The Complete Reference Manual

Essential and concise guide to mastering KiCad for the successful development of sophisticated electronic printed circuit boards.

Contributors
Jean-Pierre Charras
Fabrizio Tappero
David Jahshan
Phil Hutchinson
Christina Jarron
Melroy van den Berg
Wayne Stambaugh
Cirilo Bernardo
The KiCad Team

Feedback
Please direct any bug reports, suggestions or new versions to here:
• About KiCad document: https://github.com/KiCad/kicad-doc/issues
• About KiCad software: https://bugs.launchpad.net/kicad
• About KiCad software i18n: https://github.com/KiCad/kicad-i18n/issues

Changes to Original Documents
No changes were made to the original documents. The page format size was reduced to fit this book's page size format. Page numbers were added to this document to reflect the combination of all the individual documents contained within.

Getting Started in KiCad

August 24, 2017

Contents

Essential and concise guide to mastering KiCad for the successful development of sophisticated electronic printed circuit boards.

Copyright

Contributors

David Jahshan, Phil Hutchinson, Fabrizio Tappero, Christina Jarron, Melroy van den Berg.

Feedback

Please direct any bug reports, suggestions or new versions to here:

- About KiCad document: https://github.com/KiCad/kicad-doc/issues
- About KiCad software: https://bugs.launchpad.net/kicad
- About KiCad software i18n: https://github.com/KiCad/kicad-i18n/issues

Publication date

2015, May 16.

Chapter 1

Introduction to KiCad

KiCad is an open-source software tool for the creation of electronic schematic diagrams and PCB artwork. Beneath its singular surface, KiCad incorporates an elegant ensemble of the following stand-alone software tools:

Program name	Description	File extension
KiCad	Project manager	`*.pro`
Eeschema	Schematic editor (both schematic and component)	`*.sch, *.lib, *.net`
CvPcb	Footprint selector	`*.net`
Pcbnew	Circuit board board editor	`*.kicad_pcb`
GerbView	Gerber viewer	All the usual gerbers
Bitmap2Component	Convert bitmap images to components or footprints	`*.lib, *.kicad_mod, *.kicad_wks`
PCB Calculator	Calculator for components, track width, electrical spacing, color codes, and more···	None
Pl Editor	Page layout editor	`*.kicad_wks`

Note

The file extension list is not complete and only contains a subset of the files that KiCad works with that is useful for the basic understanding of which files are used for each KiCad unique application.

KiCad can be considered mature enough to be used for the successful development and maintenance of complex electronic boards.

KiCad does not present any board-size limitation and it can easily handle up to 32 copper layers, up to 14 technical layers and up to 4 auxiliary layers. KiCad can create all the files necessary for building printed boards, Gerber files for photo-plotters, drilling files, component location files and a lot more.

Being open source (GPL licensed), KiCad represents the ideal tool for projects oriented towards the creation of electronic hardware with an open-source flavour.

On the Internet, the home of KiCad is:

http://www.kicad-pcb.org/

1.1 Download and install KiCad

KiCad runs on GNU/Linux, Apple OS X and Windows. You can find the most up to date instructions and download links at:

http://www.kicad-pcb.org/download/

Important

KiCad stable releases occur periodically per the KiCad Stable Release Policy. New features are continually being added to the development branch. If you would like to take advantage of these new features and help out by testing them, please download the latest nightly build package for your platform. Nightly builds may introduce bugs but it is the goal of the KiCad Development Team to keep the development branch as usable as possible during new feature development.

1.2 Under GNU/Linux

Stable builds Stable releases of KiCad can be found in most distribution′ s package managers as kicad and kicad-doc. If your distribution does not provide latest stable version, please follow the instruction for unstable builds and select and install the latest stable version.

Unstable (nightly development) builds Unstable builds are built from the most recent source code. They can sometimes have bugs that cause file corruption, generate bad gerbers, etc, but are generally stable and have the latest features.

Under Ubuntu, the easiest way to install an unstable nightly build of KiCad is via *PPA* and *Aptitude*. Type the following into your Terminal:

```
sudo add-apt-repository ppa:js-reynaud/ppa-kicad
sudo aptitude update && sudo aptitude safe-upgrade
sudo aptitude install kicad kicad-doc-en
```

Under Fedora the easiest way to install an unstable nightly build is via *copr*. To install KiCad via copr type the following in to copr:

```
sudo dnf copr enable mangelajo/kicad
sudo dnf install kicad
```

Alternatively, you can download and install a pre-compiled version of KiCad, or directly download the source code, compile and install KiCad.

1.3 Under Apple OS X

Stable builds Stable builds of KiCad for OS X can be found at: http://downloads.kicad-pcb.org/osx/stable/

Unstable (nightly development) builds Unstable builds are built from the most recent source code. They can sometimes have bugs that cause file corruption, generate bad gerbers, etc, but are generally stable and have the latest features.

Unstable nightly development builds can be found at: http://downloads.kicad-pcb.org/osx/

1.4 Under Windows

Stable builds Stable builds of KiCad for Windows can be found at: http://downloads.kicad-pcb.org/windows/-stable/

Unstable (nightly development) builds Unstable builds are built from the most recent source code. They can sometimes have bugs that cause file corruption, generate bad gerbers, etc, but are generally stable and have the latest features.

For Windows you can find nightly development builds at: http://downloads.kicad-pcb.org/windows/

1.5 Support

If you have ideas, remarks or questions, or if you just need help:

- Visit the Forum
- Join the #kicad IRC channel on Freenode
- Watch Tutorials

Chapter 2

KiCad Workflow

Despite its similarities with other PCB software tools, KiCad is characterised by an interesting work-flow in which schematic components and footprints are actually two separate entities. This is often the subject of discussion on Internet forums.

2.1 KiCad Workflow overview

The KiCad work-flow is comprised of two main tasks: making the schematic and laying out the board. Both a component library and a footprint library are necessary for these two tasks. KiCad has plenty of both. Just in case that is not enough, KiCad also has the tools necessary to make new ones.

In the picture below, you see a flowchart representing the KiCad work-flow. The picture explains which steps you need to take, in which order. When applicable, the icon is added as well for convenience.

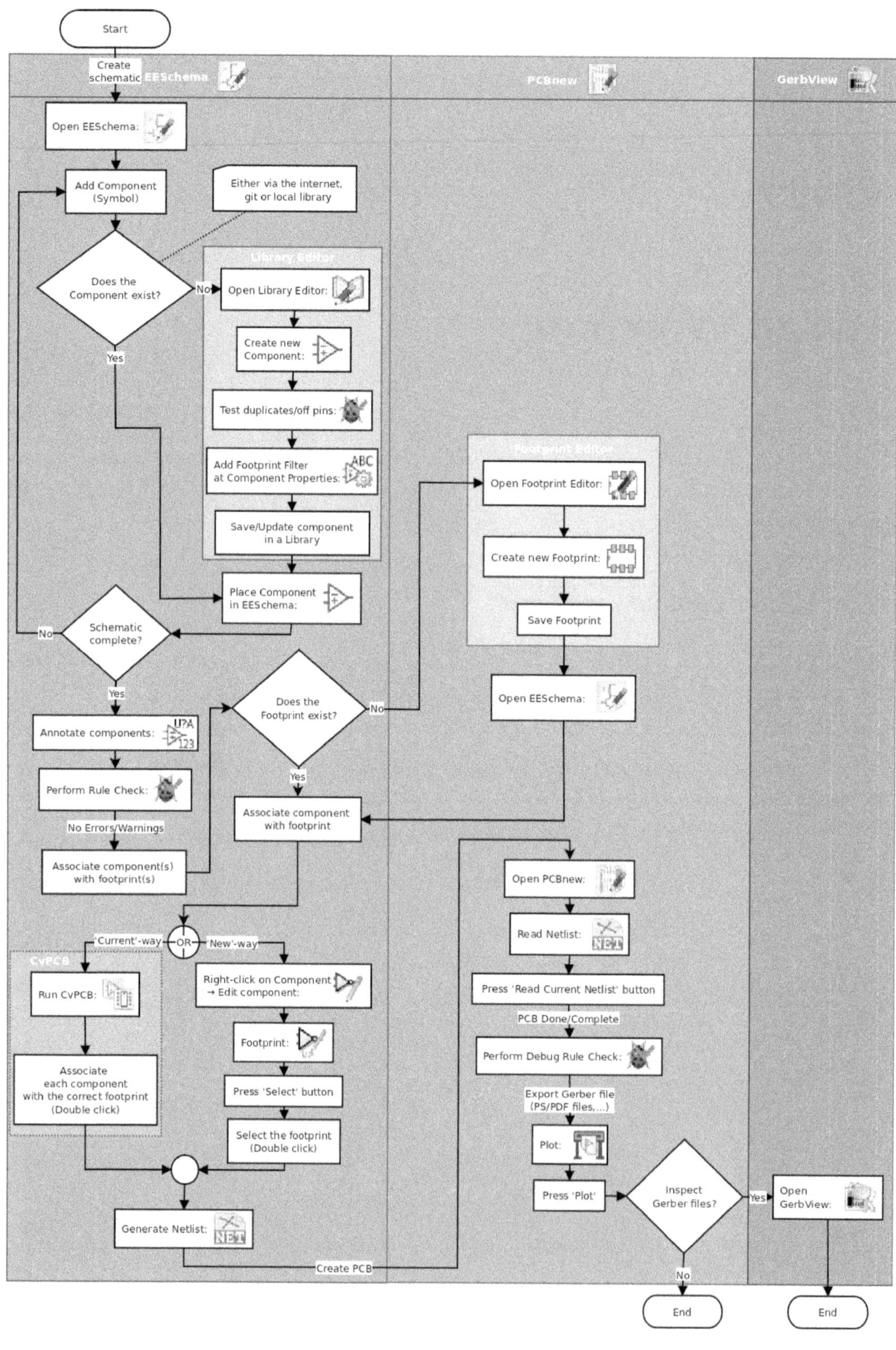
Start
Create schematic
EESchema
PCBnew
GerbView
Open EESchema:
Add Component (Symbol)
Either via the internet, git or local library
Library Editor
Does the Component exist?
No
Open Library Editor:
Create new Component:
Yes
Test duplicates/off pins:
Add Footprint Filter at Component Properties:
Save/Update component in a Library
Footprint Editor
Open Footprint Editor:
Create new Footprint:
Save Footprint
Place Component in EESchema:
Schematic complete?
Open EESchema:
Does the Footprint exist?
Annotate components:
Perform Rule Check:
No Errors/Warnings
Associate component with footprint
Associate component(s) with footprint(s)
Open PCBnew:
Read Netlist:
'Current'-way
OR
'New'-way
CvPCB
Run CvPCB:
Right-click on Component → Edit component:
Press 'Read Current Netlist' button
PCB Done/Complete
Footprint:
Perform Debug Rule Check:
Associate each component with the correct footprint (Double click)
Press 'Select' button
Export Gerber file (PS/PDF files,...)
Select the footprint (Double click)
Plot:
Press 'Plot'
Inspect Gerber files?
Open GerbView:
Generate Netlist:
Create PCB
End
End

For more information about creating a component, see the section of this document titled Make schematic components in KiCad. And for more information about how to create a new footprint, see the section of this document titled Make component footprints.

On the following site:

http://kicad.rohrbacher.net/quicklib.php

You will find an example of use of a tool that allows you to quickly create KiCad library components. For more information about quicklib, refer to the section of this document titled Make Schematic Components With quicklib.

2.2 Forward and backward annotation

Once an electronic schematic has been fully drawn, the next step is to transfer it to a PCB following the KiCad work-flow. Once the board layout process has been partially or completely done, additional components or nets might need to be added, parts moved around and much more. This can be done in two ways: Backward Annotation and Forward Annotation.

Backward Annotation is the process of sending a PCB layout change back to its corresponding schematic. Some do not consider this particular feature especially useful.

Forward Annotation is the process of sending schematic changes to a corresponding PCB layout. This is a fundamental feature because you do not really want to re-do the layout of the whole PCB every time you make a modification to your schematic. Forward Annotation is discussed in the section titled Forward Annotation.

Chapter 3

Draw electronic schematics

In this section we are going to learn how to draw an electronic schematic using KiCad.

3.1 Using Eeschema

1. Under Windows run kicad.exe. Under Linux type *kicad* in your Terminal. You are now in the main window of the KiCad project manager. From here you have access to eight stand-alone software tools: *Eeschema*, *Schematic Library Editor*, *Pcbnew*, *PCB Footprint Editor*, *GerbView*, *Bitmap2Component*, *PCB Calculator* and *Pl Editor*. Refer to the work-flow chart to give you an idea how the main tools are used.

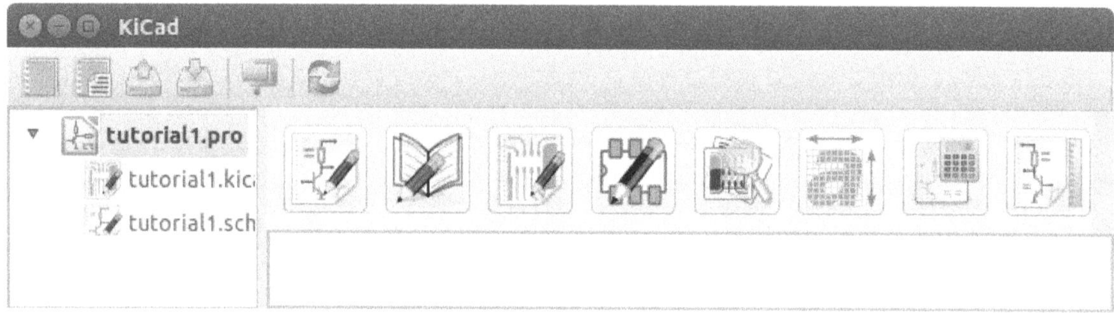

2. Create a new project: **File** → **New Project** → **New Project**. Name the project file *tutorial1*. The project file will automatically take the extension ".pro". KiCad prompts to create a dedicated directory, click "Yes" to confirm. All your project files will be saved here.

3. Let' s begin by creating a schematic. Start the schematic editor *Eeschema*, . It is the first button from the left.

4. Click on the *Page Settings* icon on the top toolbar. Set the Page Size as *A4* and enter the Title as *Tutorial 1*. You will see that more information can be entered here if necessary. Click OK. This information will populate the schematic sheet at the bottom right corner. Use the mouse wheel to zoom in. Save the whole schematic project: **File** → **Save Schematic Project**

5. We will now place our first component. Click on the *Place component* icon in the right toolbar. The same functionality is achieved by pressing the *Place component* shortcut key (*a*).

Note

You can see a list of all available shortcut keys by pressing the *?* key.

6. Click on the middle of your schematic sheet. A *Choose Component* window will appear on the screen. We' re going to place a resistor. Search / filter on the *R* of **R**esistor. You may notice the *device* heading above the Resistor. This *device* heading is the name of the library where the component is located, which is quite a generic and useful library.

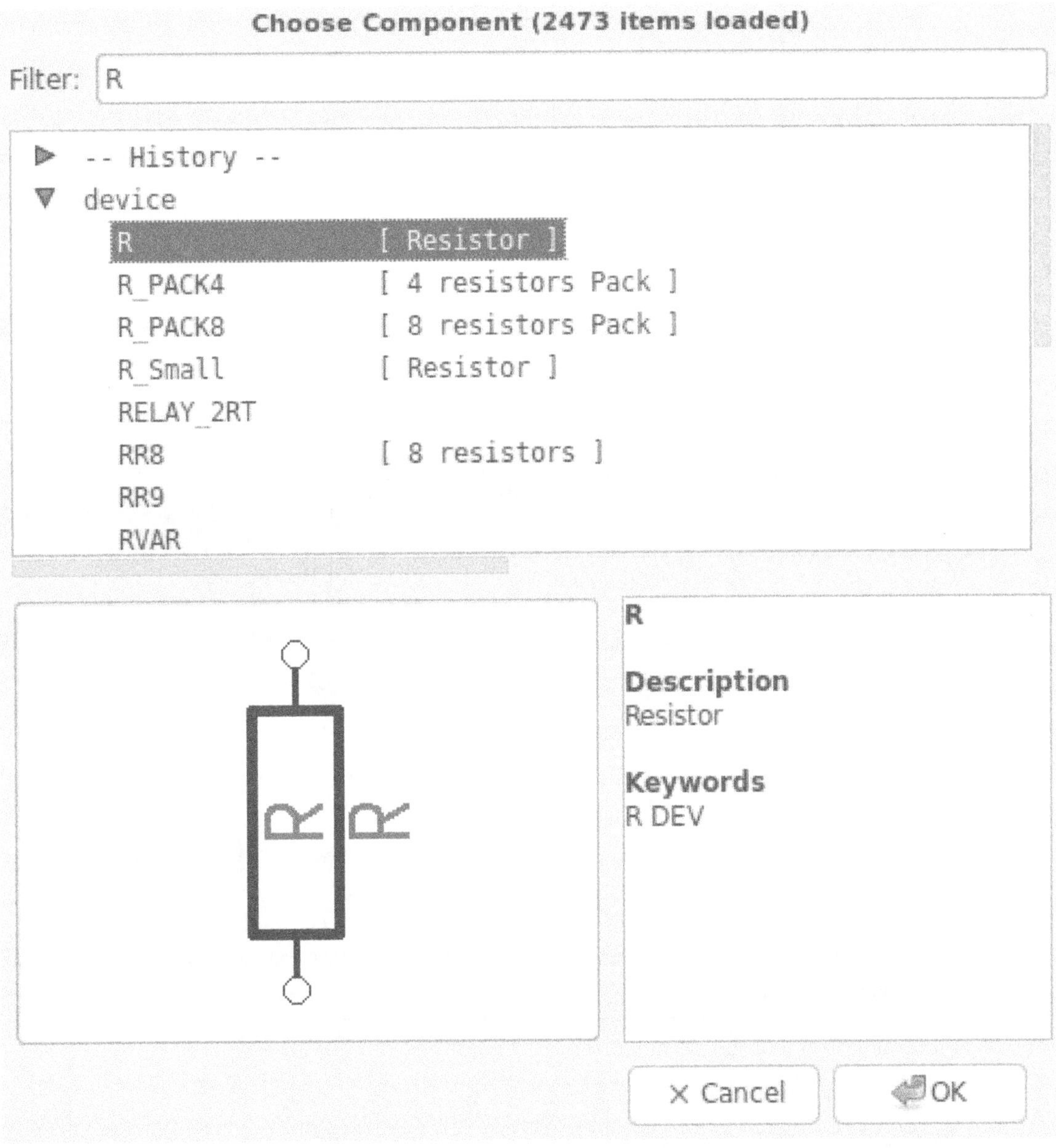

7. Double click on it. This will close the *Choose Component* window. Place the component in the schematic sheet by clicking where you want it to be.

8. Click on the magnifier icon to zoom in on the component. Alternatively, use the mouse wheel to zoom in and zoom out. Press the wheel (central) mouse button to pan horizontally and vertically.

9. Try to hover the mouse over the component *R* and press the r key. The component should rotate. You do not need to actually click on the component to rotate it.

Note

If your mouse was also over the *Field Reference* (*R*) or the *Field Value* (*R?*), a menu will appear. You will see these *Clarify Selection* menu often in KiCad, they allow working on objects that are on top of each other. In this case, tell KiCad you want to perform the action on the *Component* ···*R*···.

10. Right click in the middle of the component and select **Edit Component** → **Value**. You can achieve the same result by hovering over the component and pressing the v key. Alternatively, the e key will take you to the more general Edit window. Notice how the right-click menu below shows shortcut keys for all available actions.

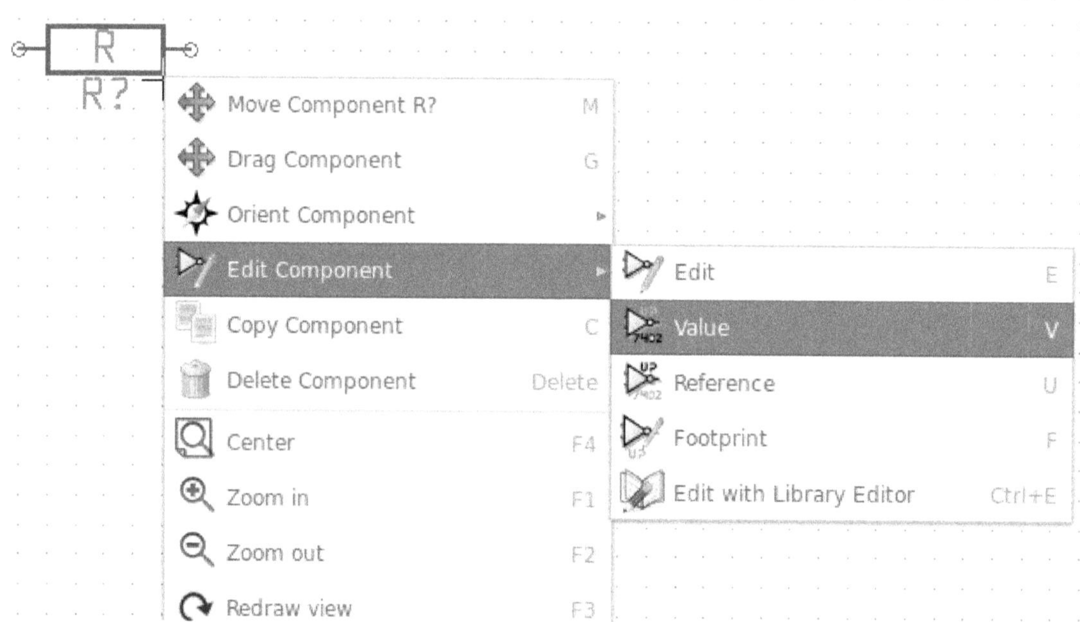

11. The Component value window will appear. Replace the current value *R* with *1 k*. Click OK.

Note

Do not change the Reference field (R?), this will be done automatically later on. The value inside the resistor should now be *1 k*.

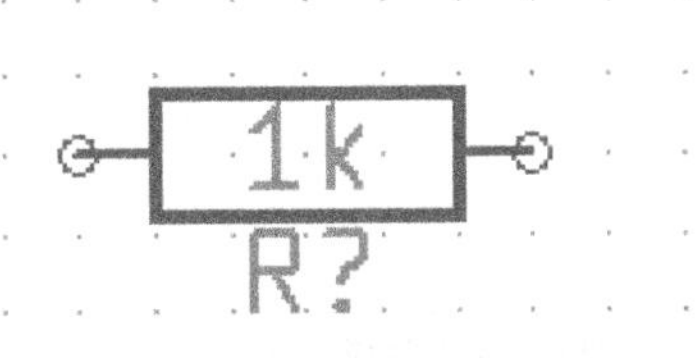

12. To place another resistor, simply click where you want the resistor to appear. The Component Selection window will appear again.
13. The resistor you previously chose is now in your history list, appearing as *R*. Click OK and place the component.

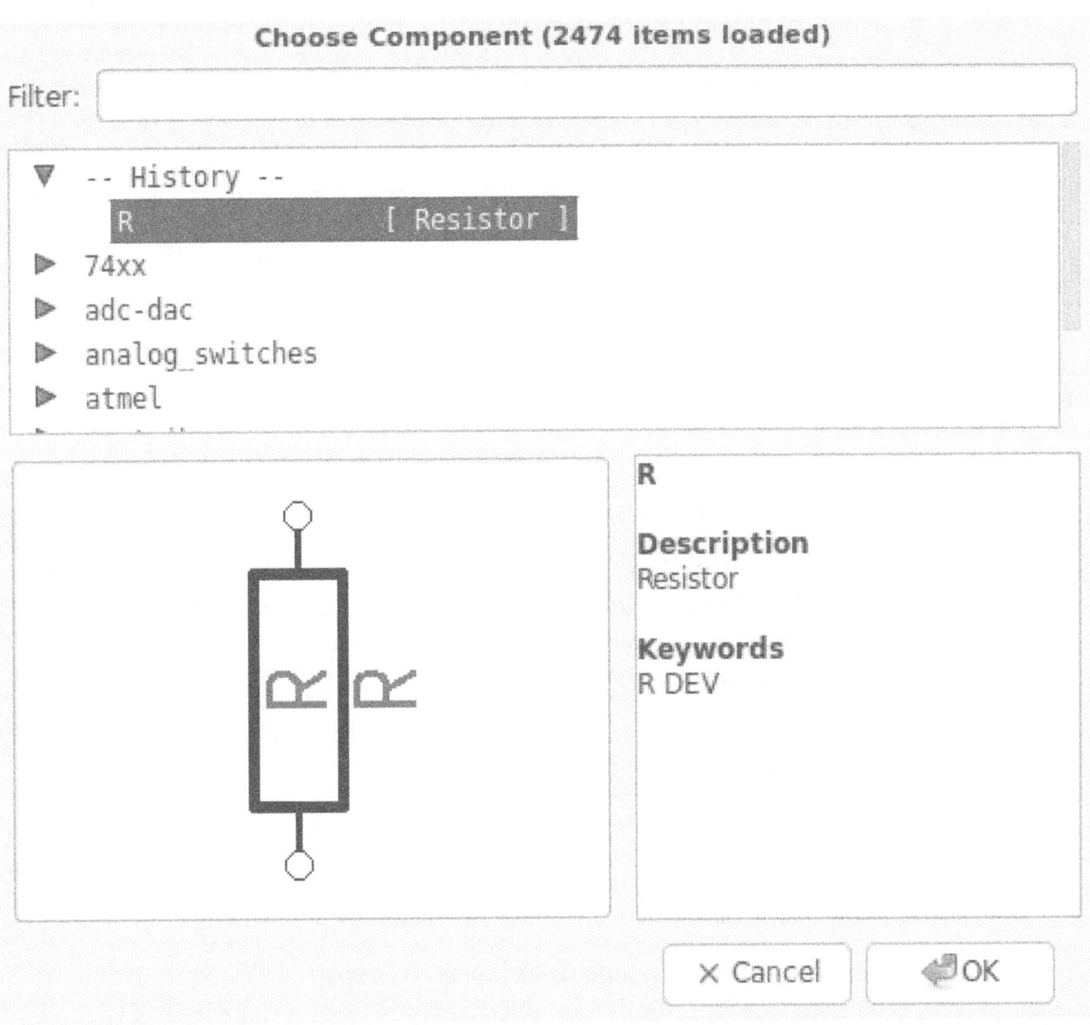

14. In case you make a mistake and want to delete a component, right click on the component and click *Delete Component.* This will remove the component from the schematic. Alternatively, you can hover over the component you want to delete and press the del key.

Note

You can edit any default shortcut key by going to **Preferences → Hotkeys → Edit hotkeys**. Any modification will be saved immediately.

15. You can also duplicate a component already on your schematic sheet by hovering over it and pressing the c key. Click where you want to place the new duplicated component.
16. Right click on the second resistor. Select *Drag Component.* Reposition the component and left click to drop. The same functionality can be achieved by hovering over the component and by pressing the g key. Use the r key to rotate the component. The x key and the y key will flip the component.

Note

Right-Click → Move component (equivalent to the m key option) is also a valuable option for moving anything around, but it is better to use this only for component labels and components yet to be connected. We will see later on why this is the case.

17. Edit the second resistor by hovering over it and pressing the v key. Replace *R* with *100.* You can undo any of your editing actions with the ctrl+z key.
18. Change the grid size. You have probably noticed that on the schematic sheet all components are snapped onto a large pitch grid. You can easily change the size of the grid by **Right-Click → Grid select**. *In general, it is recommended to use a grid of 50.0 mils for the schematic sheet.*
19. We are going to add a component from a library that isn' t configured in the default project. In the menu, choose **Preferences → Component Libraries** and click the **Add** button for **Component library files**.
20. You need to find where the official KiCad libraries are installed on your computer. Look for a `library` directory containing a hundred of `.dcm` and `.lib` files. Try in `C:\Program Files (x86)\KiCad\share\` (Windows) and `/usr/share/kicad/library/` (Linux). When you have found the directory, choose and add the *microchip_pic12mcu* library and close the window.
21. Repeat the add-component steps, however this time select the *microchip_pic12mcu* library instead of the *device* library and pick the *PIC12C508A-I/SN* component.
22. Hover the mouse over the microcontroller component. Press the y key or the x key on the keyboard. Notice how the component is flipped over its x axis or its y axis. Press the key again to return it to its original orientation.
23. Repeat the add-component steps, this time choosing the *device* library and picking the *LED* component from it.
24. Organise all components on your schematic sheet as shown below.

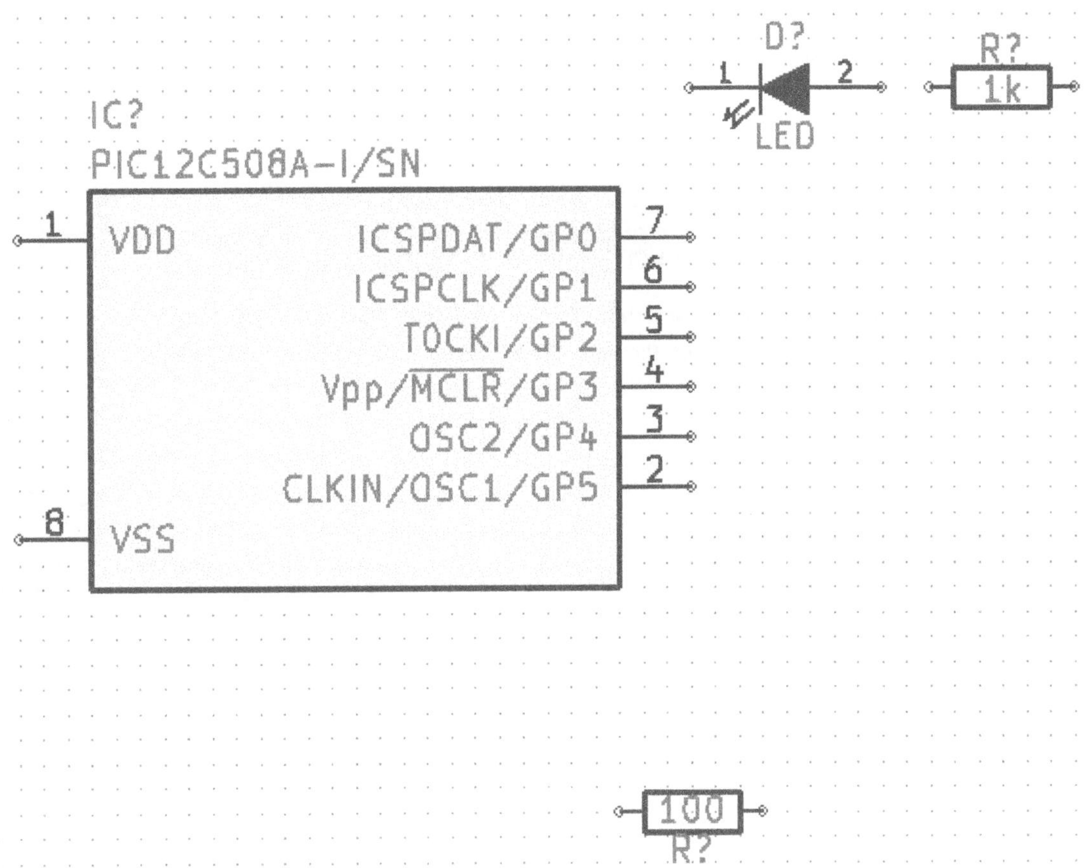

25. We now need to create the schematic component *MYCONN3* for our 3-pin connector. You can jump to the section titled Make Schematic Components in KiCad to learn how to make this component from scratch and then return to this section to continue with the board.

26. You can now place the freshly made component. Press the *a* key and pick the *MYCONN3* component in the *myLib* library.

27. The component identifier *J?* will appear under the *MYCONN3* label. If you want to change its position, right click on *J?* and click on *Move Field* (equivalent to the m key option). It might be helpful to zoom in before/ while doing this. Reposition *J?* under the component as shown below. Labels can be moved around as many times as you please.

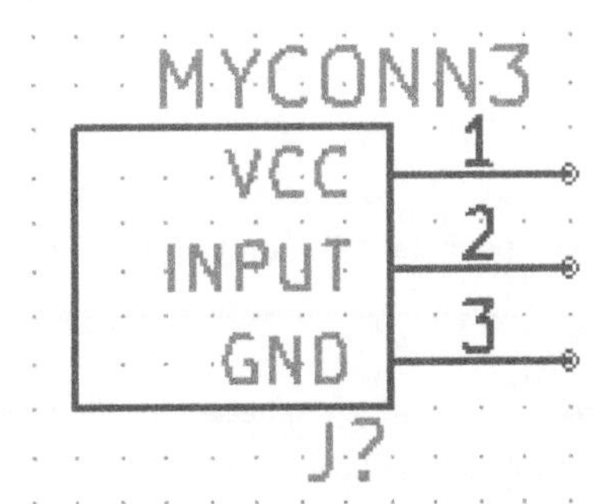

28. It is time to place the power and ground symbols. Click on the *Place a power port* button on the right toolbar. Alternatively, press the *p* key. In the component selection window, scroll down and select *VCC* from the *power* library. Click OK.

29. Click above the pin of the 1 k resistor to place the VCC part. Click on the area above the microcontroller *VDD*. In the *Component Selection history* section select *VCC* and place it next to the VDD pin. Repeat the add process again and place a VCC part above the VCC pin of *MYCONN3*.

30. Repeat the add-pin steps but this time select the GND part. Place a GND part under the GND pin of *MYCONN3*. Place another GND symbol on the right of the VSS pin of the microcontroller. Your schematic should now look something like this:

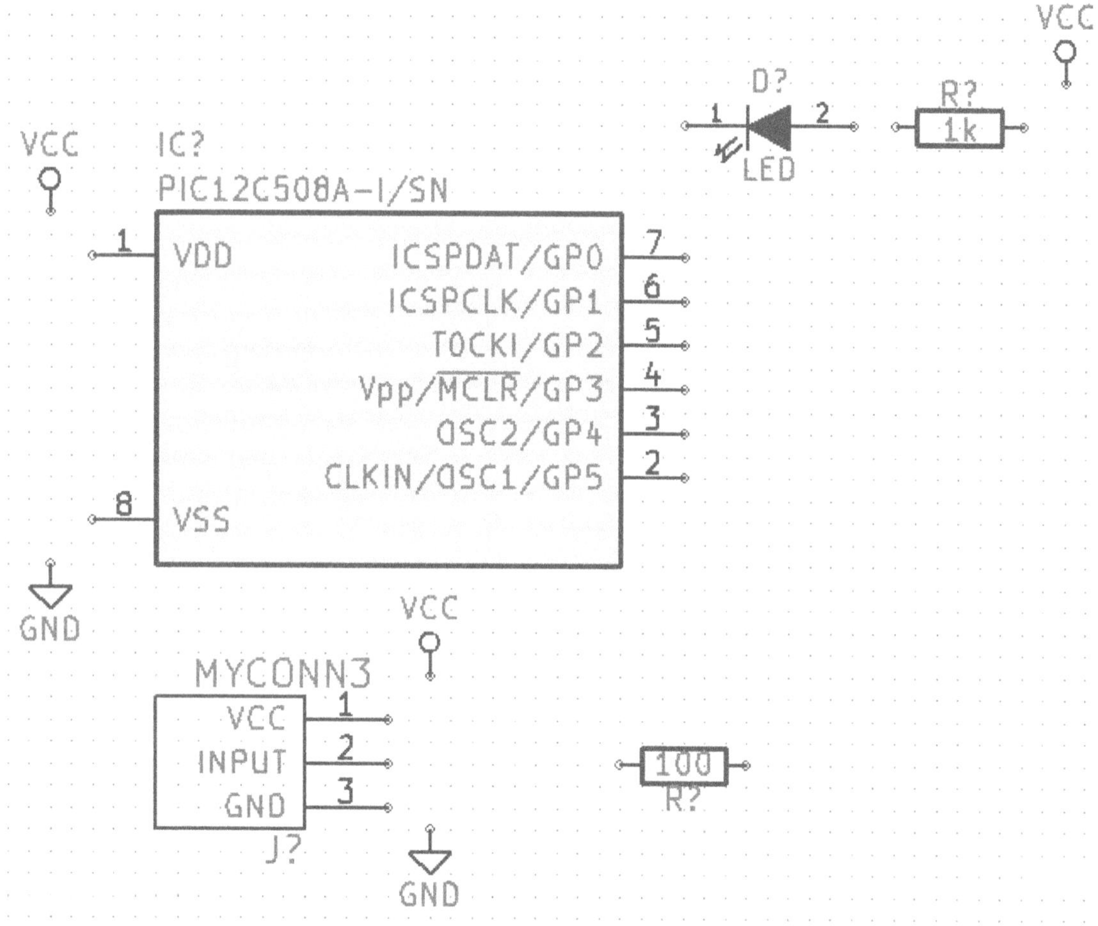

31. Next, we will wire all our components. Click on the *Place wire* icon on the right toolbar.

Note

Be careful not to pick *Place a bus*, which appears directly beneath this button but has thicker lines. The section Bus Connections in KiCad will explain how to use a bus section.

32. Click on the little circle at the end of pin 7 of the microcontroller and then click on the little circle on pin 2 of the LED. You can zoom in while you are placing the connection.

Note

If you want to reposition wired components, it is important to use the g key (grab) option and not the m key (move) option. Using the grab option will keep the wires connected. Review step 24 in case you have forgotten how to move a component.

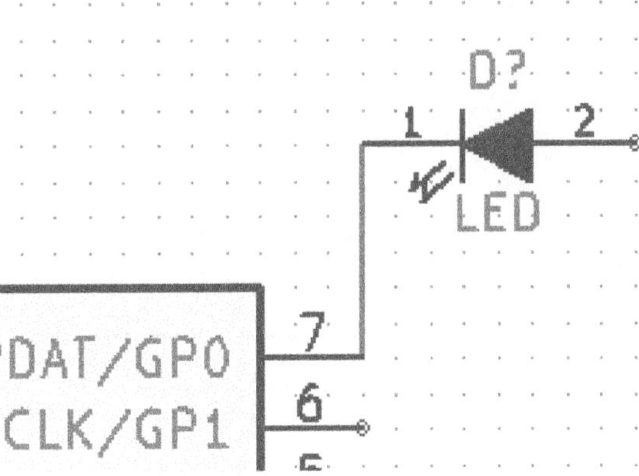

33. Repeat this process and wire up all the other components as shown below. To terminate a wire just double-click. When wiring up the VCC and GND symbols, the wire should touch the bottom of the VCC symbol and the middle top of the GND symbol. See the screenshot below.

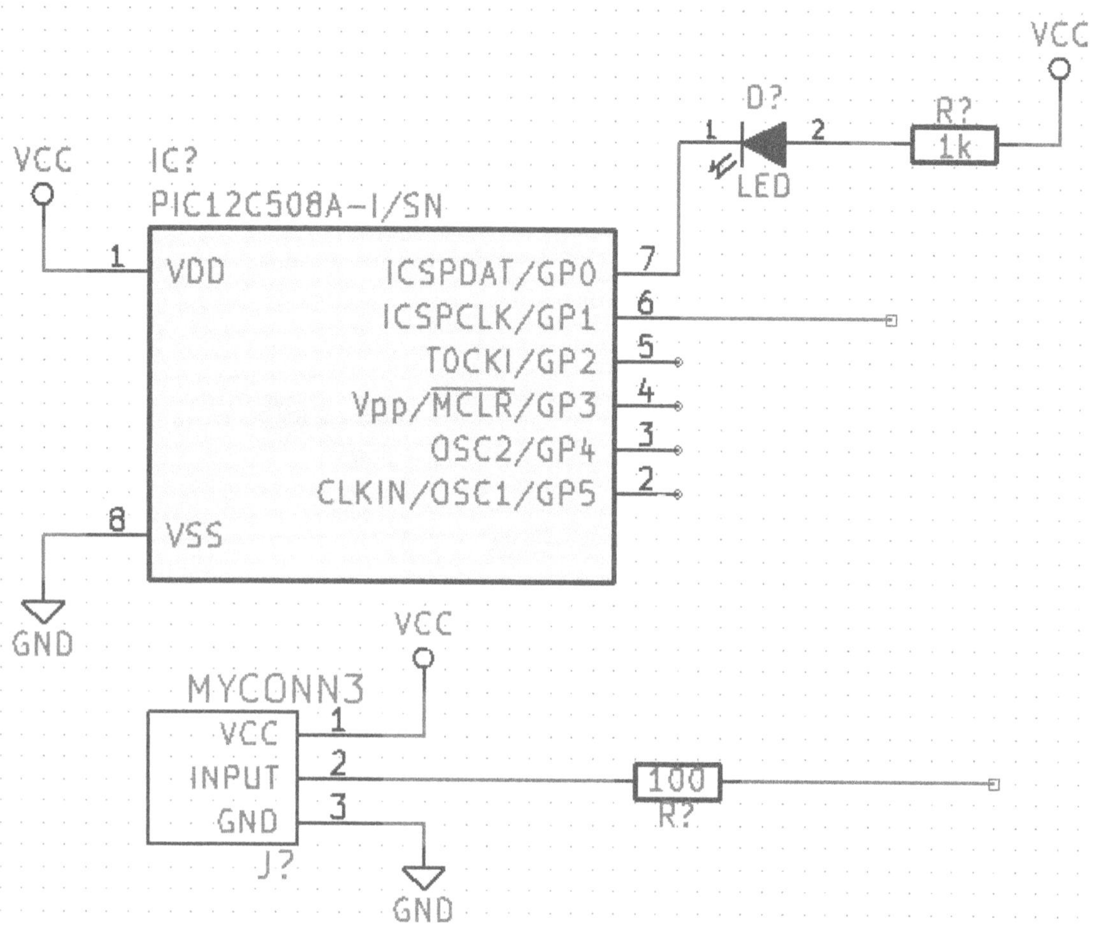

34. We will now consider an alternative way of making a connection using labels. Pick a net labelling tool by clicking on the *Place net name* icon A on the right toolbar. You can also use the l key.
35. Click in the middle of the wire connected to pin 6 of the microcontroller. Name this label *INPUT*.
36. Follow the same procedure and place another label on line on the right of the 100 ohm resistor. Also name it *INPUT*. The two labels, having the same name, create an invisible connection between pin 6 of the PIC and the 100 ohm resistor. This is a useful technique when connecting wires in a complex design where drawing the lines would make the whole schematic messier. To place a label you do not necessarily need a wire, you can simply attach the label to a pin.
37. Labels can also be used to simply label wires for informative purposes. Place a label on pin 7 of the PIC. Enter the name *uCtoLED*. Name the wire between the resistor and the LED as *LEDtoR*. Name the wire between *MYCONN3* and the resistor as *INPUTtoR*.
38. You do not have to label the VCC and GND lines because the labels are implied from the power objects they are connected to.
39. Below you can see what the final result should look like.

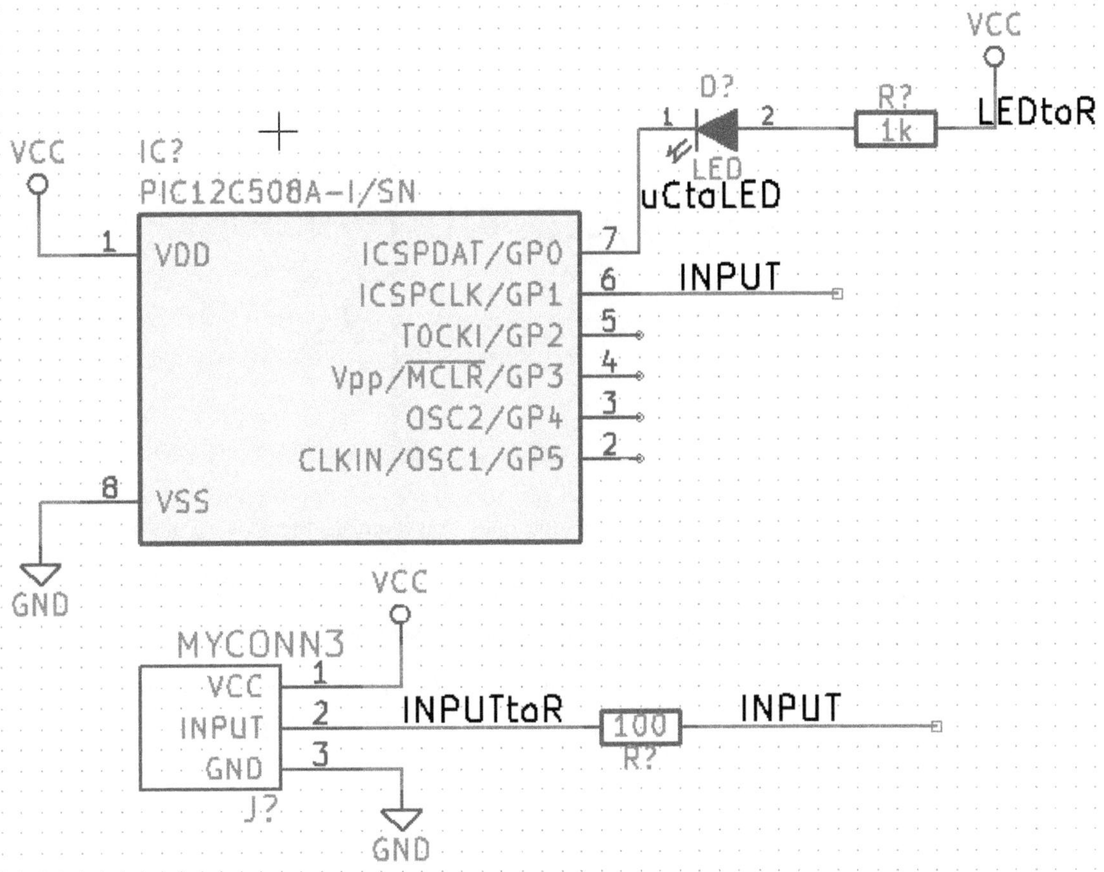

40. Let' s now deal with unconnected wires. Any pin or wire that is not connected will generate a warning when checked by KiCad. To avoid these warnings you can either instruct the program that the unconnected wires are deliberate or manually flag each unconnected wire or pin as unconnected.

41. Click on the *Place no connect flag* icon ✕ on the right toolbar. Click on pins 2, 3, 4 and 5. An X will appear to signify that the lack of a wire connection is intentional.

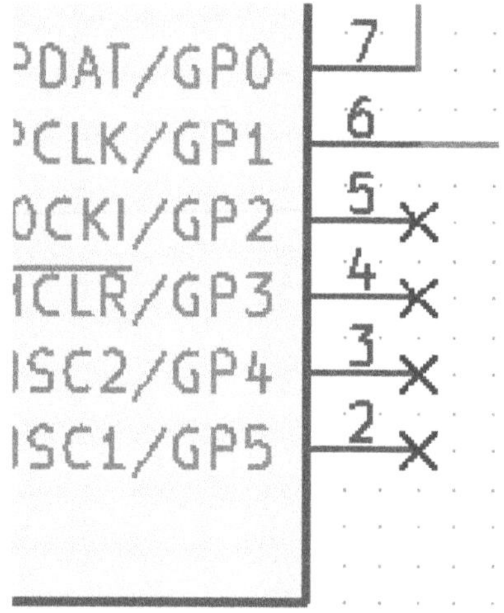

42. Some components have power pins that are invisible. You can make them visible by clicking on the *Show hidden pins* icon on the left toolbar. Hidden power pins get automatically connected if VCC and GND naming is respected. Generally speaking, you should try not to make hidden power pins.

43. It is now necessary to add a *Power Flag* to indicate to KiCad that power comes in from somewhere. Press the a key, select *List All*, double click on the *power* library and search for *PWR_FLAG*. Place two of them. Connect them to a GND pin and to VCC as shown below.

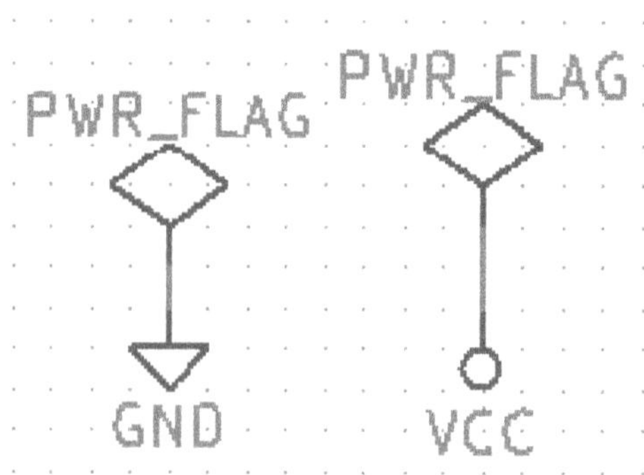

Note

This will avoid the classic schematic checking warning: Warning Pin power_in not driven (Net xx)

44. Sometimes it is good to write comments here and there. To add comments on the schematic use the *Place graphic text (comment)* icon T on the right toolbar.

45. All components now need to have unique identifiers. In fact, many of our components are still named *R?* or *J?*. Identifier assignation can be done automatically by clicking on the *Annotate schematic* icon U?A 123 on the top toolbar.

46. In the Annotate Schematic window, select *Use the entire schematic* and click on the *Annotation* button. Click OK in the confirmation message and then click *Close.* Notice how all the *?* have been replaced with numbers. Each identifier is now unique. In our example, they have been named *R1*, *R2*, *U1*, *D1* and *J1*.

47. We will now check our schematic for errors. Click on the *Perform electrical rules check* icon on the top toolbar. Click on the *Run* button. A report informing you of any errors or warnings such as disconnected wires is generated. You should have 0 Errors and 0 Warnings. In case of errors or warnings, a small green arrow will appear on the schematic in the position where the error or the warning is located. Check *Create ERC file report* and press the *Run* button again to receive more information about the errors.

Note

If you have a warning with "No default editor found you must choose it", try setting the path to `c:\windows\notepad.exe` (windows) or `/usr/bin/gedit` (Linux).

---

48. The schematic is now finished. We can now create a Netlist file to which we will add the footprint of each component. Click on the *Generate netlist* icon on the top toolbar. Click on the *Generate* button and save under the default file name.

49. After generating the Netlist file, click on the *Run Cvpcb* icon on the top toolbar. If a missing file error window pops up, just ignore it and click OK.

50. *Cvpcb* allows you to link all the components in your schematic with footprints in the KiCad library. The pane on the center shows all the components used in your schematic. Here select *D1*. In the pane on the right you have all the available footprints, here scroll down to *LEDs:LED-5MM* and double click on it.

51. It is possible that the pane on the right shows only a selected subgroup of available footprints. This is because KiCad is trying to suggest to you a subset of suitable footprints. Click on the icons , and to enable or disable these filters.

52. For *IC1* select the *Housings_DIP:DIP-8_W7.62mm* footprint. For *J1* select the *Connect:Banana_Jack_3Pin* footprint. For *R1* and *R2* select the *Discret:R1* footprint.

53. If you are interested in knowing what the footprint you are choosing looks like, you have two options. You can click on the *View selected footprint* icon for a preview of the current footprint. Alternatively, click on the *Display footprint list documentation* icon and you will get a multi-page PDF document with all available footprints. You can print it out and check your components to make sure that the dimensions match.

54. You are done. You can now update your netlist file with all the associated footprints. Click on **File → Save As**. The default name *tutorial1.net* is fine, click save. Otherwise you can use the icon . Your netlist file has now been updated with all the footprints. Note that if you are missing the footprint of any device, you will need to make your own footprints. This will be explained in a later section of this document.

55. You can close *Cvpcb* and go back to the *Eeschema* schematic editor. Save the project by clicking on **File → Save Whole Schematic Project**. Close the schematic editor.

56. Switch to the KiCad project manager.

57. The netlist file describes all components and their respective pin connections. The netlist file is actually a text file that you can easily inspect, edit or script.

    Note

    Library files (**.lib*) are text files too and they are also easily editable or scriptable.

    ---

58. To create a Bill Of Materials (BOM), go to the *Eeschema* schematic editor and click on the *Bill of materials* icon on the top toolbar. By default there is no plugin active. You add one, by clicking on **Add Plugin** button. Select the *.xsl file you want to use, in this case, we select *bom2csv.xsl.*

    Note

    The *.xsl file is located in *plugins* directory of the KiCad installation, which is located at: /usr/lib/kicad/plugins/. Or get the file via:

    ```
    wget https://raw.githubusercontent.com/KiCad/kicad-source-mirror/master/eeschema/ ↩
        plugins/bom2csv.xsl
    ```

    KiCad automatically generates the command, for example:

    ```
    xsltproc -o "%O" "/home/<user>/kicad/eeschema/plugins/bom2csv.xsl" "%I"
    ```

    You may want to add the extension, so change this command line to:

    ```
    xsltproc -o "%O.csv" "/home/<user>/kicad/eeschema/plugins/bom2csv.xsl" "%I"
    ```

    Press Help button for more info.

59. Now press *Generate.* The file (same name as your project) is located in your project folder. Open the ***.csv** file with LibreOffice Calc or Excel. An import window will appear, press OK.

You are now ready to move to the PCB layout part, which is presented in the next section. However, before moving on let' s take a quick look at how to connect component pins using a bus line.

3.2 Bus connections in KiCad

Sometimes you might need to connect several sequential pins of component A with some other sequential pins of component B. In this case you have two options: the labelling method we already saw or the use of a bus connection. Let' s see how to do it.

1. Let us suppose that you have three 4-pin connectors that you want to connect together pin to pin. Use the label option (press the l key) to label pin 4 of the P4 part. Name this label *a1*. Now let' s press the Ins key to have the same item automatically added on the pin below pin 4 (PIN 3). Notice how the label is automatically renamed *a2*.
2. Press the Ins Key two more times. The Ins key corresponds to the action *Repeat last item* and it is an infinitely useful command that can make your life a lot easier.
3. Repeat the same labelling action on the two other connectors CONN_2 and CONN_3 and you are done. If you proceed and make a PCB you will see that the three connectors are connected to each other. Figure 2 shows the result of what we described. For aesthetic purposes it is also possible to add a series of *Place wire to bus entry* using the icon and bus line using the icon , as shown in Figure 3. Mind, however, that there will be no effect on the PCB.
4. It should be pointed out that the short wire attached to the pins in Figure 2 is not strictly necessary. In fact, the labels could have been applied directly to the pins.
5. Let' s take it one step further and suppose that you have a fourth connector named CONN_4 and, for whatever reason, its labelling happens to be a little different (b1, b2, b3, b4). Now we want to connect *Bus a* with *Bus b* in a pin to pin manner. We want to do that without using pin labelling (which is also possible) but by instead using labelling on the bus line, with one label per bus.
6. Connect and label CONN_4 using the labelling method explained before. Name the pins b1, b2, b3 and b4. Connect the pin to a series of *Wire to bus entry* using the icon and to a bus line using the icon . See Figure 4.
7. Put a label (press the l key option) on the bus of CONN_4 and name it *b[1..4]*.
8. Put a label (press the l key option) on the previous a bus and name it *a[1..4]*.
9. What we can now do is connect bus a[1..4] with bus b[1..4] using a bus line with the button .
10. By connecting the two buses together, pin a1 will be automatically connected to pin b1, a2 will be connected to b2 and so on. Figure 4 shows what the final result looks like.

Note

The *Repeat last item* option accessible via the Ins key can be successfully used to repeat period item insertions. For instance, the short wires connected to all pins in Figure 2, Figure 3 and Figure 4 have been placed with this option.

---

11. The *Repeat last item* option accessible via the Ins key has also been extensively used to place the many series of *Wire to bus entry* using the icon .

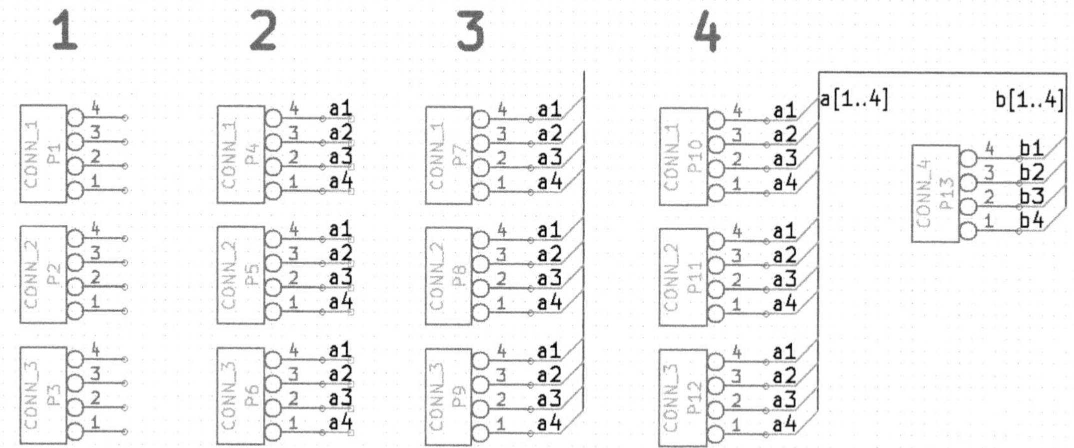
1
2
3
4
CONN_1
P1
CONN_2
P2
CONN_3
P3
CONN_1
P4
CONN_2
P5
CONN_3
P6
CONN_1
P7
CONN_2
P8
CONN_3
P9
CONN_1
P10
CONN_2
P11
CONN_3
P12
CONN_4
P13
a1
a2
a3
a4
a[1..4]
b[1..4]
b1
b2
b3
b4

Chapter 4

Layout printed circuit boards

It is now time to use the netlist file you generated to lay out the PCB. This is done with the *Pcbnew* tool.

4.1 Using Pcbnew

1. From the KiCad project manager, click on the *Pcbnew* icon . The *Pcbnew* window will open. If you get an error message saying that a **.kicad_pcb* file does not exist and asks if you want to create it, just click Yes.
2. Begin by entering some schematic information. Click on the *Page settings* icon on the top toolbar. Set *paper size* as *A4* and *title* as *Tutorial1.*
3. It is a good idea to start by setting the **clearance** and the **minimum track width** to those required by your PCB manufacturer. In general you can set the clearance to *0.25* and the minimum track width to *0.25.* Click on the **Design Rules** → **Design Rules** menu. If it does not show already, click on the *Net Classes Editor* tab. Change the *Clearance* field at the top of the window to *0.25* and the *Track Width* field to *0.25* as shown below. Measurements here are in mm.

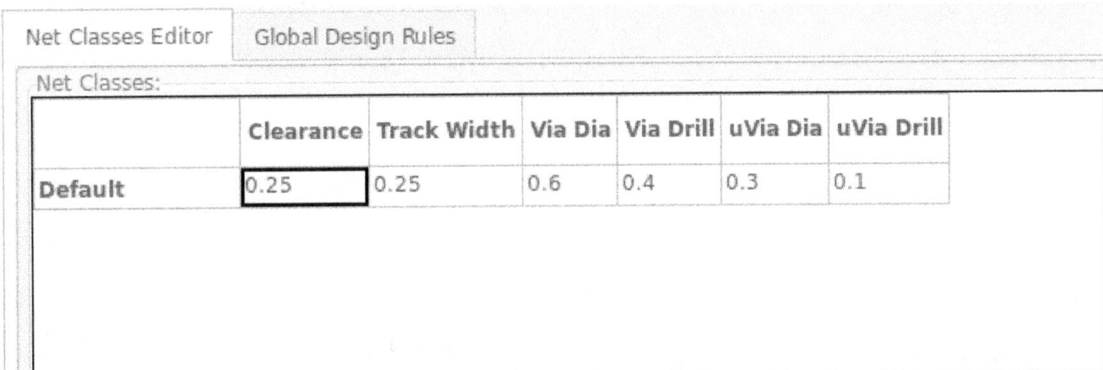

Net Classes Editor
Global Design Rules
Net Classes:
Clearance
Track Width
Via Dia
Via Drill
uVia Dia
uVia Drill
Default
0.25
0.25
0.6
0.4
0.3
0.1

4. Click on the *Global Design Rules* tab and set *Min track width* to 0.25'. Click the OK button to commit your changes and close the Design Rules Editor window.

5. Now we will import the netlist file. Click on the *Read Netlist* icon on the top toolbar. Click on the *Browse Netlist Files* button, select *tutorial1.net* in the File selection dialogue, and click on *Read Current Netlist.* Then click the *Close* button.

6. All components should now be visible in the top left hand corner just above the page. Scroll up if you cannot see them.

7. Select all components with the mouse and move them to the middle of the board. If necessary you can zoom in and out while you move the components.

8. All components are connected via a thin group of wires called *ratsnest.* Make sure that the *Hide board ratsnest* button is pressed. In this way you can see the ratsnest linking all components.

Note

The tool-tip is backwards; pressing this button actually displays the ratsnest.

9. You can move each component by hovering over it and pressing the g key. Click where you want to place them. Move all components around until you minimise the number of wire crossovers.

Note

If instead of grabbing the components (with the g key) you move them around using the m key you will later note that you lose the track connection (the same occurs in the schematic editor). Bottom line, always use the g key option.

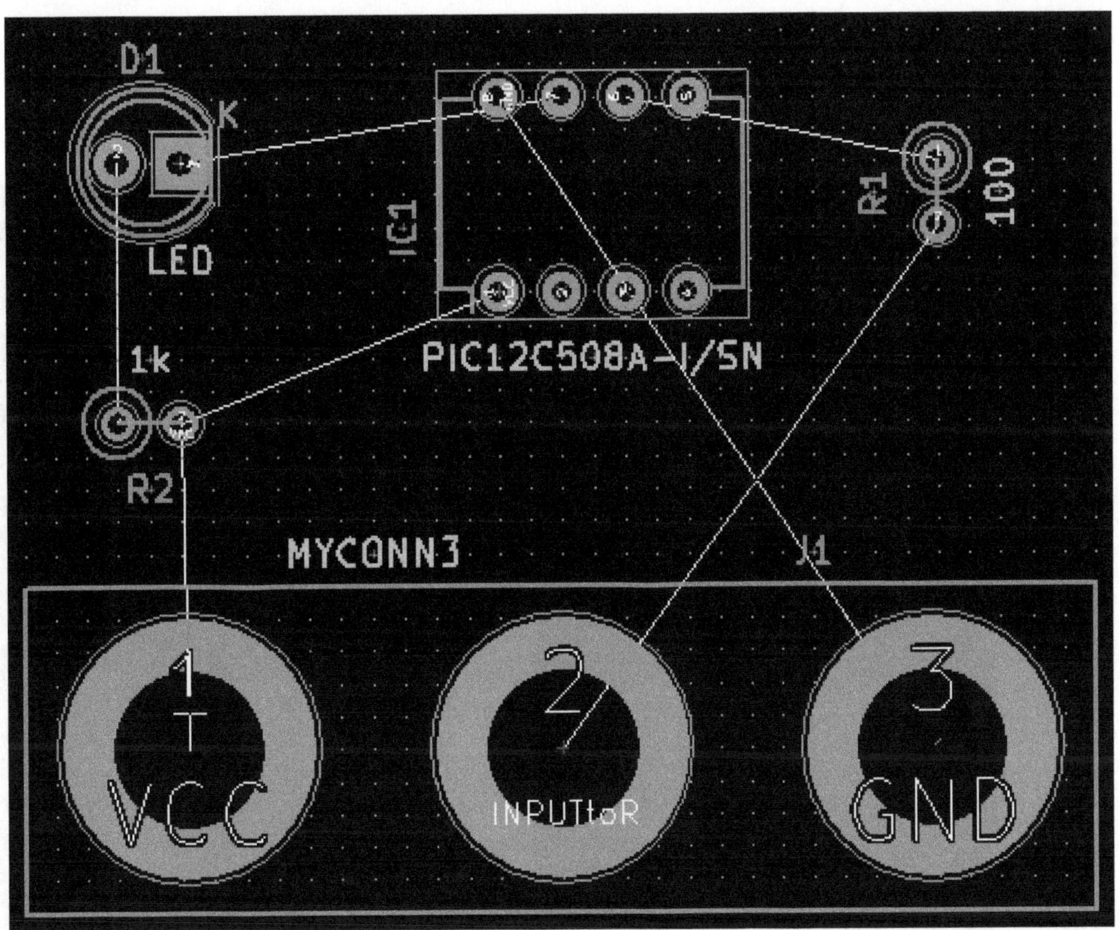

10. If the ratsnest disappears or the screen gets messy, right click and click *Redraw view.* Note how one pin of the 100 ohm resistor is connected to pin 6 of the PIC component. This is the result of the labelling method used to connect pins. Labels are often preferred to actual wires because they make the schematic much less messy.

11. Now we will define the edge of the PCB. Select *Edge.Cuts* from the drop-down menu in the top toolbar. Click on the *Add graphic line or polygon* icon on the right toolbar. Trace around the edge of the board, clicking at each corner, and remember to leave a small gap between the edge of the green and the edge of the PCB.

12. Next, connect up all the wires except GND. In fact, we will connect all GND connections in one go using a ground plane placed on the bottom copper (called *B.Cu*) of the board.

13. Now we must choose which copper layer we want to work on. Select *F.Cu (PgUp)* in the drop-down menu on the top toolbar. This is the front top copper layer.

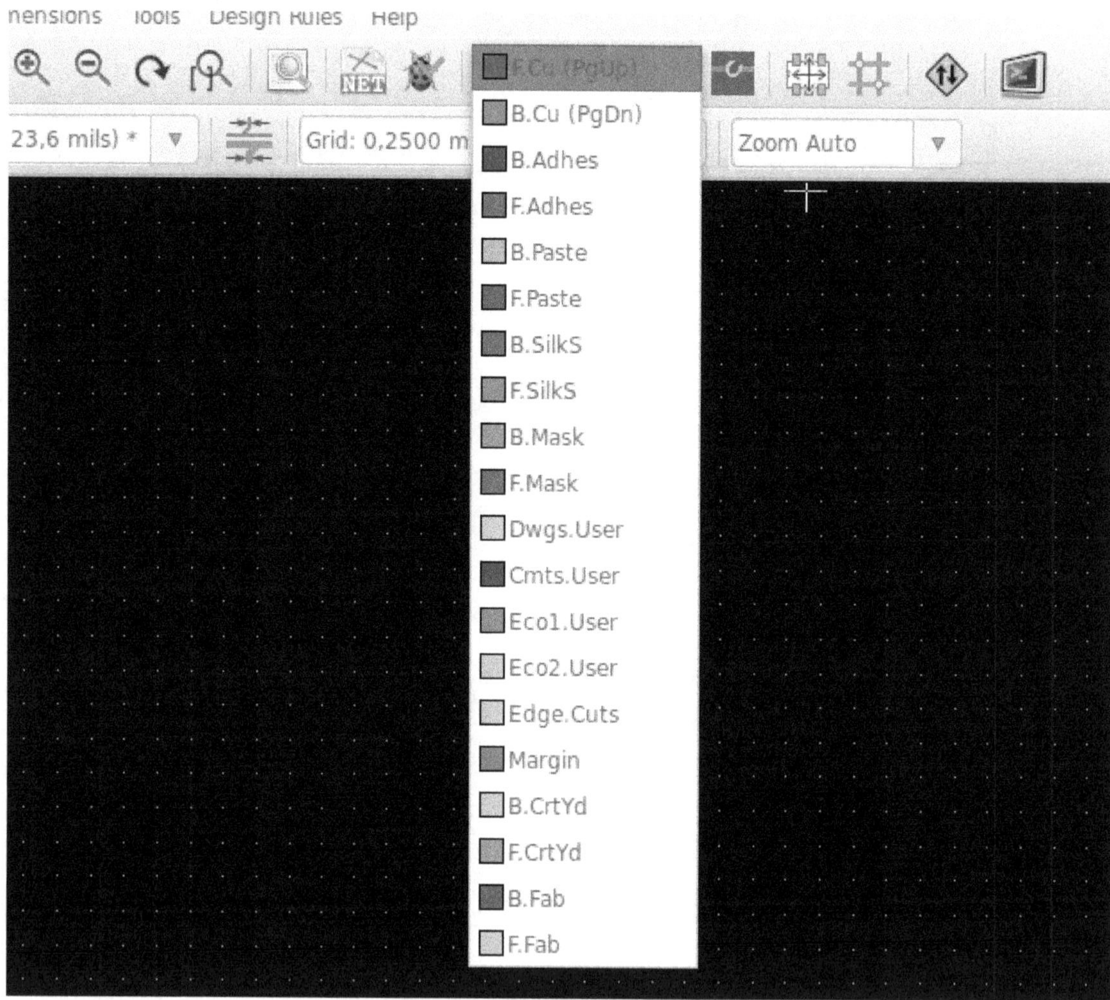

14. If you decide, for instance, to do a 4 layer PCB instead, go to **Design Rules** → **Layers Setup** and change *Copper Layers* to 4. In the *Layers* table you can name layers and decide what they can be used for. Notice that there are very useful presets that can be selected via the *Preset Layer Groupings* menu.

15. Click on the *Add Tracks and vias* icon on the right toolbar. Click on pin 1 of *J1* and run a track to pad *R2*. Double-click to set the point where the track will end. The width of this track will be the default 0.250 mm. You can change the track width from the drop-down menu in the top toolbar. Mind that by default you have only one track width available.

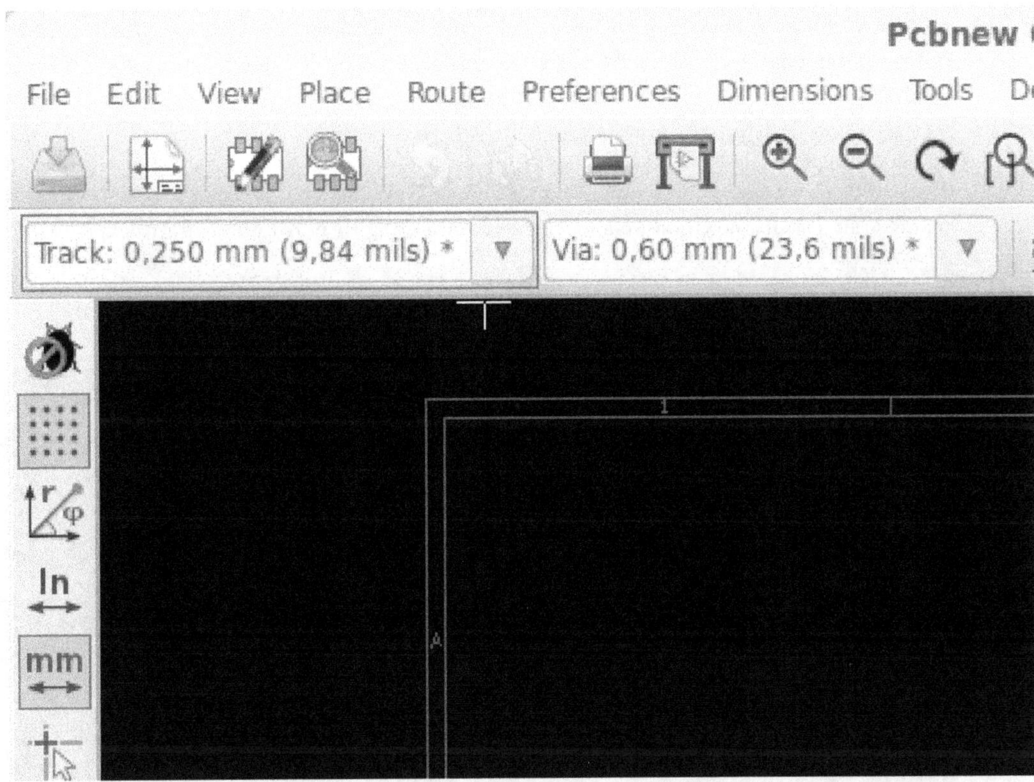

16. If you would like to add more track widths go to: **Design Rules** → **Design Rules** → **Global Design Rules** tab and at the bottom right of this window add any other width you would like to have available. You can then choose the widths of the track from the drop-down menu while you lay out your board. See the example below (inches).

Custom Track Widths:

	Width
Track 1	0.0100
Track 2	0.0200
Track 3	0.0500
Track 4	0.0800
Track 5	0.1000
Track 6	0.1500
Track 7	0.2000

17. Alternatively, you can add a Net Class in which you specify a set of options. Go to **Design Rules → Design Rules → Net Classes Editor** and add a new class called *power*. Change the track width from 8 mil (indicated as 0.0080) to 24 mil (indicated as 0.0240). Next, add everything but ground to the *power* class (select *default* at left and *power* at right and use the arrows).

18. If you want to change the grid size, **Right click → Grid Select**. Be sure to select the appropriate grid size before or after laying down the components and connecting them together with tracks.

19. Repeat this process until all wires, except pin 3 of J1, are connected. Your board should look like the example below.

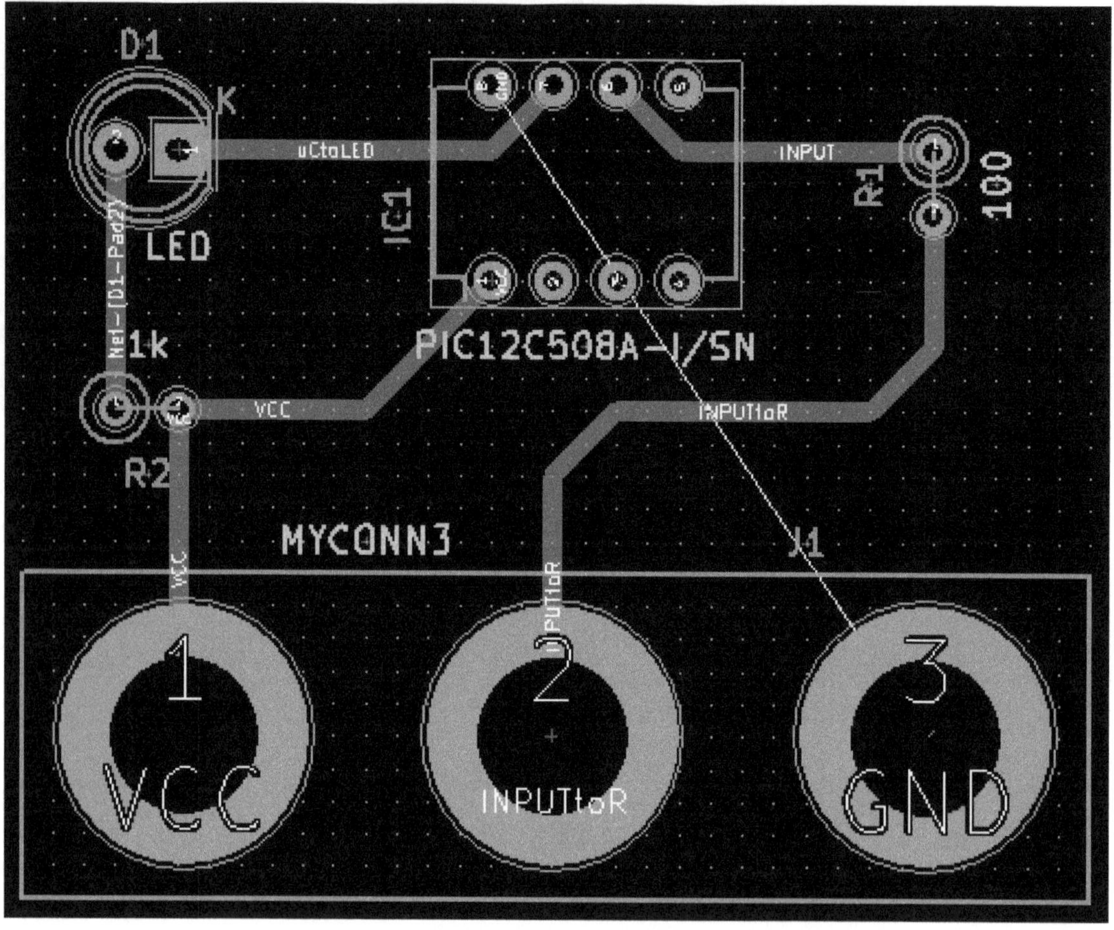

20. Let' s now run a track on the other copper side of the PCB. Select *B.Cu* in the drop-down menu on the top toolbar. Click on the *Add tracks and vias* icon . Draw a track between pin 3 of J1 and pin 8 of U1. This is actually not necessary since we could do this with the ground plane. Notice how the colour of the track has changed.

21. **Go from pin A to pin B by changing layer**. It is possible to change the copper plane while you are running a track by placing a via. While you are running a track on the upper copper plane, right click and select *Place Via* or simply press the v key. This will take you to the bottom layer where you can complete your track.

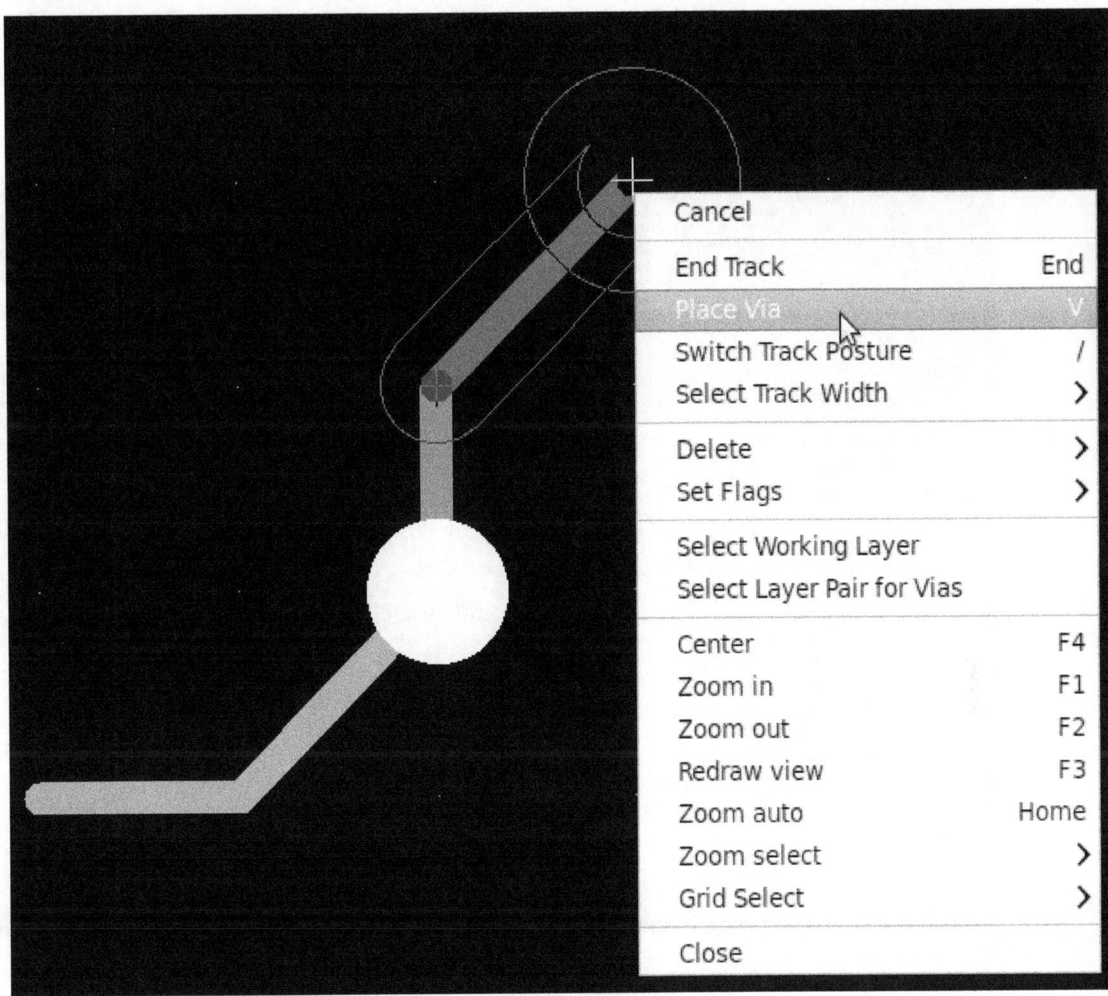

22. When you want to inspect a particular connection you can click on the *Net highlight* icon on the right toolbar. Click on pin 3 of J1. The track itself and all pads connected to it should become highlighted.

23. Now we will make a ground plane that will be connected to all GND pins. Click on the *Add Zones* icon on the right toolbar. We are going to trace a rectangle around the board, so click where you want one of the corners to be. In the dialogue that appears, set *Pad in Zone* to *Thermal relief* and *Zone edges orient* to *H,V* and click OK.

24. Trace around the outline of the board by clicking each corner in rotation. Double-click to finish your rectangle. Right click inside the area you have just traced. Click on *Fill or Refill All Zones.* The board should fill in with green and look something like this:

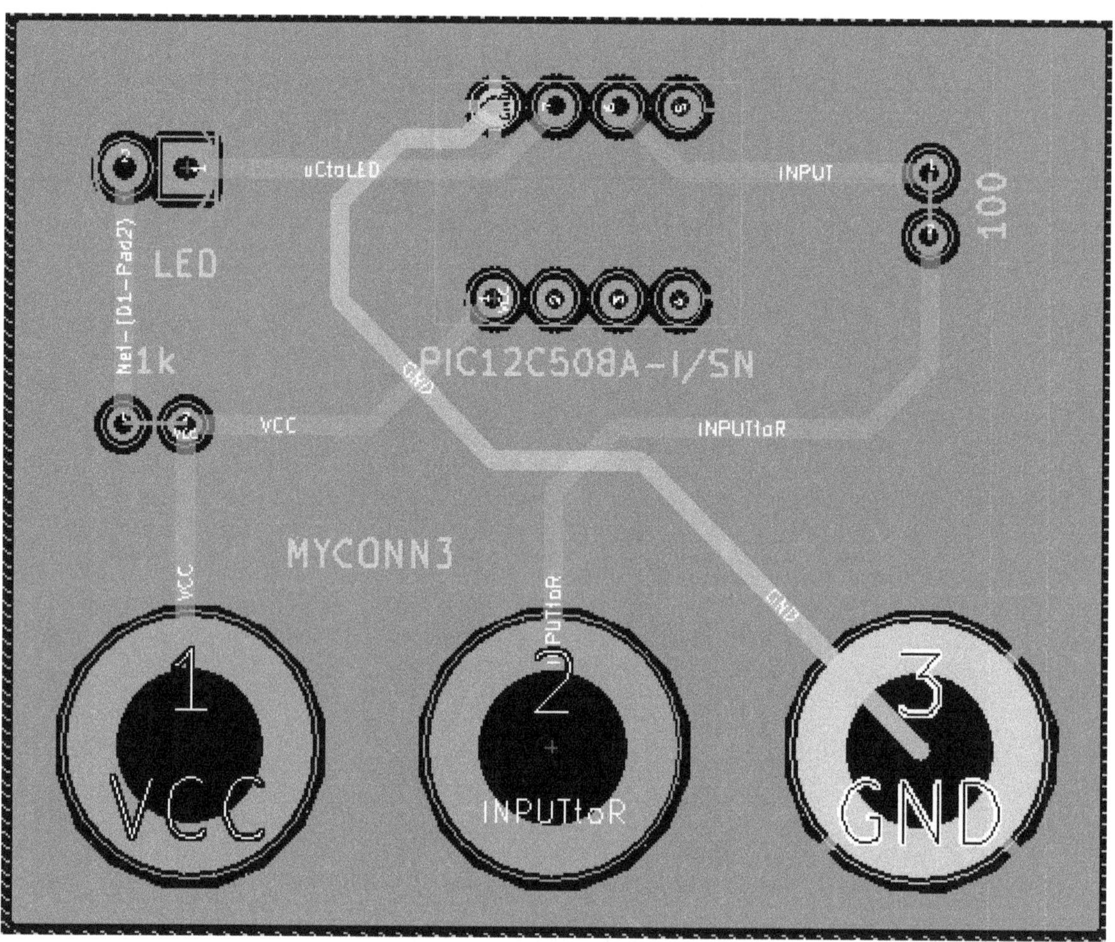

25. Run the design rules checker by clicking on the *Perform Design Rules Check* icon on the top toolbar. Click on *Start DRC*. There should be no errors. Click on *List Unconnected*. There should be no unconnected track. Click OK to close the DRC Control dialogue.

26. Save your file by clicking on **File** → **Save**. To admire your board in 3D, click on **View** → **3D Viewer**.

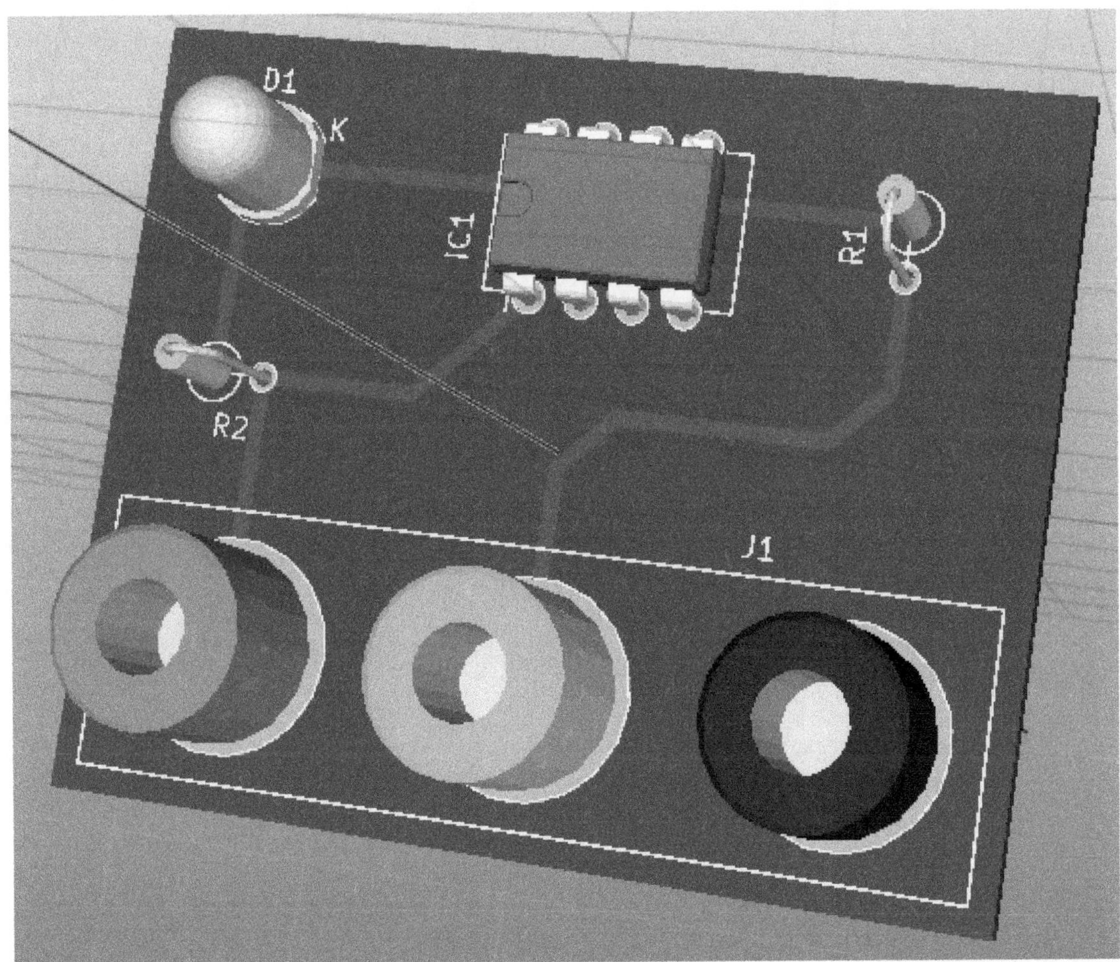

27. You can drag your mouse around to rotate the PCB.

28. Your board is complete. To send it off to a manufacturer you will need to generate all Gerber files.

4.2 Generate Gerber files

Once your PCB is complete, you can generate Gerber files for each layer and send them to your favourite PCB manufacturer, who will make the board for you.

1. From KiCad, open the *Pcbnew* software tool and load your board file by clicking on the icon .

2. Click on **File → Plot**. Select *Gerber* as the *Plot Format* and select the folder in which to put all Gerber files. Proceed by clicking on the *Plot* button.

3. These are the layers you need to select for making a typical 2-layer PCB:

Layer	KiCad Layer Name	Old KiCad Layer Name	Default Gerber Extension	"Use Protel filename extensions" is enabled
Bottom Layer	B.Cu	Copper	.GBR	.GBL
Top Layer	F.Cu	Component	.GBR	.GTL
Top Overlay	F.SilkS	SilkS_Cmp	.GBR	.GTO
Bottom Solder Resist	B.Mask	Mask_Cop	.GBR	.GBS
Top Solder Resist	F.Mask	Mask_Cmp	.GBR	.GTS
Edges	Edge.Cuts	Edges_Pcb	.GBR	.GM1

4.3 Using GerbView

1. To view all your Gerber files go to the KiCad project manager and click on the *GerbView* icon. On the drop-down menu select *Layer 1*. Click on **File → Load Gerber file** or click on the icon . Load all generated Gerber files one at a time. Note how they all get displayed one on top of the other.
2. Use the menu on the right to select/deselect which layer to show. Carefully inspect each layer before sending them for production.
3. To generate the drill file, from *Pcbnew* go again to the **File → Plot** option. Default settings should be fine.

4.4 Automatically route with FreeRouter

Routing a board by hand is quick and fun, however, for a board with lots of components you might want to use an autorouter. Remember that you should first route critical traces by hand and then set the autorouter to do the boring bits. Its work will only account for the unrouted traces. The autorouter we will use here is FreeRouter from *freerouting.net*.

Note

Freerouter is an open source java application, and it is needed to build by yourself to use with KiCad. Source code of Freerouter can be found on this site: https://github.com/nikropht/FreeRouting

---

1. From *Pcbnew* click on **File → Export → Specctra DSN** or click on **Tools → FreeRoute → Export a Specctra Design (*.dsn) file** and save the file locally. Launch FreeRouter and click on the *Open Your Own Design* button, browse for the *dsn* file and load it.

   Note

   The **Tools → FreeRoute** dialog has a nice help button that opens a file viewer with a little document inside named **Freerouter Guidelines**. Please follow these guidelines to use FreeRoute effectively.

   ---

2. FreeRouter has some features that KiCad does not currently have, both for manual routing and for automatic routing. FreeRouter operates in two main steps: first, routing the board and then optimising it. Full optimisation can take a long time, however you can stop it at any time need be.

3. You can start the automatic routing by clicking on the *Autorouter* button on the top bar. The bottom bar gives you information about the on-going routing process. If the *Pass* count gets above 30, your board probably can not be autorouted with this router. Spread your components out more or rotate them better and try again. The goal in rotation and position of parts is to lower the number of crossed airlines in the ratsnest.

4. Making a left-click on the mouse can stop the automatic routing and automatically start the optimisation process. Another left-click will stop the optimisation process. Unless you really need to stop, it is better to let FreeRouter finish its job.

5. Click on the **File → Export Specctra Session File** menu and save the board file with the *.ses* extension. You do not really need to save the FreeRouter rules file.

6. Back to *Pcbnew*. You can import your freshly routed board by clicking on the link **Tools → FreeRoute** and then on the icon *Back Import the Spectra Session (.ses) File* and selecting your *.ses* file.

If there is any routed trace that you do not like, you can delete it and re-route it again, using the del key and the routing tool, which is the *Add tracks* icon on the right toolbar.

Chapter 5

Forward annotation in KiCad

Once you have completed your electronic schematic, the footprint assignment, the board layout and generated the Gerber files, you are ready to send everything to a PCB manufacturer so that your board can become reality.

Often, this linear work-flow turns out to be not so uni-directional. For instance, when you have to modify/extend a board for which you or others have already completed this work-flow, it is possible that you need to move components around, replace them with others, change footprints and much more. During this modification process, what you do not want to do is to re-route the whole board again from scratch. Instead, this is how you do it:

1. Let' s suppose that you want to replace a hypothetical connector CON1 with CON2.
2. You already have a completed schematic and a fully routed PCB.
3. From KiCad, start *Eeschema*, make your modifications by deleting CON1 and adding CON2. Save your schematic project with the icon and c lick on the *Netlist generation* icon NET on the top toolbar.
4. Click on *Netlist* then on *save*. Save to the default file name. You have to rewrite the old one.
5. Now assign a footprint to CON2. Click on the *Run Cvpcb* icon on the top toolbar. Assign the footprint to the new device CON2. The rest of the components still have the previous footprints assigned to them. Close *Cvpcb*.
6. Back in the schematic editor, save the project by clicking on *File → Save Whole Schematic Project*. Close the schematic editor.
7. From the KiCad project manager, click on the *Pcbnew* icon. The *Pcbnew* window will open.
8. The old, already routed, board should automatically open. Let' s import the new netlist file. Click on the *Read Netlist* icon NET on the top toolbar.
9. Click on the *Browse Netlist Files* button, select the netlist file in the file selection dialogue, and click on *Read Current Netlist*. Then click the *Close* button.

10. At this point you should be able to see a layout with all previous components already routed. On the top left corner you should see all unrouted components, in our case the CON2. Select CON2 with the mouse. Move the component to the middle of the board.

11. Place CON2 and route it. Once done, save and proceed with the Gerber file generation as usual.

The process described here can easily be repeated as many times as you need. Beside the Forward Annotation method described above, there is another method known as Backward Annotation. This method allows you to make modifications to your already routed PCB from Pcbnew and updates those modifications in your schematic and netlist file. The Backward Annotation method, however, is not that useful and is therefore not described here.

Chapter 6

Make schematic components in KiCad

Sometimes a component that you want to place on your schematic is not in a KiCad library. This is quite normal and there is no reason to worry. In this section we will see how a new schematic component can be quickly created with KiCad. Nevertheless, remember that you can always find KiCad components on the Internet. For instance from here:

http://per.launay.free.fr/kicad/kicad_php/composant.php

In KiCad, a component is a piece of text that starts with a *DEF* and ends with *ENDDEF*. One or more components are normally placed in a library file with the extension *.lib*. If you want to add components to a library file you can just use the cut and paste commands.

6.1 Using Component Library Editor

1. We can use the *Component Library Editor* (part of *Eeschema*) to make new components. In our project folder *tutorial1* let' s create a folder named *library*. Inside we will put our new library file *myLib.lib* as soon as we have created our new component.
2. Now we can start creating our new component. From KiCad, start *Eeschema*, click on the *Library Editor* icon and then click on the *New component* icon . The Component Properties window will appear. Name the new component *MYCONN3*, set the *Default reference designator* as *J*, and the *Number of parts per package* as *1*. Click OK. If the warning appears just click yes. At this point the component is only made of its labels. Let' s add some pins. Click on the *Add Pins* icon on the right toolbar. To place the pin, left click in the centre of the part editor sheet just below the *MYCONN3* label.
3. In the Pin Properties window that appears, set the pin name to *VCC*, set the pin number to *1*, and the *Electrical type* to *Passive* then click OK.

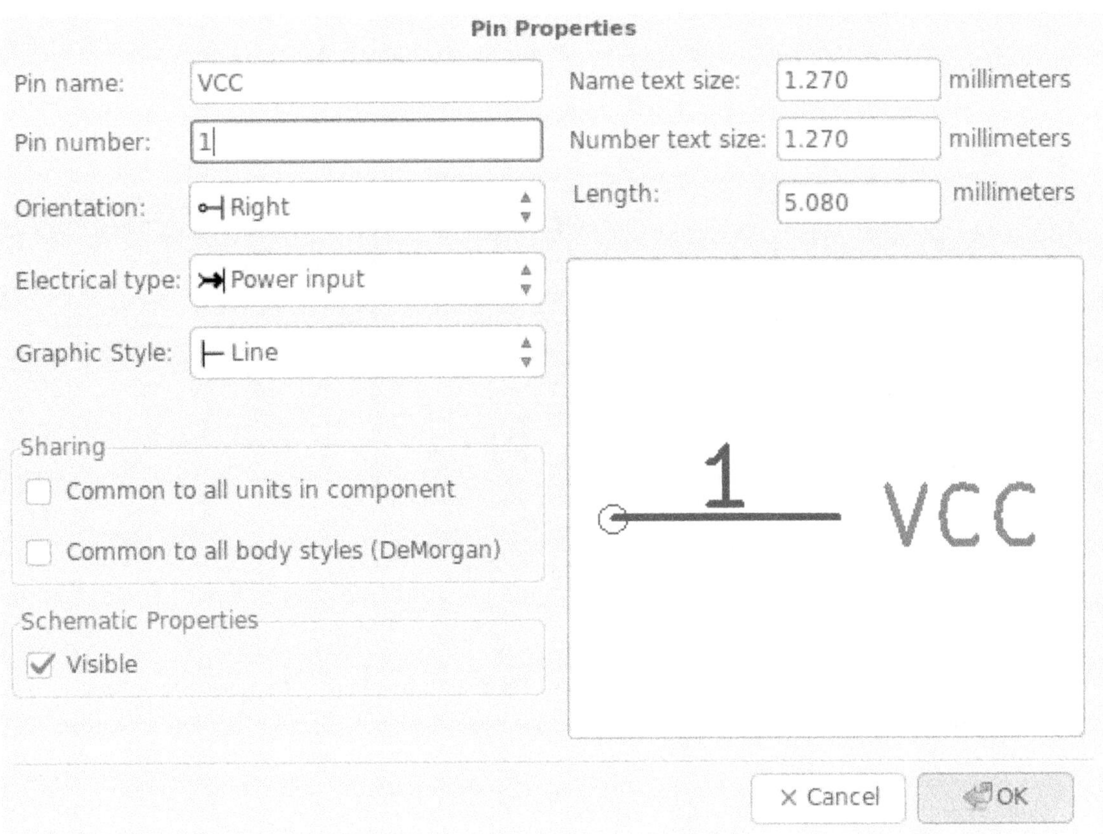

4. Place the pin by clicking on the location you would like it to go, right below the *MYCONN3* label.
5. Repeat the place-pin steps, this time *Pin name* should be *INPUT*, *Pin number* should be *2*, and *Electrical Type* should be *Passive*.
6. Repeat the place-pin steps, this time *Pin name* should be *GND*, *Pin number* should be *3*, and *Electrical Type* should be *Passive*. Arrange the pins one on top of the other. The component label *MYCONN3* should be in the centre of the page (where the blue lines cross).
7. Next, draw the contour of the component. Click on the *Add rectangle* icon . We want to draw a rectangle next to the pins, as shown below. To do this, click where you want the top left corner of the rectangle to be (do not hold the mouse button down). Click again where you want the bottom right corner of the rectangle to be.

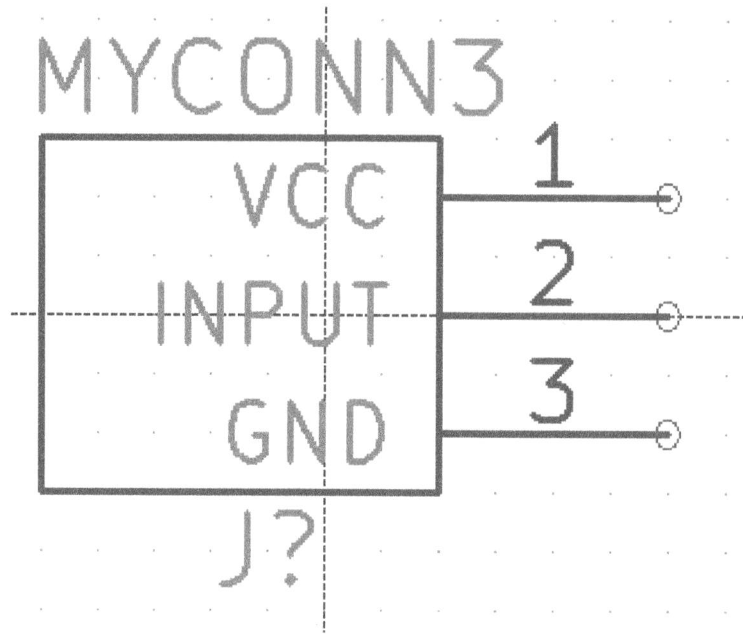

8. If you want to fill the rectangle with yellow, set the fill colour to *yellow 4* in **Preferences → Select color scheme**, then select the rectangle in the editing screen and edit (E), selecting *Fill background.*

9. Save the component in your library *myLib.lib*. Click on the *New Library* icon, navigate into *tutorial1/ library/* folder and save the new library file with the name *myLib.lib*.

10. Go to **Preferences → Component Libraries** and add both *tutorial1/library/* in *User defined search path* and *myLib.lib in Component library files.*

11. Click on the *Select working library* icon. In the Select Library window click on *myLib* and click OK. Notice how the heading of the window indicates the library currently in use, which now should be *myLib.*

12. Click on the *Update current component in current library* icon in the top toolbar. Save all changes by clicking on the *Save current loaded library on disk* icon in the top toolbar. Click *Yes* in any confirmation messages that appear. The new schematic component is now done and available in the library indicated in the window title bar.

13. You can now close the Component library editor window. You will return to the schematic editor window. Your new component will now be available to you from the library *myLib.*

14. You can make any library *file.lib* file available to you by adding it to the library path. From *Eeschema*, go to **Preferences → Library** and add both the path to it in *User defined search path* and *file.lib* in *Component library files.*

6.2 Export, import and modify library components

Instead of creating a library component from scratch it is sometimes easier to start from one already made and modify it. In this section we will see how to export a component from the KiCad standard library *device* to your own library *myOwnLib.lib* and then modify it.

1. From KiCad, start *Eeschema*, click on the *Library Editor* icon, click on the *Select working library* icon and choose the library *device*. Click on *Load component to edit from the current lib* icon and import the *RELAY_2RT*.
2. Click on the *Export component* icon, navigate into the *library/* folder and save the new library file with the name *myOwnLib.lib*.
3. You can make this component and the whole library *myOwnLib.lib* available to you by adding it to the library path. From *Eeschema*, go to **Preferences → Component Libraries** and add both *library/* in *User defined search path* and *myOwnLib.lib* in the *Component library files*. Close the window.
4. Click on the *Select working library* icon. In the Select Library window click on *myOwnLib* and click OK. Notice how the heading of the window indicates the library currently in use, it should be *myOwnLib*.
5. Click on the *Load component to edit from the current lib* icon and import the *RELAY_2RT*.
6. You can now modify the component as you like. Hover over the label *RELAY_2RT*, press the e key and rename it *MY_RELAY_2RT*.
7. Click on *Update current component in current library* icon in the top toolbar. Save all changes by clicking on the *Save current loaded library on disk* icon in the top toolbar.

6.3 Make schematic components with quicklib

This section presents an alternative way of creating the schematic component for MYCONN3 (see MYCONN3 above) using the Internet tool *quicklib*.

1. Head to the *quicklib* web page: http://kicad.rohrbacher.net/quicklib.php
2. Fill out the page with the following information: Component name: MYCONN3 Reference Prefix: J Pin Layout Style: SIL Pin Count, N: 3
3. Click on the *Assign Pins* icon. Fill out the page with the following information: Pin 1: VCC Pin 2: input Pin 3: GND. Type : Passive for all 3 pins.

4. Click on the icon *Preview it* and, if you are satisfied, click on the *Build Library Component.* Download the file and rename it *tutorial1/library/myQuickLib.lib.*. You are done!

5. Have a look at it using KiCad. From the KiCad project manager, start *Eeschema*, click on the *Library Editor* icon, click on the *Import Component* icon, navigate to *tutorial1/library/* and select *myQuickLib.lib.*

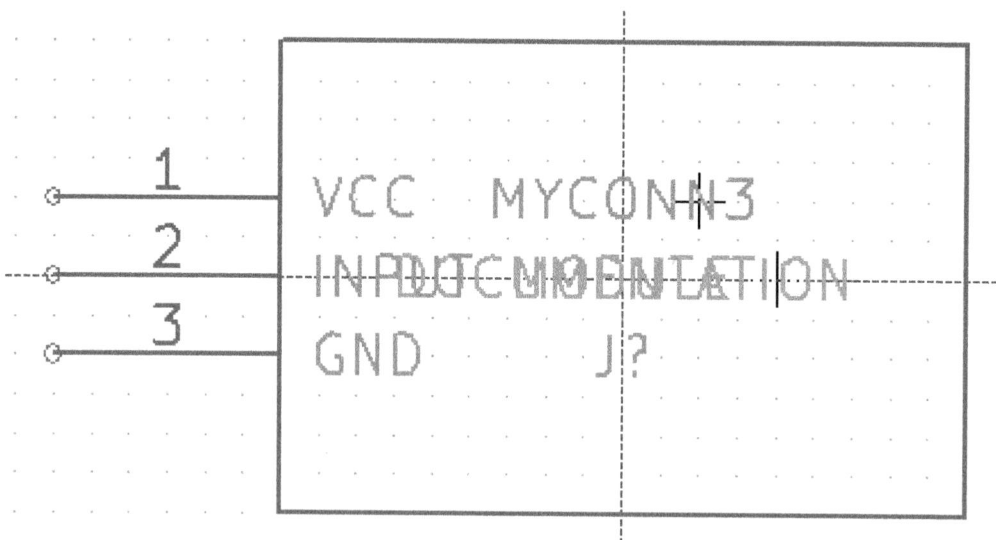

6. You can make this component and the whole library *myQuickLib.lib* available to you by adding it to the KiCad library path. From *Eeschema*, go to **Preferences** → **Component Libraries** and add *library* in *User defined search path* and *myQuickLib.lib* in *Component library files.*

As you might guess, this method of creating library components can be quite effective when you want to create components with a large pin count.

6.4 Make a high pin count schematic component

In the section titled *Make Schematic Components in quicklib* we saw how to make a schematic component using the *quicklib* web-based tool. However, you will occasionally find that you need to create a schematic component with a high number of pins (some hundreds of pins). In KiCad, this is not a very complicated task.

1. Suppose that you want to create a schematic component for a device with 50 pins. It is common practise to draw it using multiple low pin-count drawings, for example two drawings with 25 pins each. This component representation allows for easy pin connection.

2. The best way to create our component is to use *quicklib* to generate two 25-pin components separately, re-number their pins using a Python script and finally merge the two by using copy and paste to make them into one single DEF and ENDDEF component.

3. You will find an example of a simple Python script below that can be used in conjunction with an *in.txt* file and an *out.txt* file to re-number the line: `X PIN1 1 -750 600 300 R 50 50 1 1 I` into `X PIN26 26 -750 600 300 R 50 50 1 1 I` this is done for all lines in the file *in.txt.*

Simple script

```
#!/usr/bin/env python
''' simple script to manipulate KiCad component pins numbering'''
import sys, re
try:
    fin=open(sys.argv[1],'r')
    fout=open(sys.argv[2],'w')
except:
    print "oh, wrong use of this app, try:", sys.argv[0], "in.txt out.txt"
    sys.exit()
for ln in fin.readlines():
    obj=re.search("(X PIN)(\d*)(\s)(\d*)(\s.*)",ln)
if obj:
    num = int(obj.group(2))+25
    ln=obj.group(1) + str(num) + obj.group(3) + str(num) + obj.group(5) +'\n'
    fout.write(ln)
fin.close(); fout.close()
#
# for more info about regular expression syntax and KiCad component generation:
# http://gskinner.com/RegExr/
# http://kicad.rohrbacher.net/quicklib.php
```

1. While merging the two components into one, it is necessary to use the Library Editor from Eeschema to move the first component so that the second does not end up on top of it. Below you will find the final .lib file and its representation in *Eeschema*.

Contents of a *.lib file

```
EESchema-LIBRARY Version 2.3
#encoding utf-8
# COMP
DEF COMP U 0 40 Y Y 1 F N
F0 "U" -1800 -100 50 H V C CNN
F1 "COMP" -1800 100 50 H V C CNN
DRAW
S -2250 -800 -1350 800 0 0 0 N
S -450 -800 450 800 0 0 0 N
X PIN1 1 -2550 600 300 R 50 50 1 1 I

...

X PIN49 49 750 -500 300 L 50 50 1 1 I
ENDDRAW
ENDDEF
#End Library
```

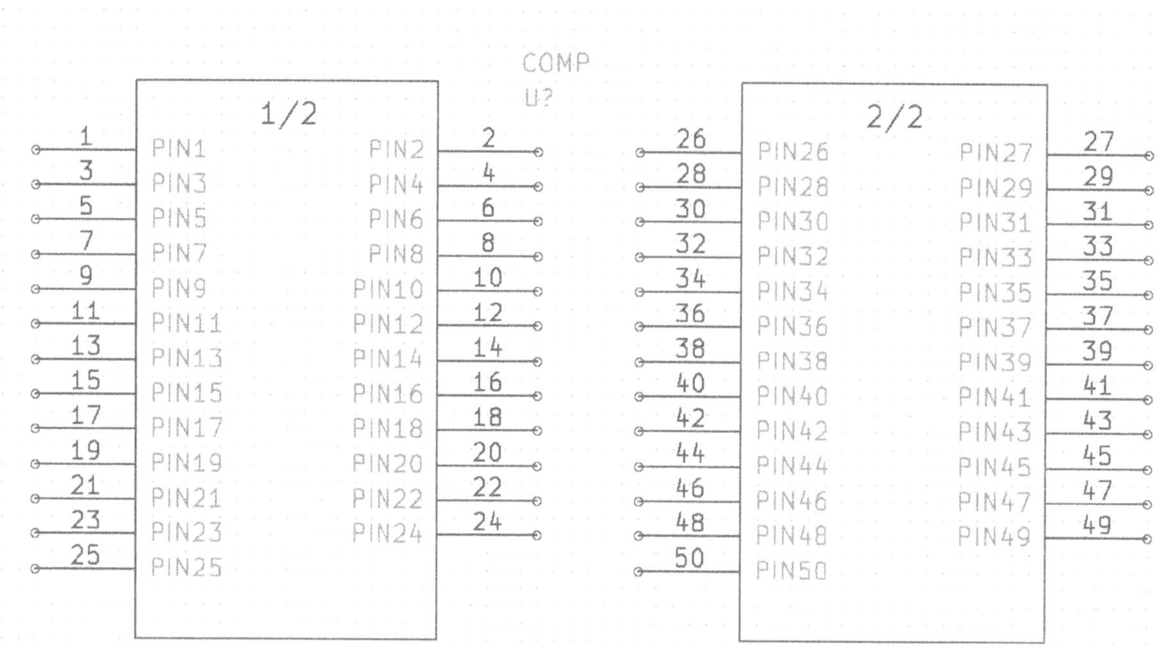

1. The Python script presented here is a very powerful tool for manipulating both pin numbers and pin labels. Mind, however, that all its power comes for the arcane and yet amazingly useful Regular Expression syntax: *http://gskinner.com/RegExr/*.

Chapter 7

Make component footprints

Unlike other EDA software tools, which have one type of library that contains both the schematic symbol and the footprint variations, KiCad *.lib* files contain schematic symbols and *.kicad_mod* files contain footprints. *Cvpcb* is used to successfully map footprints to symbols.

As for *.lib* files, *.kicad_mod* library files are text files that can contain anything from one to several parts.

There is an extensive footprint library with KiCad, however on occasion you might find that the footprint you need is not in the KiCad library. Here are the steps for creating a new PCB footprint in KiCad:

7.1 Using Footprint Editor

1. From the KiCad project manager start the *Pcbnew* tool. Click on the *Open Footprint Editor* icon on the top toolbar. This will open the *Footprint Editor.*
2. We are going to save the new footprint *MYCONN3* in the new footprint library *myfootprint.* Create a new folder *myfootprint.pretty* in the *tutorial1/* project folder. Click on the **Preferences → Footprint Libraries Manager** and press *Append Library* button. In the table, enter "myfootprint" as Nickname, enter "${KIPRJMOD}/ myfootprint.pretty" as Library Path and enter "KiCad" as Plugin Type. Press OK to close the PCB Library Tables window. Click on the *Select active library* icon on the top toolbar. Select the *myfootprint* library.
3. Click on the *New Footprint* icon on the top toolbar. Type *MYCONN3* as the *footprint name.* In the middle of the screen the *MYCONN3* label will appear. Under the label you can see the *REF* label. Right click on* MYCONN3 *and move it above* REF*. Right click on *REF__**, select *Edit Text* and rename it to *SMD.* Set the *Display* value to *Invisible.*
4. Select the *Add Pads* icon on the right toolbar. Click on the working sheet to place the pad. Right click on the new pad and click *Edit Pad.* You can otherwise use the e key shortcut.

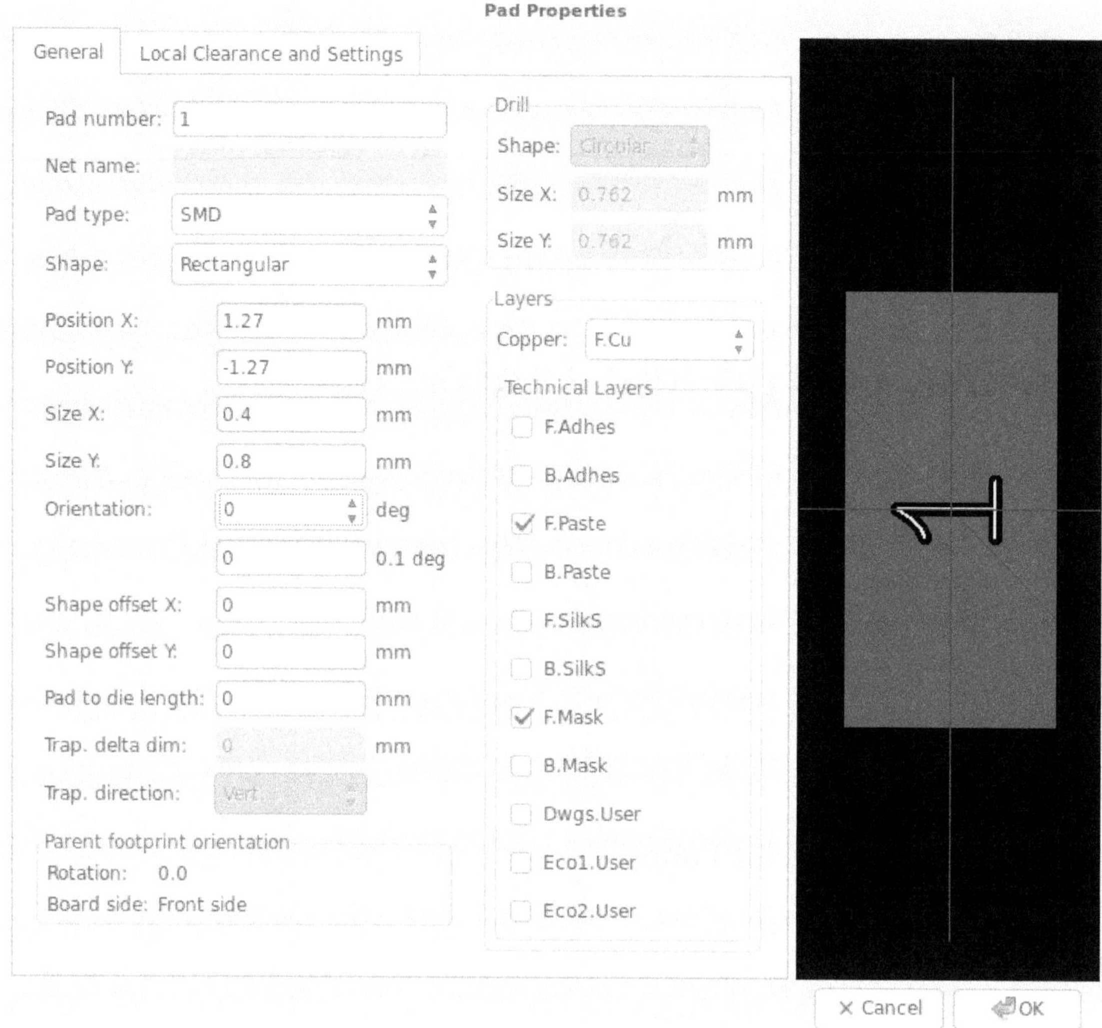

5. Set the *Pad Num* to *1*, *Pad Shape* to *Rect*, *Pad Type* to *SMD*, *Shape Size X* to *0.4*, and *Shape Size Y* to *0.8*. Click OK. Click on *Add Pads* again and place two more pads.

6. If you want to change the grid size, **Right click** → **Grid Select**. Be sure to select the appropriate grid size before laying down the components.

7. Move the *MYCONN3* label and the *SMD* label out of the way so that it looks like the image shown above.

8. When placing pads it is often necessary to measure relative distances. Place the cursor where you want the relative coordinate point *(0,0)* to be and press the space bar. While moving the cursor around, you will see a relative indication of the position of the cursor at the bottom of the page. Press the space bar at any time to set the new origin.

9. Now add a footprint contour. Click on the *Add graphic line or polygon* button in the right toolbar. Draw an outline of the connector around the component.

10. Click on the *Save Footprint in Active Library* icon on the top toolbar, using the default name MYCONN3.

Chapter 8

Note about portability of KiCad project files

What files do you need to send to someone so that they can fully load and use your KiCad project?

When you have a KiCad project to share with somebody, it is important that the schematic file *.sch*, the board file *.kicad_pcb*, the project file *.pro* and the netlist file *.net*, are sent together with both the schematic parts file *.lib* and the footprints file *.kicad_mod*. Only this way will people have total freedom to modify the schematic and the board.

With KiCad schematics, people need the *.lib* files that contain the symbols. Those library files need to be loaded in the *Eeschema* preferences. On the other hand, with boards (*.kicad_pcb* files), footprints can be stored inside the *.kicad_pcb* file. You can send someone a *.kicad_pcb* file and nothing else, and they would still be able to look at and edit the board. However, when they want to load components from a netlist, the footprint libraries (*.kicad_mod* files) need to be present and loaded in the *Pcbnew* preferences just as for schematics. Also, it is necessary to load the *.kicad_mod* files in the preferences of *Pcbnew* in order for those footprints to show up in *Cvpcb*.

If someone sends you a *.kicad_pcb* file with footprints you would like to use in another board, you can open the Footprint Editor, load a footprint from the current board, and save or export it into another footprint library. You can also export all the footprints from a *.kicad_pcb* file at once via **Pcbnew → File → Archive → Footprints → Create footprint archive**, which will create a new *.kicad_mod* file with all the board' s footprints.

Bottom line, if the PCB is the only thing you want to distribute, then the board file *.kicad_pcb* is enough. However, if you want to give people the full ability to use and modify your schematic, its components and the PCB, it is highly recommended that you zip and send the following project directory:

```
tutorial1/
|-- tutorial1.pro
|-- tutorial1.sch
|-- tutorial1.kicad_pcb
|-- tutorial1.net
|-- library/
|   |-- myLib.lib
|   |-- myOwnLib.lib
|   \-- myQuickLib.lib
|
|-- myfootprint.pretty/
|   \-- MYCONN3.kicad_mod
```

```
|
\-- gerber/
    |-- ...
    \-- ...
```

Chapter 9

More about KiCad documentation

This has been a quick guide on most of the features in KiCad. For more detailed instructions consult the help files which you can access through each KiCad module. Click on **Help** → **Manual**.

KiCad comes with a pretty good set of multi-language manuals for all its four software components.

The English version of all KiCad manuals are distributed with KiCad.

In addition to its manuals, KiCad is distributed with this tutorial, which has been translated into other languages. All the different versions of this tutorial are distributed free of charge with all recent versions of KiCad. This tutorial as well as the manuals should be packaged with your version of KiCad on your given platform.

For example, on Linux the typical locations are in the following directories, depending on your exact distribution:

```
/usr/share/doc/kicad/help/en/
/usr/local/share/doc/kicad/help/en
```

On Windows it is in:

```
<installation directory>/share/doc/kicad/help/en
```

On OS X:

```
/Library/Application Support/kicad/help/en
```

9.1 KiCad documentation on the Web

Latest KiCad documentations are available in multiple languages on the Web.

http://kicad-pcb.org/help/documentation/

KiCad

August 24, 2017

Contents

Reference manual

Copyright

Contributors

Jean-Pierre Charras, Fabrizio Tappero.

Feedback

Please direct any bug reports, suggestions or new versions to here:

- About KiCad document: https://github.com/KiCad/kicad-doc/issues
- About KiCad software: https://bugs.launchpad.net/kicad
- About KiCad software i18n: https://github.com/KiCad/kicad-i18n/issues

Publication date and software version

2015, may 21.

Chapter 1

Introduction

1.1 KiCad

KiCad is an open-source software tool for the creation of electronic schematic diagrams and PCB artwork. Beneath its singular surface, KiCad incorporates an elegant ensemble of the following software tools:

- **KiCad** : project manager
- **Eeschema** : schematic editor and component editor
- **CvPcb** : footprint selector helper (always run from Eeschema)
- **Pcbnew** : circuit board layout editor and footprint editor
- **GerbView** : Gerber viewer

3 utilities are included

- **Bitmap2Component**: component maker for logos. It creates a schematic component or a footprint from a bitmap picture.
- **PcbCalculator**: A calculator that is helpful to calculate components for regulators, track width versus current, transmission lines···
- **PlEditor**: Page Layout Editor.

These tools are usually run from the project manager, but can be also run as stand-alone tools.

At the time of writing, KiCad is considered mature and can be used for the successful development and maintenance of complex electronic boards.

KiCad does not present any board-size limitation and it can handle up to 32 copper layers, 14 technical layers and 4 auxiliary layers.

KiCad can create all the files necessary for building printed boards:

- Gerber files for photo-plotters
- drilling files
- component location files
- and a lot more.

Being open source (GPL licensed), KiCad represents the ideal tool for projects oriented towards the creation of electronic hardware with an open-source flavour.

KiCad is available for Linux, Windows and Apple OS X (still experimental, but is now working well).

1.2 KiCad files and folders

KiCad creates and uses files with the following specific file extensions (and folders) for schematic and board editing.

Project manager file:

*.pro	Small file containing a few parameters for the current project, including the component library list.

Schematic editor files:

*.sch	Schematic files, which do not contain the components themselves.
*.lib	Schematic component library files, containing the component descriptions: graphic shape, pins, fields.
*.dcm	Schematic component library documentation, containing some component descriptions: comments, keywords, reference to data sheets.
*_cache.lib	Schematic component library cache file, containing a copy of the components used in the schematic project.

Board editor files and folders:

*.kicad_pcb	Board file containing all info but the page layout.
*.pretty	Footprint **library folders**. The folder itself is the library.
*.kicad_mod	Footprint files, containing one footprint description each.
*.brd	Board file in the legacy format. Can be read, but not written by the board editor.
*.mod	Footprint library in the legacy format. Can be read by the footprint or the board editor, but not written.
fp-lib-table	Footprint library list (*footprint libraries table*): list of footprint libraries (various formats) which are loaded by the board or the footprint editor or CvPcb.

Common files:

*.kicad_wks	The page layout description files, for people who want a worksheet with a custom look.

*.net	Netlist file created by the schematic, and read by the board editor. This file is associated to the .cmp file, for users who prefer a separate file for the component/ footprint association.

Special file:

*.cmp	Stores the association between components used in the schematic and their footprints. It can be created by Pcbnew, and imported by Eeschema. The purpose is a back import from Pcbnew to Eeschema, for users who change footprints inside Pcbnew (for instance using *Exchange Footprints* command) and want to import these changes in schematic.

Other files:

They are generated by KiCad for fabrication or documentation.

*.gbr	Gerber files, for fabrication
*.drl	Drill files (Excellon format), for fabrication.
*.pos	Position files (ascii format), for automatic insertion machines.
*.rpt	Report files (ascii format), for documentation.
*.ps	Plot files (postscript), for documentation.
*.pdf	Plot files (pdf format), for documentation.
*.svg	Plot files (svg format), for documentation.
*.dxf	Plot files (dxf format), for documentation.
*.plt	Plot files (HPGL format), for documentation.

Chapter 2

Installation and configuration

2.1 Display options

Pcbnew needs the support of OpenGL v2.1 or more.

2.2 Initialization of the default configuration

A default configuration file named *kicad.pro* is supplied in kicad/template. It serves as a template for any new project.

If another default configuration file named *fp-lib-table* exists, it will be used only once to create a footprint library list. (or else, this list will be created from scratch)

The default file *kicad.pro* can be freely modified if necessary, mainly to set the list of library files loaded by Eeschema.

A few other parameters (default text size, default line thickness, mainly for Pcbnew) are stored here.

Verify that you have write access to kicad/template/kicad.pro

Run KiCad and load *kicad.pro* project.

Run Eeschema via KiCad. Modify and update the Eeschema configuration, and mainly the list of libraries you want to use each time you create new projects.

Run Pcbnew via KiCad. Modify and update the Pcbnew configuration, especially the footprint library list. Pcbnew will create or update a library list file called **footprint library table**. There are 2 library list files (named fp-lib-table). The first (located in the user home directory) is global for all projects. The second, if it exists (located in the project directory) is specific to the project.

2.3 Initialization of some options and utilities

When using KiCad, a text editor and a PDF viewer are useful. Setting them is a good idea.

These settings are accessible from the Preference menu

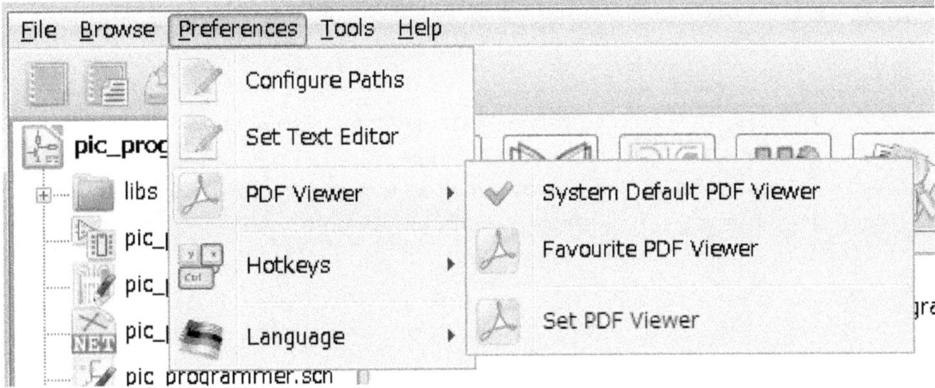

3 options are especially important:

- Configure Paths
- PDF Viewer
- Set Text Editor

2.4 Configuration of paths

In KiCad, one can define some paths using an *environment variable.* A few environment variables are internally defined by KiCad, and can be used to define paths (for libraries, 3D shapes, etc).

This is useful when absolute paths are not known or are subject to change. This is the case for "official" libraries built for KiCad:

- for the path of these libraries, when installed on your disk
- for the path of 3D shapes files used in footprint definitions.

For instance, the full path of *connect.pretty* footprint library is defined like this, when using the KISYSMOD environment variable to define the full path: ${KISYSMOD}/connect.pretty

Obviously, one can use a usual full path definition, if this full path is well known, and never changes.

This option allows you to define some paths from an environment variable, and add your own environment variables, to define personal paths, if needed.

KIGITHUB	frequently used in footprint lib tables examples. If you are using this variable, it must be defined.
KISYS3DMOD	default base path of 3D shapes files, and must be defined, because an absolute path is not usually used.
KISYSMOD	default base path of footprint library folders, and must be defined, if an absolute path is not used in footprint library names.

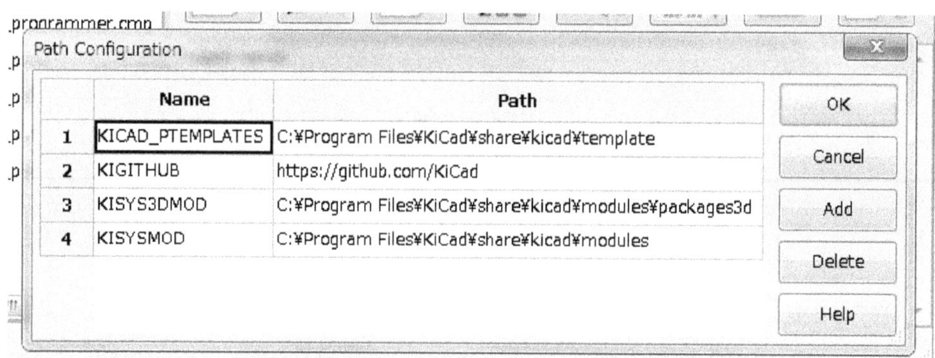

Note also the environment variable

- **KIPRJMOD**

is **always** internally defined by KiCad, and is the **current project absolute path**.

For instance, ***${KIPRJMOD}/connect.pretty*** is always the ***connect.pretty*** folder (the pretty footprint library) found ***inside the current project folder***.

- **If you modify the configuration of paths, please quit and rerun KiCad, to avoid any issues in path handling.**

2.5 Initialization of the text editor

Before using a text editor to browse/edit files in the current project, you have to choose the text editor you want to use. The menu:

Preferences/SetText Editor

allows you to set the text editor to use.

2.6 Initialization of the PDF viewer

You can use the default PDF viewer or choose your own PDF viewer.

Select *Preferences/PDF Viewer/Favourite PDF Viewer* to choose your favourite (default) PDF Viewer.

Your own (non default) viewer is chosen by using the *Preferences/PDF Viewer/SetPDF Viewer* menu.

On Linux, the default PDF viewer is known to be sometimes strange, so using *Favourite PDF Viewer* after selecting a suitable PDF viewer is mandatory.

2.7 KiCad: principles of use

In order to manage a KiCad project: schematic files, printed circuit board files, supplementary libraries, manufacturing files for photo-tracing, drilling and automatic component placement files, it is recommended to create a project as follows:

- **Create a working directory for the project** (using KiCad or by other means).
- **In this directory, use KiCad to create a project file** (file with extension .pro) via the "Create a new project" or "Create a new project from template" icon.

Warning

It is recommended to use a unique directory for each KiCad project. Do not combine multiple projects into a single directory.

KiCad creates a file with a .pro extension that maintains a number of parameters for project management (such as the list of libraries used in the schematic). Default names of both main schematic file and printed circuit board file are derived from the name of the project. Thus, if a project called *example.pro* was created in a directory called *example* , the default files will be created:

example.pro	project management file.
example.sch	main schematic file.
example.kicad_pcb	printed circuit board file.
example.net	netlist file.
example.xxx	various files created by the other utility programs.
example-cache.lib	library file automatically created and used by the schematic editor. (It contains a backup of the components used in the schematic).

Chapter 3

Use KiCad Manager

The KiCad Manager (kicad or kicad.exe file) is a tool which can easily run the other tools (editors, gerber viewer and utility tools) when creating a design.

Running the other tools from KiCad manager has some advantages:

- cross probing between schematic editor and board editor.
- cross probing between schematic editor and footprint selector (CvPcb).

But you can only edit the current project files.

(When these tools are run in *stand alone* mode, you can open any file in any project but cross probing between tools can give strange results)

3.1 Main window

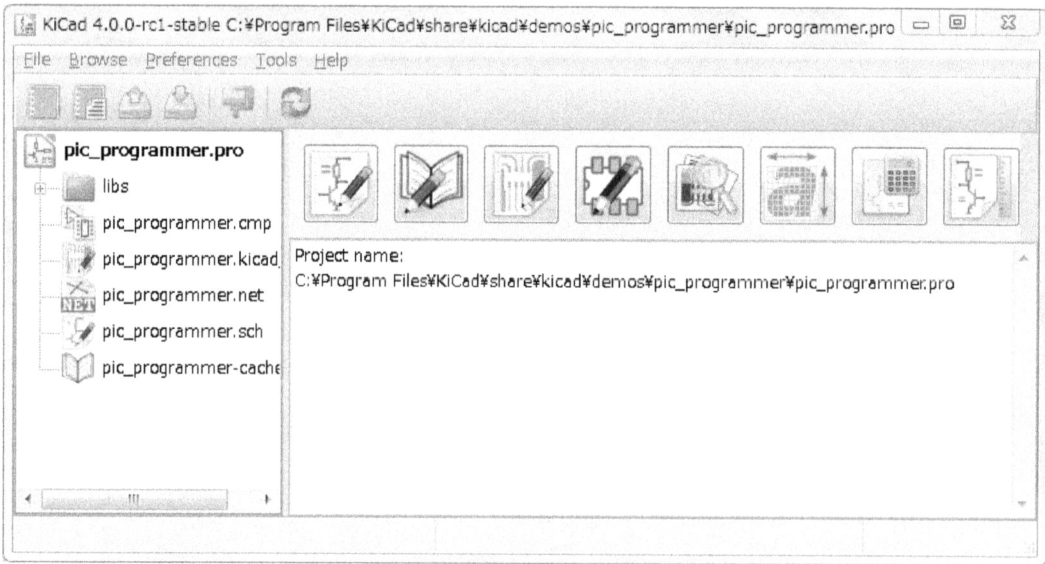

The main KiCad window is composed of a project tree view, a launch pane containing buttons used to run the various software tools, and a message window. The menu and the toolbar can be used to create, read and save project files.

3.2 Utility launch pane

KiCad allows you to run all stand alone software tools that come with it.

The launch pane is made of the 8 buttons below that correspond to the following commands (1 to 8, from left to right):

1	**Eeschema**	The schematic editor.
2	**LibEdit**	The component editor and component library manager.
3	**Pcbnew**	The board layout editor.
4	**FootprintEditor**	The footprint editor and footprint library manager.
5	**Gerbview**	A GERBER file viewer. It can also show drill files.
6	**Bitmap2component**	A tool to build a footprint or a component from a B&W bitmap image to create logos.
7	**Pcb Calculator**	A tool to calculate track widths, and many other things.
8	**Pl Editor**	The Page Layout editor, to create/customize frame references.

3.3 Project tree view

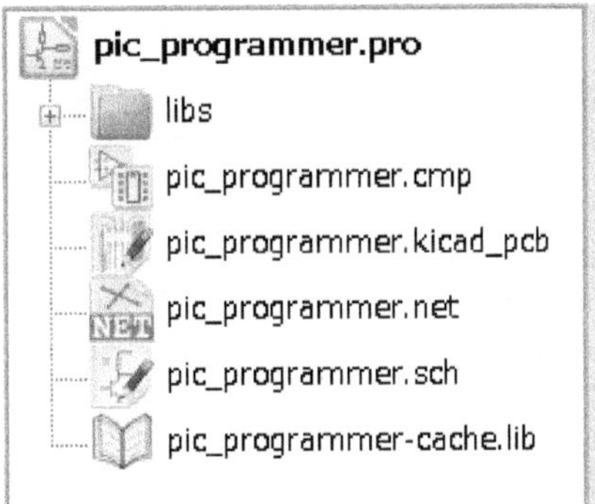

- Double-clicking on the Eeschema icon runs the schematic editor which in this case will open the file pic_programmer.sch.
- Double-clicking on the Pcbnew icon runs the layout editor, in this case opening the file pic_programmer.kicad_pcb.
- Right clicking on any of the files in the project tree allows generic file manipulation.

3.4 Top toolbar

KiCad top toolbar allows for some basic files operation (from left to right).

	Create a project file. If the template kicad.pro is found in kicad/template, it is copied into the working directory.
	Create a project from a template.
	Open an existing project.
	Update and save the current project tree.
	Create a zip archive of the whole project. This includes schematic files, libraries, pcb, etc.
	Rebuild and redraw the tree list, sometimes needed after a tree change.

Chapter 4

Using templates

4.1 Definitions

A template is a directory of files, which includes a directory of metadata.

The template system name (SYSNAME) is the directory name under which the template files are stored. The metadata directory (METADIR) contains pre-defined files which provide information about the template.

All files and directories in a template are copied to the new project path when a project is created using a template, except METADIR.

All files and directories which start with SYSNAME will have SYSNAME replaced by the new project file name, excluding the file extension.

4.2 Templates

They facilitate the easy setup of projects which have common attributes such as pre-defined board outlines, connector positions, schematic elements, design rules, etc. .

4.2.1 Metadata

A template' s METADIR must contain the required files, and might optionally contain any of the optional files.

4.2.2 Required Files:

meta/info.html

Contains html formatted information about the template which is used by the user to determine if the template is what they are after. The <title> tag determines the actual name of the template that is exposed to the user for template selection.

Using html to format this document means that images can be in-lined without having to invent a new scheme.

Only a basic HTML language can be used to format this document.

4.2.3 Optional Files:

meta/icon.png

A 64 x 64 pixels PNG icon file which is used as a clickable icon in the template selection dialog.

4.2.4 Example:

Here is a template for a raspberrypi-gpio board:

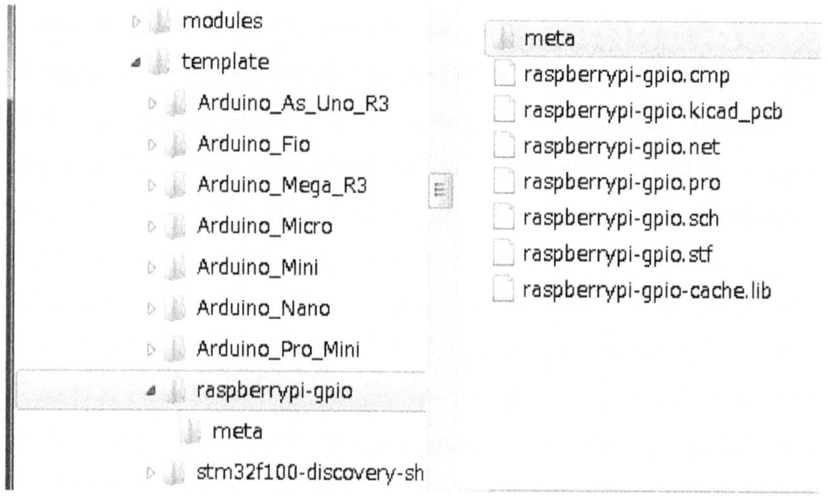

And the meta data info:

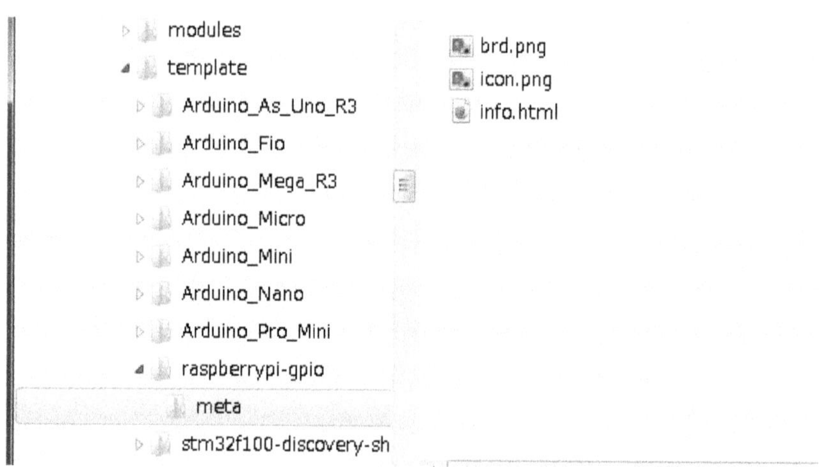

brd.png is an optional file.

Here is an info.html file sample:

```
<!DOCTYPE HTML PUBLIC "-//W3C//DTD HTML 4.0 Transitional//EN">
<HTML>
<HEAD>
```

```
<META HTTP-EQUIV="CONTENT-TYPE" CONTENT="text/html;
charset=windows-1252">
<TITLE>Raspberry Pi - Expansion Board</TITLE>
<META NAME="GENERATOR" CONTENT="LibreOffice 3.6 (Windows)">
<META NAME="CREATED" CONTENT="0;0">
<META NAME="CHANGED" CONTENT="20121015;19015295">
</HEAD>
<BODY LANG="fr-FR" DIR="LTR">
<P>This project template is the basis of an expansion board for the
<A HREF="http://www.raspberrypi.org/" TARGET="blank">Raspberry Pi $25
ARM board.</A> <BR><BR>This base project includes a PCB edge defined
as the same size as the Raspberry-Pi PCB with the connectors placed
correctly to align the two boards. All IO present on the Raspberry-Pi
board is connected to the project through the 0.1&quot; expansion
headers. <BR><BR>The board outline looks like the following:
</P>
<P><IMG SRC="brd.png" NAME="brd" ALIGN=BOTTOM WIDTH=680 HEIGHT=378
BORDER=0><BR><BR><BR><BR>
</P>
<P>(c)2012 Brian Sidebotham<BR>(c)2012 KiCad Developers</P>
</BODY>
</HTML>
```

4.2.5 Operation

The KiCad File menu New shows 2 option:

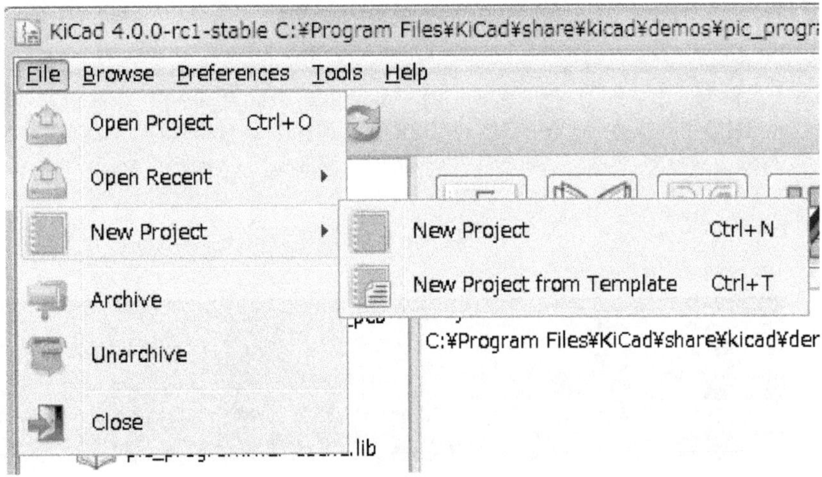

- **New Project** Create a blank project by just copying template/kicad.pro to the current folder.
- **Project from Template** Opens the template selection dialog. The template selection dialog has a list of icons, and a display window. A single click on a template' s icon on the top will load that template' s info.html metadata file and display it in the display window. A click on the OK button starts the new project creation. The template

will be copied to the new project location (excluding METADIR as mentioned earlier) and any files that match the string replacement rules will be renamed to reflect the new project' s name.

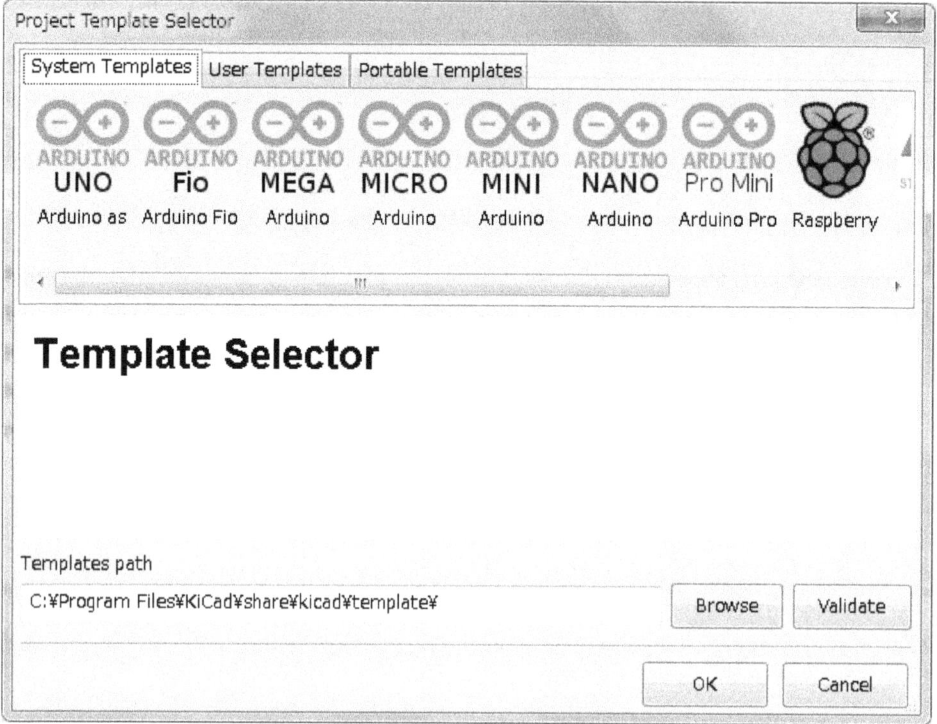

After selection of a template:

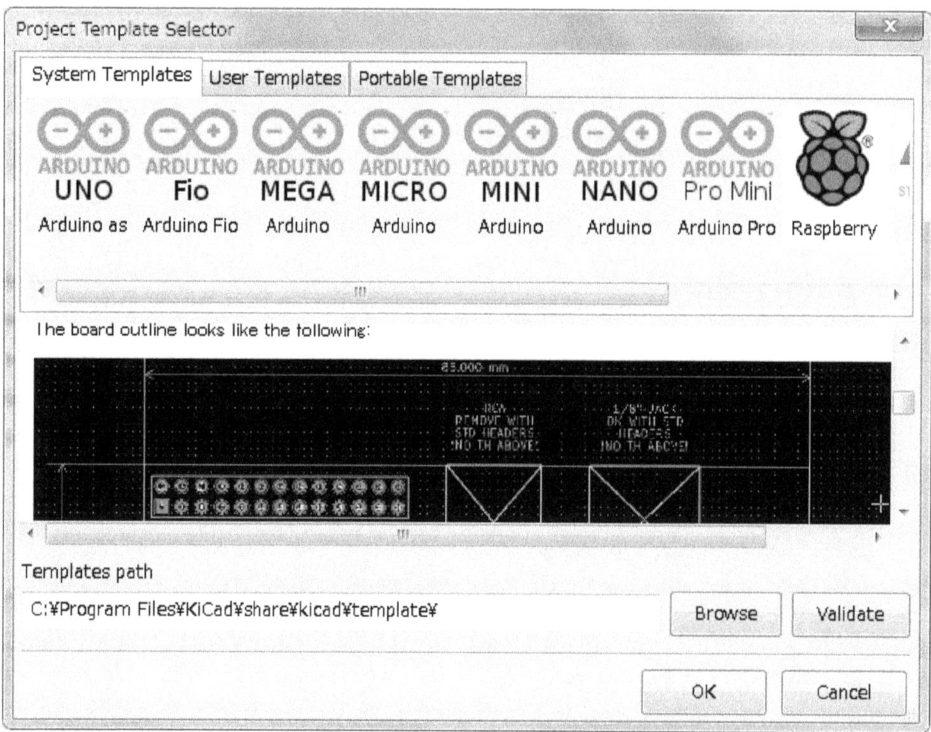

4.2.6 Templates Location:

The list of available templates are gathered from the following sources:

- For system templates: <kicad bin dir>/../share/template/
- For user templates:
  - on Unix: ~/kicad/templates/
  - on Windows: C:\Documents and Settings\username\My Documents\kicad\templates
  - on Mac: ~/Documents/kicad/templates/
- When the environment variable KICAD_PTEMPLATES is defined, there is a third page: Portable Templates, which lists templates found in KICAD_PTEMPLATES path.

Eeschema

August 24, 2017

Contents

Reference manual

Copyright

Contributors

Jean-Pierre Charras, Fabrizio Tappero.

Feedback

Please direct any bug reports, suggestions or new versions to here:

- About KiCad document: https://github.com/KiCad/kicad-doc/issues
- About KiCad software: https://bugs.launchpad.net/kicad
- About KiCad software i18n: https://github.com/KiCad/kicad-i18n/issues

Publication date and software version

Published on may 30, 2015.

Chapter 1

Introduction to Eeschema

1.1 Description

Eeschema is powerful schematic capture software distributed as part of KiCad and available under the following operating systems:

- Linux
- Apple OS X
- Windows

Regardless of the OS, all Eeschema files are 100% compatible from one OS to another.

Eeschema is an integrated application where all functions of drawing, control, layout, library management and access to the PCB design software are carried out within Eeschema itself.

Eeschema is intended to work with PcbNew, which is KiCad' s printed circuit design software. It can also export netlist files, which list all the electrical connections, for other packages.

Eeschema includes a component symbol editor, which can create and edit components and manage libraries. It also integrates the following additional but essential functions needed for modern schematic capture software:

- Electrical rules check (ERC) for the automatic control of incorrect and missing connections
- Export of plot files in many formats (Postscript, PDF, HPGL, and SVG)
- Bill of Materials generation (via Python scripts, which allow many configurable formats).

1.2 Technical overview

Eeschema is limited only by the available memory. There is thus no real limitation to the number of components, component pins, connections, or sheets. In the case of multi-sheet diagrams, the representation is hierarchical.

Eeschema can use multi-sheet diagrams of these types:

- Simple hierarchies (each schematic is used only once).
- Complex hierarchies (some schematics are used more than once with multiple instances).
- Flat hierarchies (schematics are not explicitly connected in a master diagram).

Chapter 2

Generic Eeschema commands

2.1 Access to Eeschema commands

You can reach the various commands by:

- Clicking on the menu bar (top of screen).
- Clicking on the icons on top of the screen (general commands).
- Clicking on the icons on the right side of the screen (particular commands or "tools").
- Clicking on the icons on the left side of the screen (display options).
- Pressing the mouse buttons (important complementary commands). In particular a right click opens a contextual menu for the element under the cursor (Zoom, grid and editing of the elements).
- Function keys (F1, F2, F3, F4, Insert and space keys). Specifically: The "Escape" key often allows the canceling of a command in progress. The "Insert" key allows the duplication of the last element created.

Here are the various possible command locations:

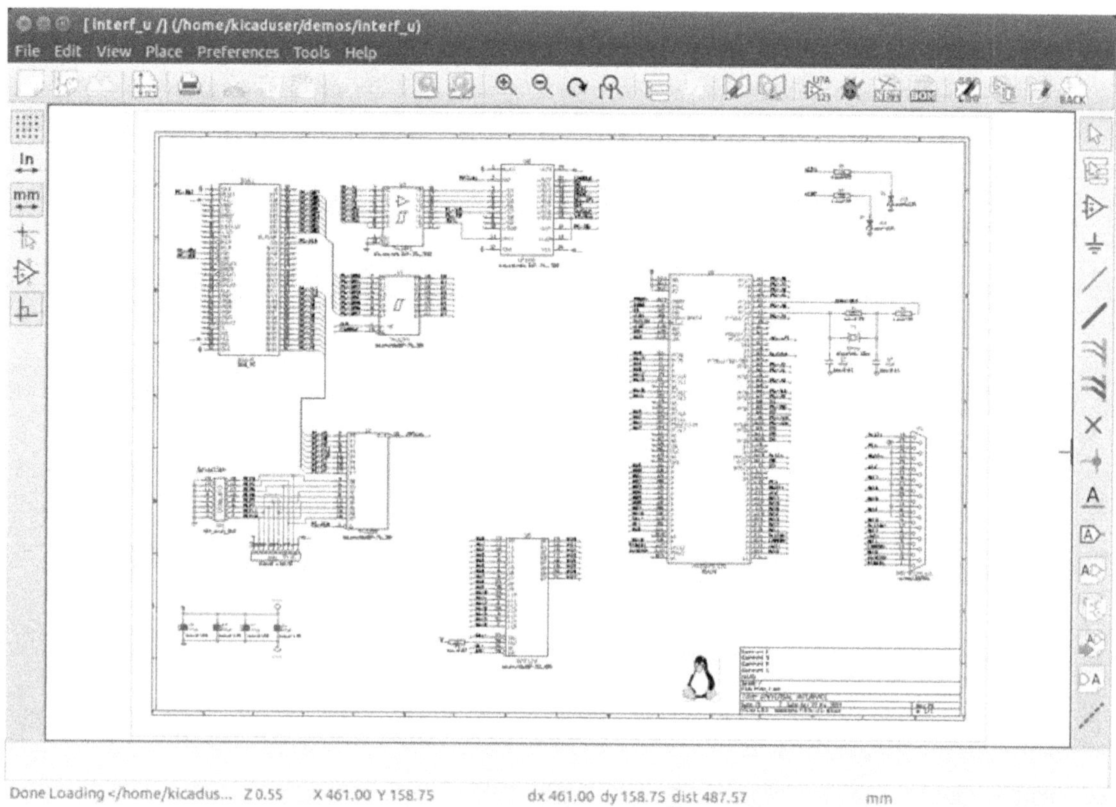

2.2 Mouse commands

2.2.1 Basic commands

Left button

- Single click: displays the characteristics of the component or text under the cursor in the status bar.
- Double click: edit (if the element is editable) the component or text.

Right button

- Opens a pop-up menu.

2.2.2 Operations on blocks

You can move, drag, copy and delete selected areas in all Eeschema menus.

Areas are selected by dragging a box around them using the left mouse button.

Holding "Shift", "Ctrl", or "Shift + Ctrl" during selection respectively performs copying, dragging, and deletion:

left mouse button	Move selection.
Shift + left mouse button	Copy selection.
Ctrl + left mouse button	Drag selection.
Ctrl + Shift + left mouse button	Delete selection.

When dragging or copying, you can:

- Click again to place the elements.
- Click the right button to cancel.

If a block move command has started, another command can be selected via the pop-up menu (mouse, right button):

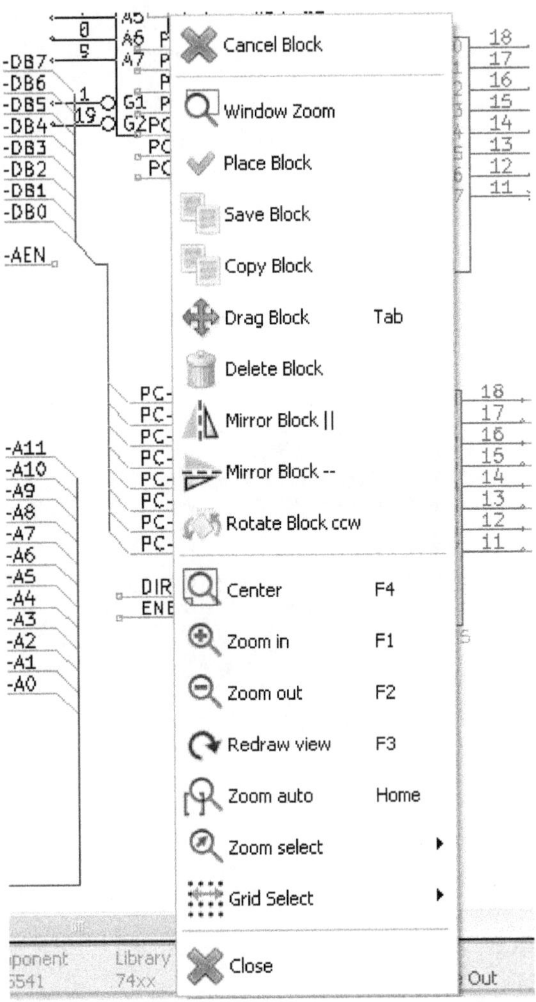

2.3 Hotkeys

- The "?" key displays the current hotkey list.

- Hotkeys can be managed by choosing "Edit Hotkeys" in the Preferences menu.

Here is the default hot key list:

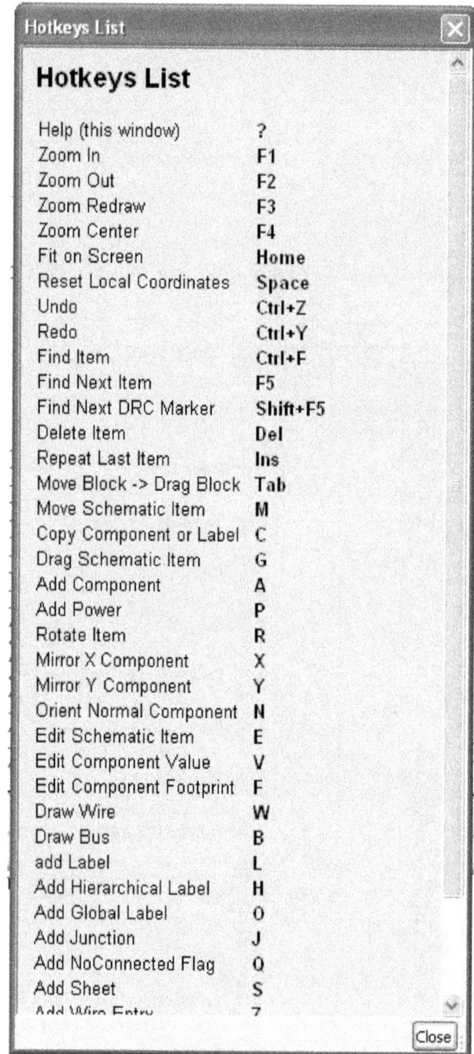

All hot keys can be redefined by the user via the hotkey editor:

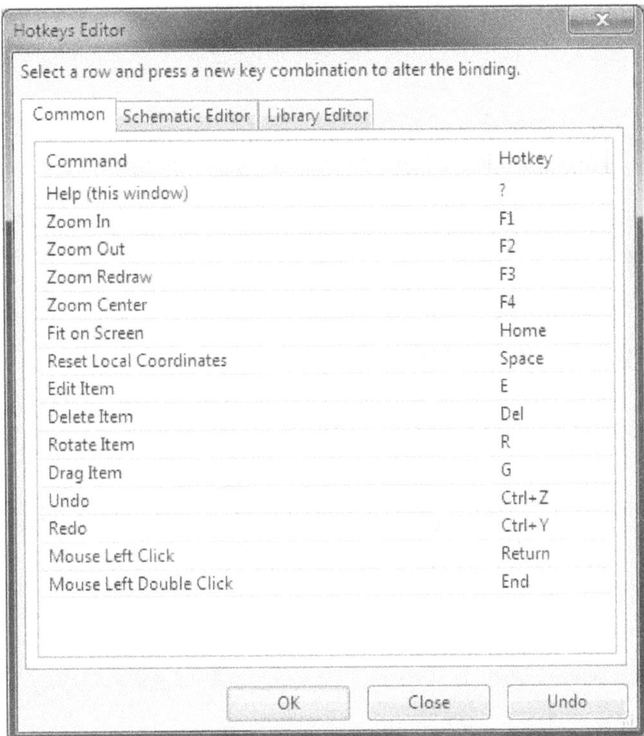

2.4 Selecting grid size

In Eeschema, the cursor moves over a grid, which can be displayed or hidden. The grid is always displayed in the library manager.

You can change the grid size via the pop-up menu or via the Preferences/Options menu.

The default grid size is 50 mil (0.050") or 1,27 millimeters.

This is the prefered grid to place components and wires in a schematic, and to place pins when designing a symbol in the Component Editor.

One can also work with a smaller grid from 25 mil to 10 mil. This is only intended for designing the component body or placing text and comments, not for placing pins and wires.

2.5 Zoom selection

To change the zoom level:

- Right click to open the Pop-up menu and select the desired zoom.
- Or use the function keys:
  - F1: Zoom in
  - F2: Zoom out

- F4 or simply click on the middle mouse button (without moving the mouse): Center the view around the cursor pointer position

- Window Zoom:
  - Mouse wheel: Zoom in/out
  - Shift+Mouse wheel: Pan up/down
  - Ctrl+Mouse wheel: Pan left/right

2.6 Displaying cursor coordinates

The display units are in inches or millimeters. However, Eeschema always works internally in 0.001-inch (mil/thou) units.

The following information is displayed at the bottom right hand side of the window:

- The zoom factor
- The absolute position of the cursor
- The relative position of the cursor

The relative coordinates can be reset to zero with the space bar. This is useful for making measurements between two points.

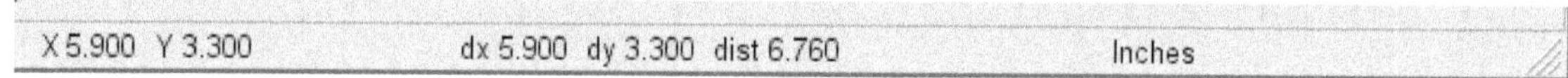

2.7 Top menu bar

The top menu bar allows the opening and saving of schematics, program configuration, and viewing the documentation.

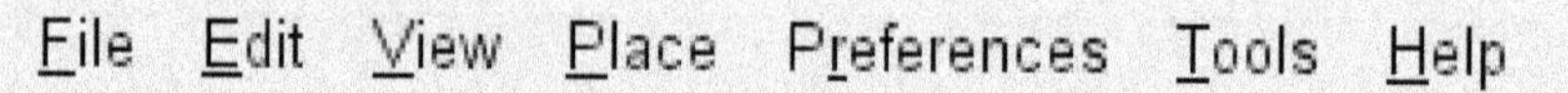

2.8 Upper toolbar

This toolbar gives access to the main functions of Eeschema.

If Eeschema is run in standalone mode, this is the available tool set:

If Eeschema is run from the project manager (KiCad), this is the available tool set:

Tools to initialize a project are not available, because these tools are in the *Project Manager*.

	Create a new schematic (only in standalone mode).
	Open a schematic (only in standalone mode).
	Save complete (hierarchical) schematic.
	Select the sheet size and edit the title block.
	Open print dialog.
	Remove the selected elements during a block move.
	Copy selected elements to the clipboard during a block move.
	Copy last selected element or block in the current sheet.
	Undo: Cancel the last change (up to 10 levels).
	Redo (up to 10 levels).
	Call the dialog to search components and texts in the schematic.
	Call the dialog to search and replace texts in the schematic.
	Zoom in and out.
	Refresh screen; zoom to fit.
	View and navigate the hierarchy tree.
	Leave the current sheet and go up in the hierarchy.
	Call component editor *Libedit* to view and modify libraries and component symbols.
	Display libraries (Viewlib).
U?A 123	Annotate components.
	Electrical rules check (ERC), automatically validate electrical connections.

	Export a netlist (Pcbnew, SPICE, and other formats).
	Generate the BOM (Bill of Materials).
	Edit footprint.
	Call CvPcb to assign footprints to components.
	Call Pcbnew to perform a PCB layout.
	Back-import component footprints (selected using CvPcb) into the "footprint" fields.

2.9 Right toolbar icons

This toolbar contains tools to:

- Place components, wires, buses, junctions, labels, text, etc.
- Create hierarchical sub-sheets and connection symbols

	Cancel the active command or tool.
	Hierarchy navigation: this tool makes it possible to open the subsheet of the displayed schematic (click in the symbol of this subsheet), or to go back up in the hierarchy (click in a free area of the schematic).
	Display the component selector.
	Display the power symbol selector.
	Draw a wire.
	Draw a bus.
	Draw wire-to-bus entry points. These elements are only graphical and do not create a connection, thus they should not be used to connect wires together.
	Draw bus-to-bus entry points.
	Place a "No Connect" flag. These are placed on component pins which are not to be connected. This is useful in the ERC function to check if pins are intentionally left not connected or are missed.
	Place a junction. This connects two crossing wires, or a wire and a pin, when it can be ambiguous. (i.e. if an end of the wire or pin is not connected to one of the ends of the other wire).
A	Local label placement. Two wires may be connected with identical labels **in the same sheet**. For connections between two different sheets, you have to use global or hierarchical labels.
A	Place a global label. All global labels with the same name are connected, even between different sheets.

		Place a hierarchical label. This makes it possible to place a connection between a sheet and the parent sheet that contains it.
		Place a hierarchical subsheet. You must specify the file name for this subsheet.
		Import hierarchical labels from a subsheet. These hierarchical labels must already be placed in the subsheet. These are equivalent to pins on a component, and must be connected using wires.
		Place hierarchical label in a subsheet symbol. This is placed by name and does not require the label to already exist in the subsheet itself.
		Draw a line. These are only graphical and do not connect anything.
	T	Place textual comments. These are only graphical.
		Place a bitmap image.
		Delete selected element. If several superimposed elements are selected, the priority is given to the smallest (in the decreasing priorities: junction, "No Connect", wire, bus, text, component). This also applies to hierarchical sheets. Note: the "Undelete" function of the general toolbar allows you to cancel last deletions.

2.10 Left toolbar icons

This toolbar manages the display options:

	Show/Hide the grid.
In	Switch to inches.
mm	Switch to millimeters.
	Choose the cursor shape.
	Visibility of "invisible" pins.
	Allowed orientation of wires and buses.

2.11 Pop-up menus and quick editing

A right-click opens a contextual menu for the selected element. This contains:

- Zoom factor.
- Grid adjustment.
- Commonly edited parameters of the selected element.

Pop-up without selected element.

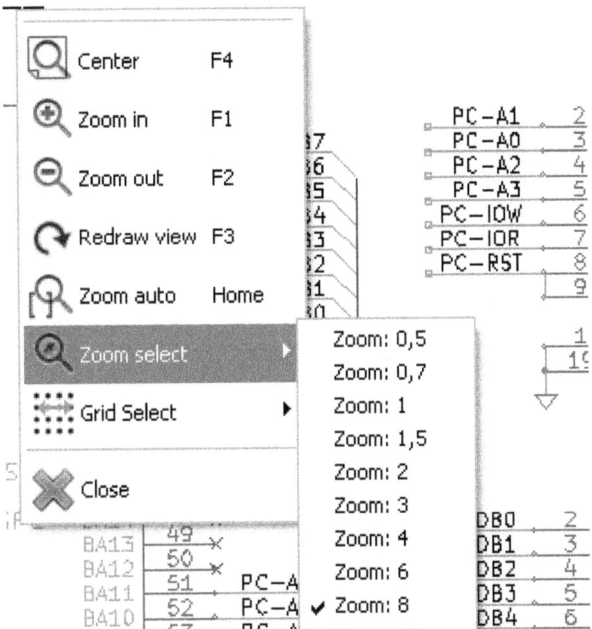

Editing of a label.

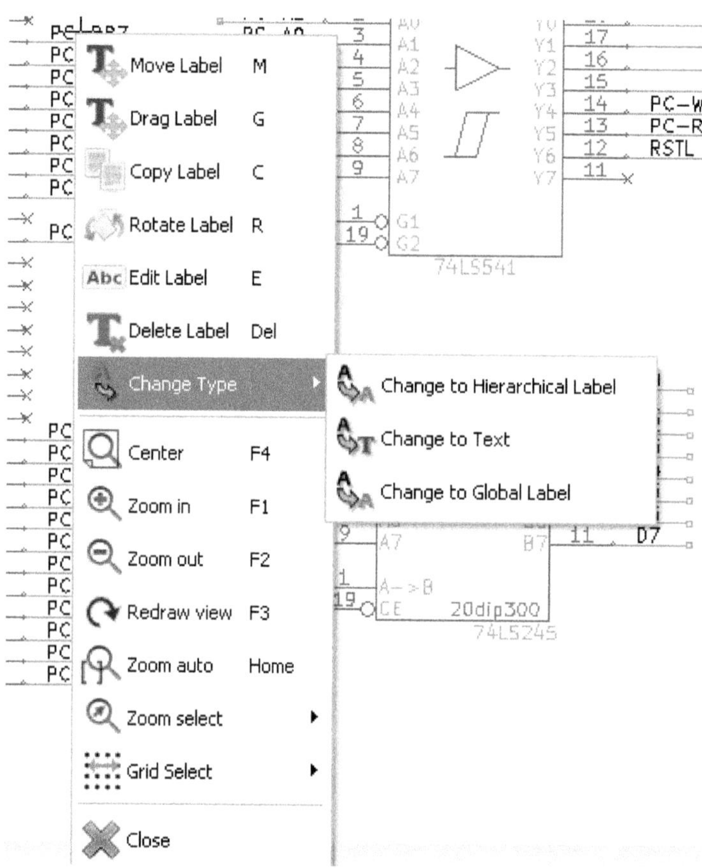

Editing a component.

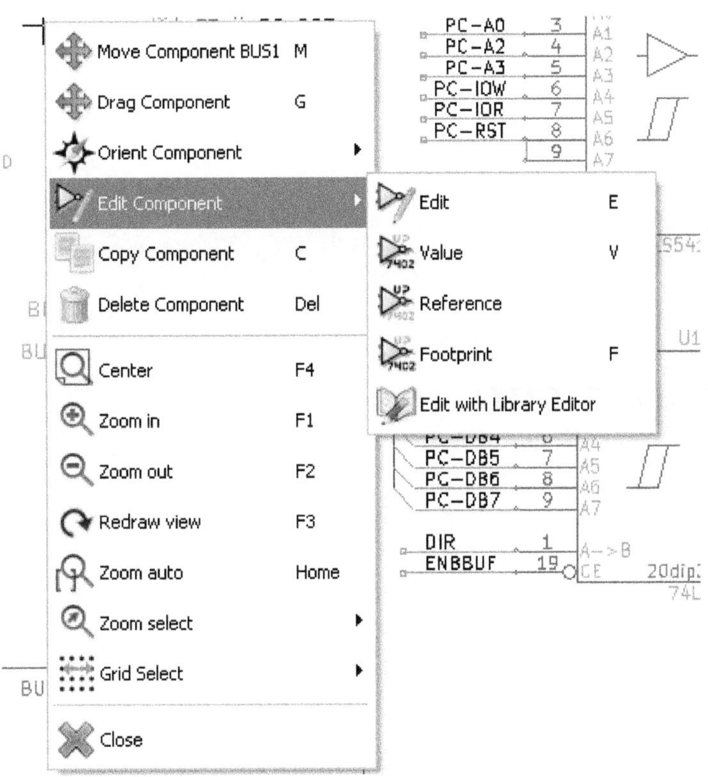
Move Component BUS1 M
Drag Component G
Orient Component
Edit Component
Copy Component C
Delete Component Del
Center F4
Zoom in F1
Zoom out F2
Redraw view F3
Zoom auto Home
Zoom select
Grid Select
Close
Edit E
Value V
Reference
Footprint F
Edit with Library Editor
PC-A0
PC-A2
PC-A3
PC-IOW
PC-IOR
PC-RST
PC-DB5
PC-DB6
PC-DB7
DIR
ENBBUF

Chapter 3

Main top menu

3.1 File menu

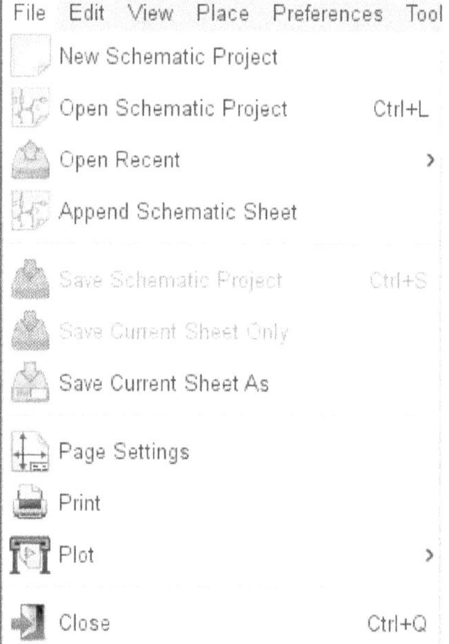

New Schematic Project	Clear current schematic and initialize a new one
Open Schematic Project	Load a schematic hierarchy
Open Recent	Open a list of recently opened files
Append Schematic Sheet	Insert the contents of another sheet into the current one
Save Schematic Project	Save current sheet and all its hierarchy.
Save Current Sheet Only	Save current sheet, but not others in a hierarchy.
Save Current Sheet As···	Save current sheet with a new name.
Page Settings	Configure page dimensions and title block.
Print	Print schematic hierarchy (See also chapter Plot and Print).

Plot	Export to PDF, PostScript, HPGL or SVG format (See chapter Plot and Print).
Close	Quit without saving.

3.2 Preferences menu

3.2.1 Preferences

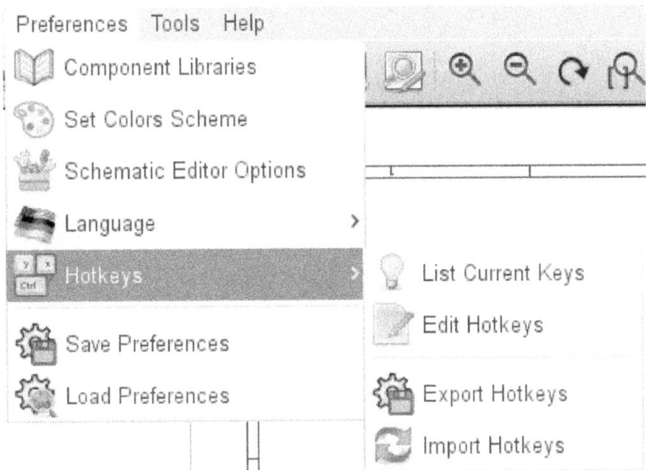

Component Libraries	Select libraries and library search path.
Set Colors Scheme	Select colors for display, print and plot.
Schematic Editor Options	General options (units, grid size, field names, etc.).
Language	Select interface language.
Hotkeys	List, edit, export, and import hotkey settings.
Save Preferences	Save the project settings to the .pro file.
Load Preferences	Load the project settings from a .pro file.

3.2.2 Preferences menu / Component Libraries

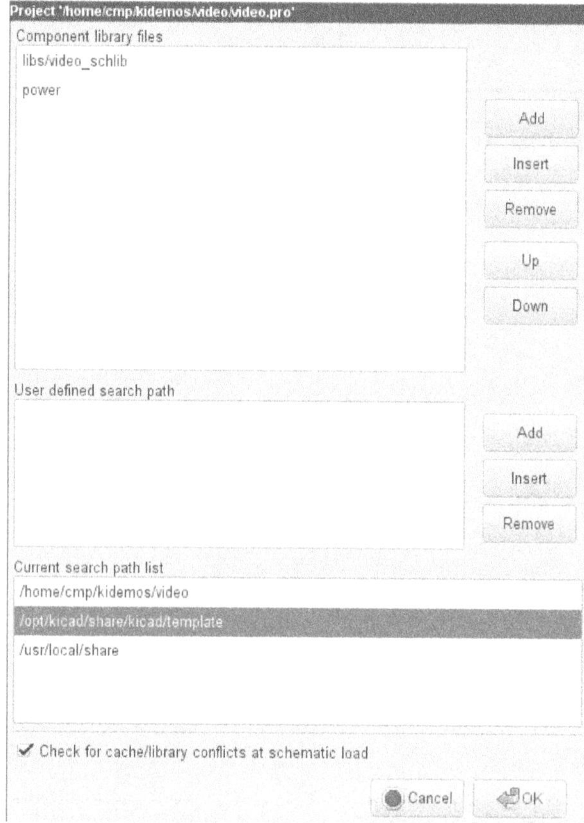

This dialog is used to configure component libraries and search paths. The configuration parameters are saved in the .pro file. Different configuration files in different directories are also possible.

Eeschema searches, in order:

1. The configuration file (projectname.pro) in the current directory.
2. The kicad.pro configuration file in the KiCad directory. This file can thus be the default configuration.
3. Default values if no file is found. It will at least then be necessary to fill out the list of libraries to load, and then save the configuration.

The *Check for cache/library conflicts at schematic load* box is used to configure the library conflict rescue behavior. See Rescuing Cached Components for more information about that.

3.2.3 Preferences menu / Set Color Scheme

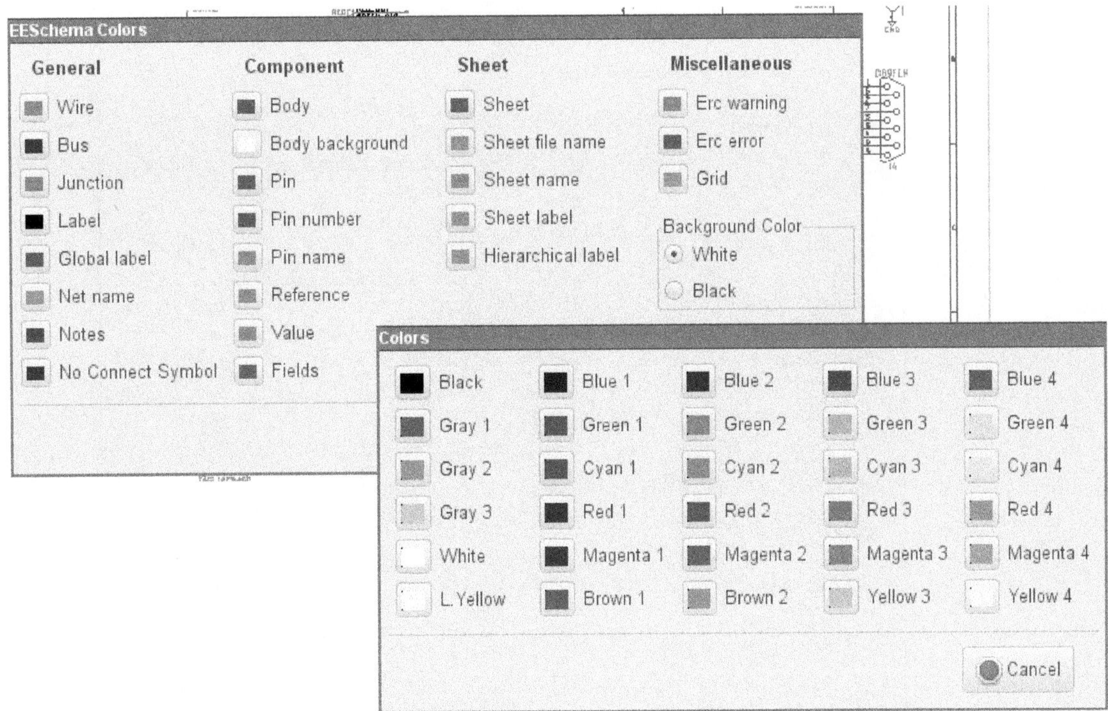

Color scheme for various graphic elements, and background color selection (either black or white).

3.2.4 Preferences menu / Schematic Editor Options

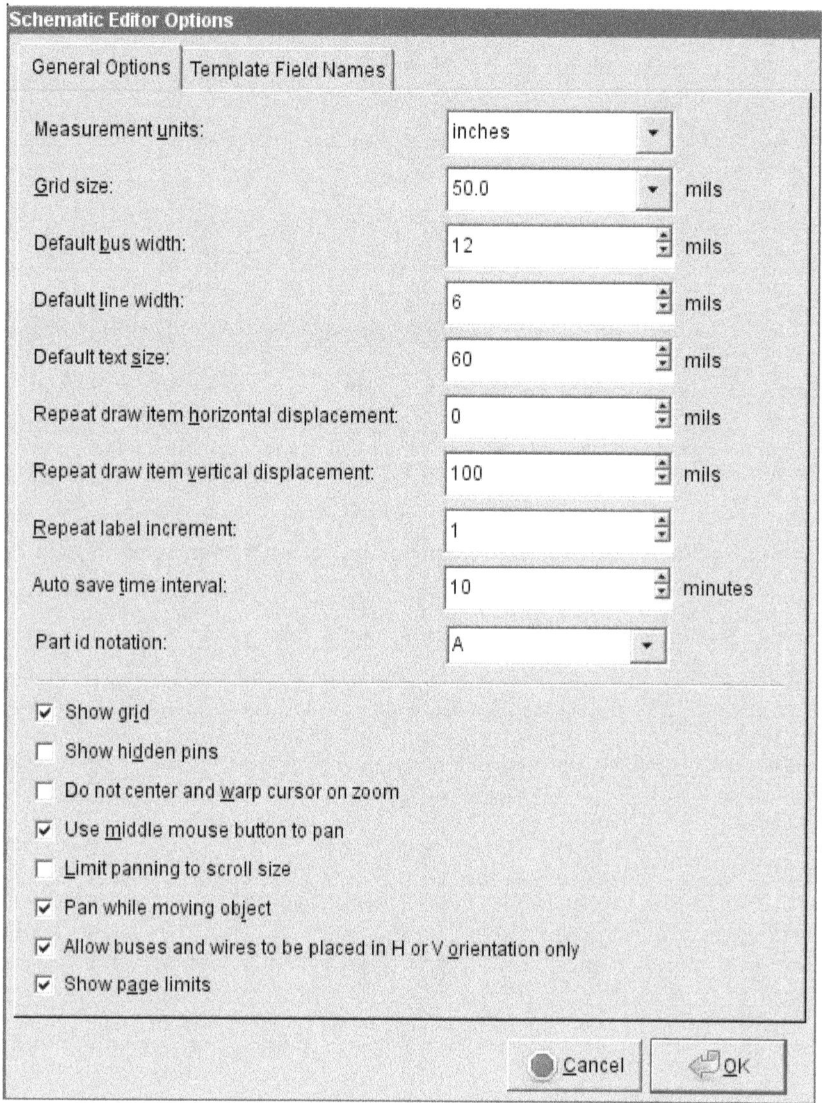

Measurement units:	Select the display and the cursor coordinate units (inches or millimeters).
Grid Size:	Grid size selection. **It is recommended to work with normal grid (0.050 inches or 1,27 mm).** *Smaller grids are used for component building.*
Default bus width:	Pen size used to draw buses.
Default line width:	Pen size used to draw objects that do not have a specified pen size.
Default text size:	Text size used when creating new text items or labels

Repeat draw item horizontal displacement	increment on X axis during element duplication (usual value 0) (after placing an item like a component, label or wire, a duplication is made by the *Insert* key)
Repeat draw item vertical displacement	increment on Y axis during element duplication (usual value is 0.100 inches or 2,54 mm)
Repeat label increment:	Increment of label value during duplication of texts ending in a number, such as bus members (usual value 1 or -1).
Auto save time interval:	Time in minutes between saving backups.
Part id notation:	Style of suffix that is used to denote component parts (U1A, U1.A, U1-1, etc.)
Show Grid:	If checked: display grid.
Show hidden pins:	Display invisible (or *hidden*) pins, typically power pins. If checked, allows the display of power pins.
Do not center and warp cursor on zoom:	When zooming, keep the position and cursor where they are.
Use middle mouse button to pan	When enabled, the sheet can be dragged around using the middle mouse button.
Limit panning to scroll size	When enabled, the middle mouse button cannot move the sheet area outside the displayed area.
Pan while moving object	If checked, automatically shifts the window if the cursor leaves the window during drawing or moving.
Allow buses and wires to be placed in H or V orientation only	If checked, buses and wires can only be vertical or horizontal. Otherwise, buses and wires can be placed at any orientation.
Show page limits	If checked, shows the page boundaries on screen.

3.2.5 Preferences and Language

Use default mode. Other languages are available mainly for development purposes.

3.3 Help menu

Access to on-line help (this document) for an extensive tutorial about KiCad. Use "Copy Version Information" when submitting bug reports to identify your build and system.

Chapter 4

General Top Toolbar

4.1 Sheet management

The Sheet Settings icon, , allows you to define the sheet size and the contents of the title block.

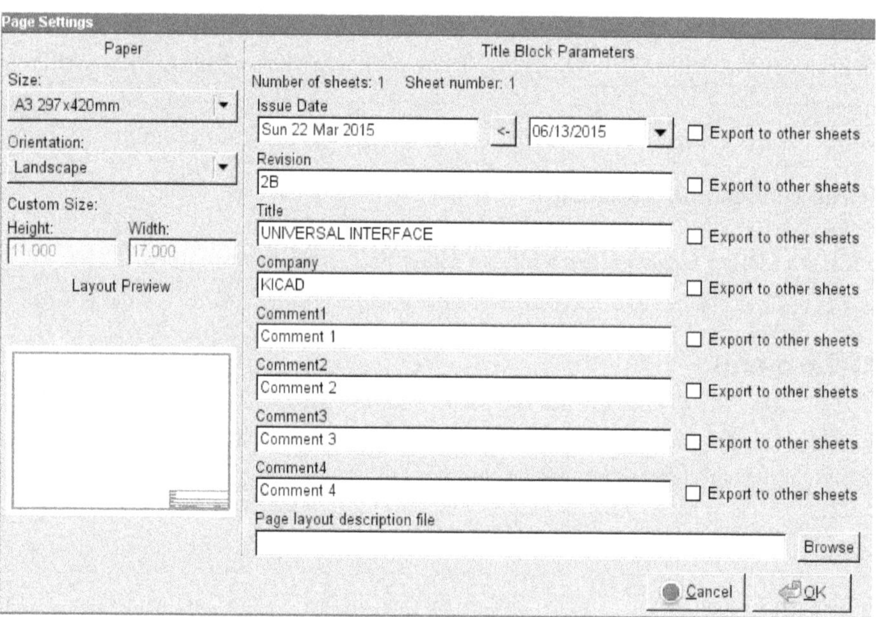

Sheet numbering is automatically updated. You can set the date to today by pressing the left arrow button by "Issue Date", but it will not be automatically changed.

4.2 Options of the schematic editor

4.2.1 General options

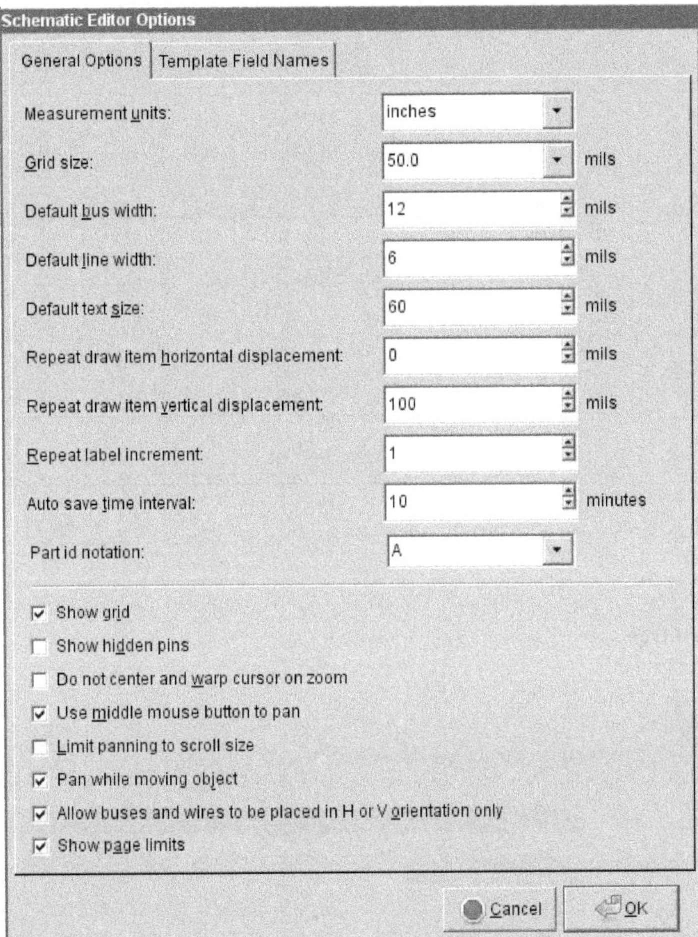

4.2.2 Template fields names

You can define custom fields that will exist by default in each component (even if left empty).

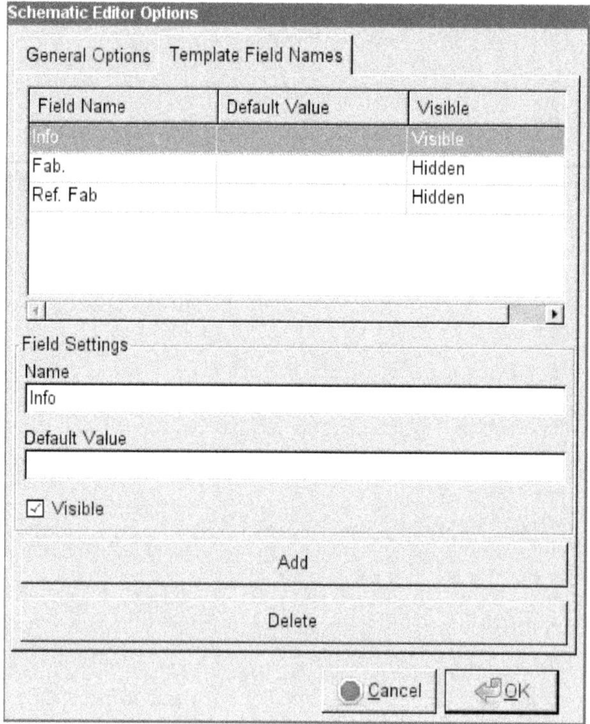

4.3 Search tool

The Find icon, , can be used to access the search tool.

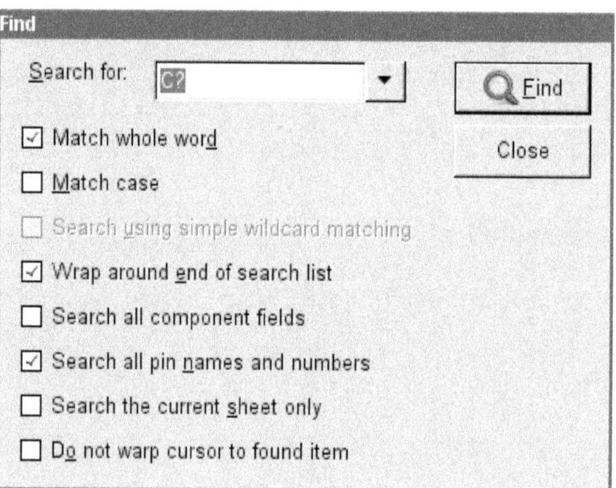

You can search for a reference, a value, or a text string in the current sheet or in the whole hierarchy. Once found, the cursor will be positioned on the found element in the relevant sub-sheet.

4.4 Netlist tool

The Netlist icon, NET, opens the netlist generation tool.

The netlist file it creates describes all connections in the entire hierarchy.

In a multisheet hierarchy, any local label is visible only inside the sheet to which it belongs. Thus, the label TOTO of sheet 3 is different from the label TOTO of sheet 5 (if no connection has been intentionally introduced to connect them). This is due to the fact that the sheet name path is internally associated with the local label.

Note 1:

Label lengths have no limitations in Eeschema, but the software exploiting the generated netlist can be limited on this point.

Note 2:

Avoid spaces in the labels, because they will appear as separated words. It is not a limitation of Eeschema, but of many netlist formats, which often assume that a label has no spaces.

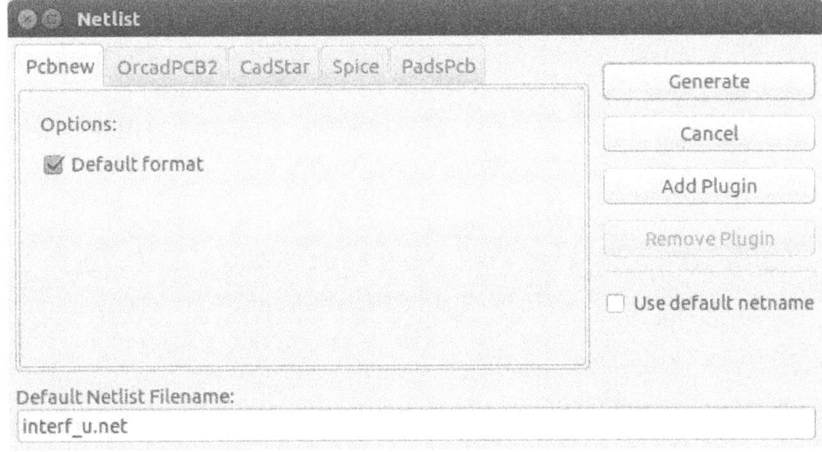

Option:

Default Format:

Check to select Pcbnew as the default format.

Other formats can also be generated:

- Orcad PCB2
- CadStar
- Spice, for simulators

External plugins can be launched to extend the netlist formats list (a PadsPcb Plugin was added here).

4.5 Annotation tool

The icon U?A 123 gives access to the annotation tool. This tool performs an automatic naming of all components in the schematic.

For multi-part components (such as 7400 TTL which contains 4 gates), a multi-part suffix is also allocated (thus a 7400 TTL designated U3 will be divided into U3A, U3B, U3C and U3D).

You can unconditionally annotate all the components, or only the new components, i.e. those which were not previously annotated.

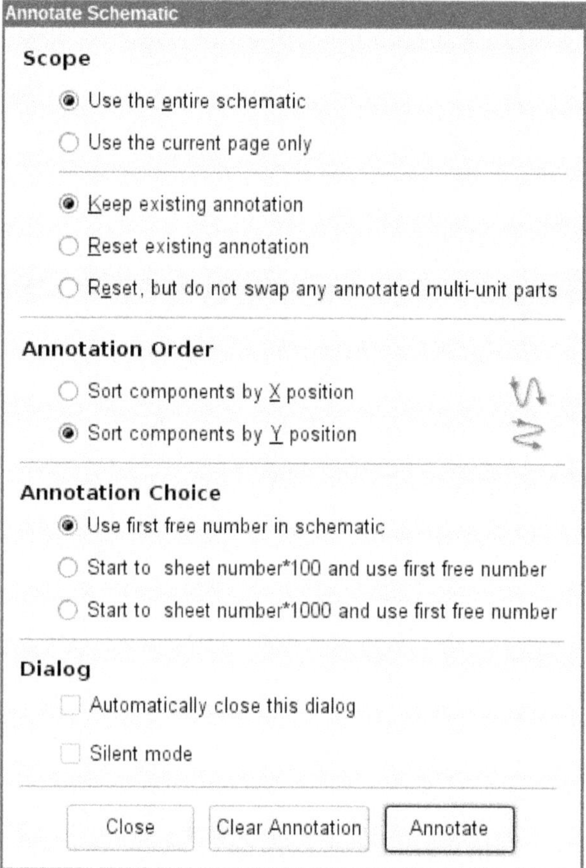

Scope

1. Use the entire schematic. All the sheets are re-annotated (usual Option).
2. Use the current page only. Only the current sheet is re-annotated (this option is to be used only in special cases, for example to evaluate the amount of resistors in the current sheet.).
3. Keep existing annotation. Conditional annotation, only the new components will be re-annotated (usual option).
4. Reset existing annotation. Unconditional annotation, all the components will be re-annotated (this option is to be used when there are duplicated references).

5. Reset, but do not swap any annotated multi-unit parts. This keeps all groups of multiple units (e.g. U2A, U2B) together when reannotating.

Annotation Order

Selects the order in which components will be numbered.

Annotation Choice

Selects the method by which numbers will be selected.

4.6 Electrical Rules Check tool

The icon 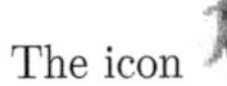 gives access to the electrical rules check (ERC) tool.

This tool performs a design verification and is particularly useful to detect forgotten connections, and inconsistencies.

Once you have run the ERC, Eeschema places markers to highlight problems. The diagnosis can then be given by left clicking on the marker. An error file can also be generated.

4.6.1 Main ERC dialog

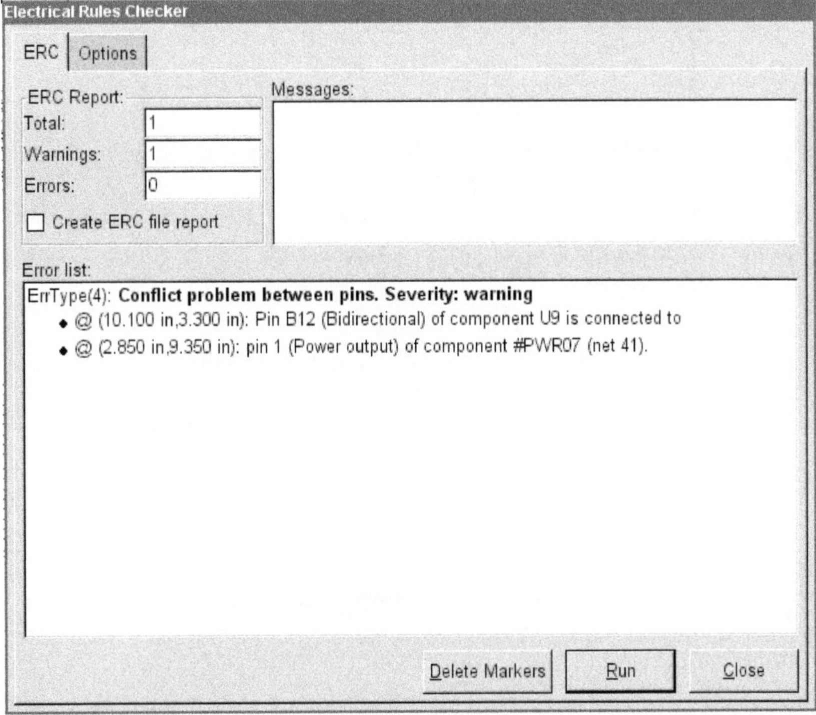

Errors are displayed in the Electrical Rules Checker dialog box:

- Total count of errors and warnings.

- Errors count.
- Warnings count.

Option:

- Create ERC file report: check this option to generate an ERC report file.

Commands:

- Delete Markers: to remove all ERC error/warnings markers.
- Run: to perform an Electrical Rules Check.
- Close: to exit this dialog box.

Note:

- Clicking on an error message jumps to the corresponding marker in the schematic.

4.6.2 ERC options dialog

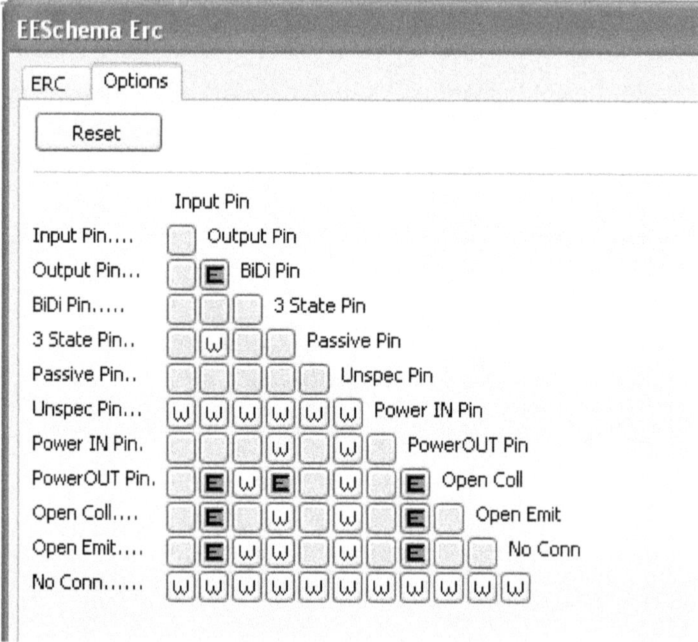

This tab allows you to establish connectivity rules between pins; you can choose between 3 options for each case:

- No error
- Warning
- Error

Each square of the matrix can be modified by clicking on it.

4.7 Bill of Material tool

The icon gives access to the bill of materials (BOM) generator. This menu allows the generation of a file listing of the components and/or hierarchical connections (global labels).

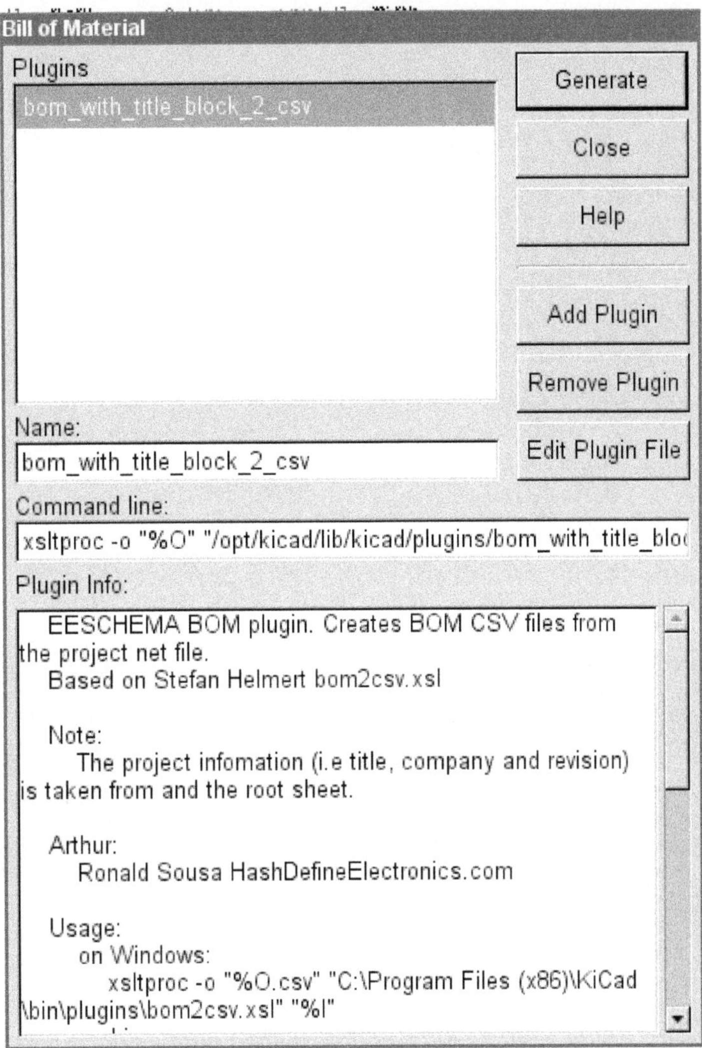

Eeschema' s BOM generator makes use of external plugins, generally in XSLT or Python form. Some are provided, and will be installed inside the KiCad program files directory.

A useful set of component properties to use for a BOM are:

- Value - unique name for each part used.
- Footprint - either manually entered or back-annotated (see below).
- Field1 - Manufacturer' s name.

- Field2 - Manufacturer' s Part Number.
- Field3 - Distributor' s Part Number.

For example:

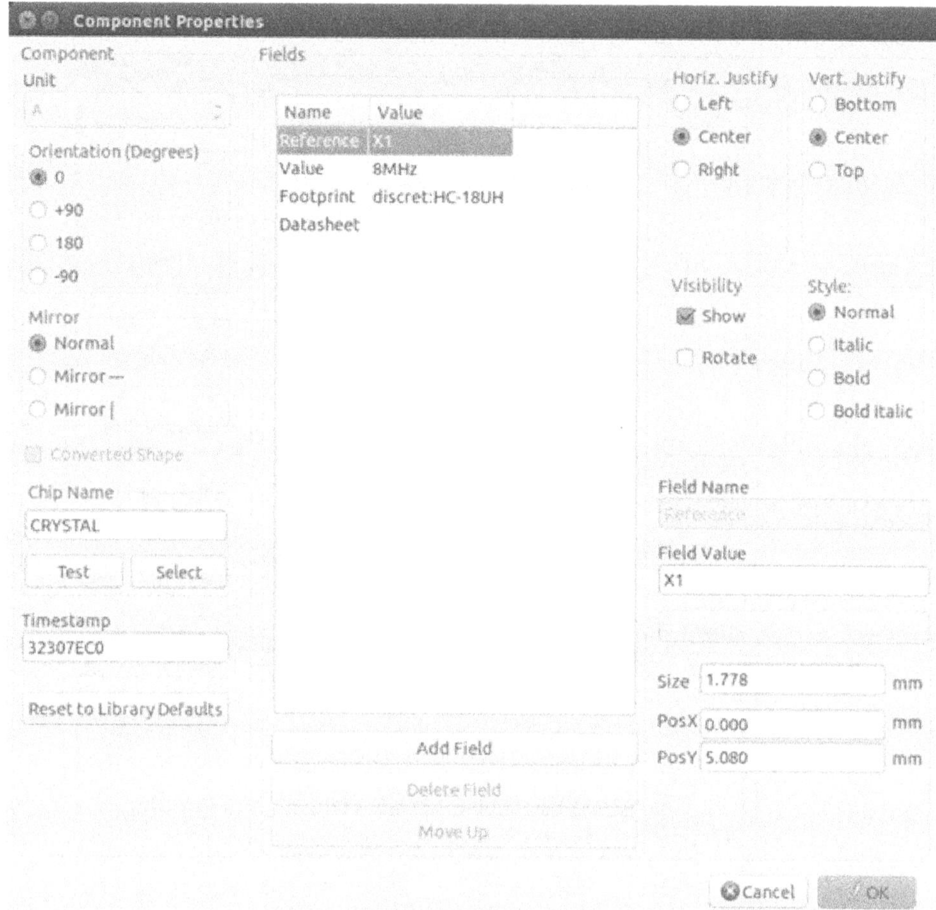

4.8 Import tool for footprint assignment:

4.8.1 Access:

The icon BACK gives access to the back-annotate tool.

This tool allows footprint changes made in PcbNew to be imported back into the footprint fields in Eeschema.

Chapter 5

Schematic Creation and Editing

5.1 Introduction

A schematic can be represented by a single sheet, but, if big enough, it will require several sheets.

A schematic represented by several sheets is hierarchical, and all its sheets (each one represented by its own file) constitute an Eeschema project. The manipulation of hierarchical schematics will be described in the Hierarchical Schematics chapter.

5.2 General considerations

A schematic designed with Eeschema is more than a simple graphic representation of an electronic device. It is normally the entry point of a development chain that allows for:

- Validating against a set of rules (Electrical Rules Check) to detect errors and omissions.
- Automatically generating a bill of materials (BOM).
- Generating a netlist for simulation software such as SPICE.
- Generating a netlist for transferring to PCB layout.

A schematic mainly consists of components, wires, labels, junctions, buses and power ports. For clarity in the schematic, you can place purely graphical elements like bus entries, comments, and polylines.

5.3 The development chain

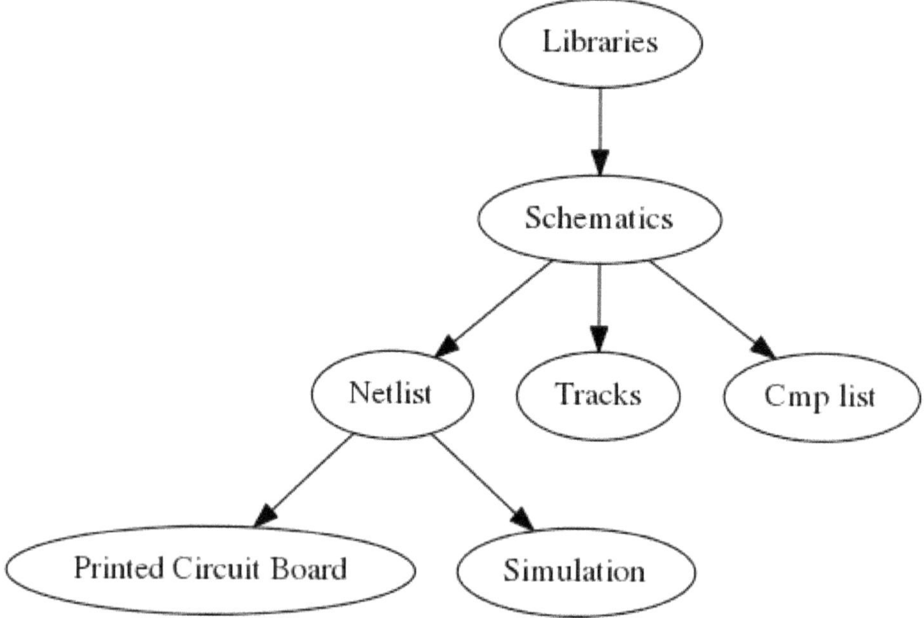

Components are added to the schematic from component libraries. After the schematic is made, a netlist is generated, which is later used to import the set of connections and footprints into PcbNew.

5.4 Component placement and editing

5.4.1 Find and place a component

To load a component into your schematic you can use the icon . A dialog box allows you to type the name of the component to load.

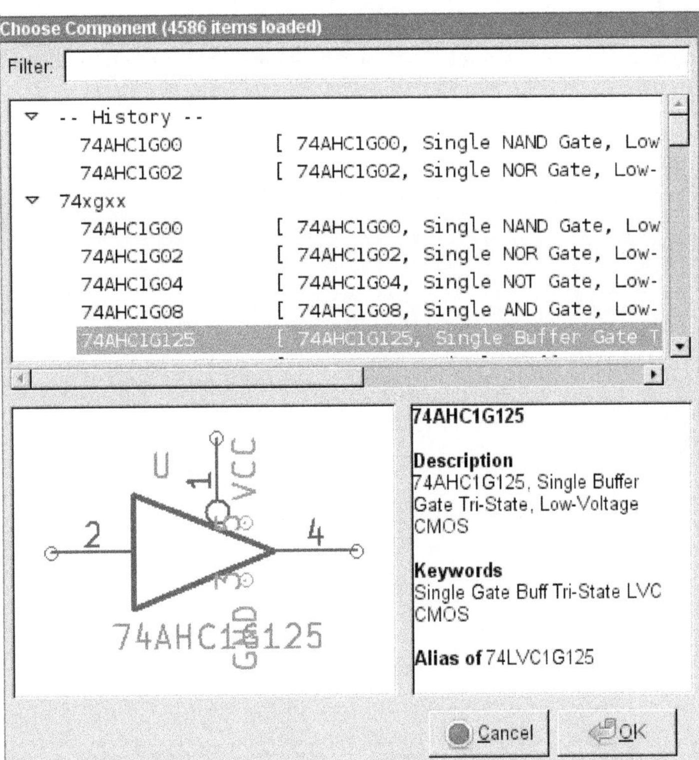

The Choose Component dialog will filter components by name, keywords, and description according to what you type into the search field.

Before placing the component in the schematic, you can rotate it, mirror it, and edit its fields, by either using the hotkeys or the right-click context menu. This can be done the same way after placement.

Here is a component during placement:

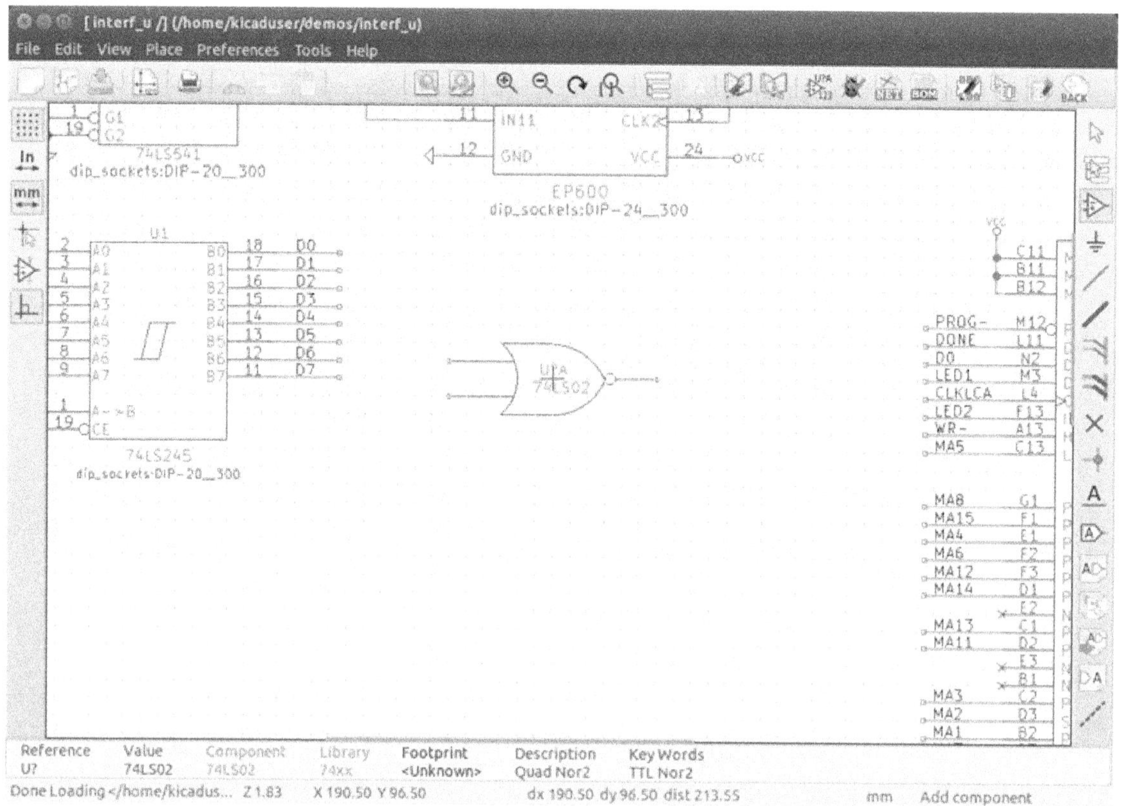

5.4.2 Power ports

A power port symbol is a component (the symbols are grouped in the "power" library), so they can be placed using the component chooser. However, as power placements are frequent, the tool is available. This tool is similar, except that the search is done directly in the "power" library.

5.4.3 Component Editing and Modification (already placed component)

There are two ways to edit a component:

- Modification of the component itself: position, orientation, unit selection on a multi-unit component.
- Modification of one of the fields of the component: reference, value, footprint, etc.

When a component has just been placed, you may have to modify its value (particularly for resistors, capacitors, etc.), but it is useless to assign to it a reference number right away, or to select the unit (except for components with locked units, which you have to assign manually). This can be done automatically by the annotation function.

5.4.3.1 Component modification

To modify some feature of a component, position the cursor on the component, and then either:

- Double-click on the component to open the full editing dialog.
- Right-click to open the context menu and use one of the commands: Move, Orientation, Edit, Delete, etc.

5.4.3.2 Text fields modification

You can modify the reference, value, position, orientation, text size and visibility of the fields:

- Double-click on the text field to modify it.
- Right-click to open the context menu and use one of the commands: Move, Rotate, Edit, Delete, etc.

For more options, or in order to create fields, double-click on the component to open the Component Properties dialog.

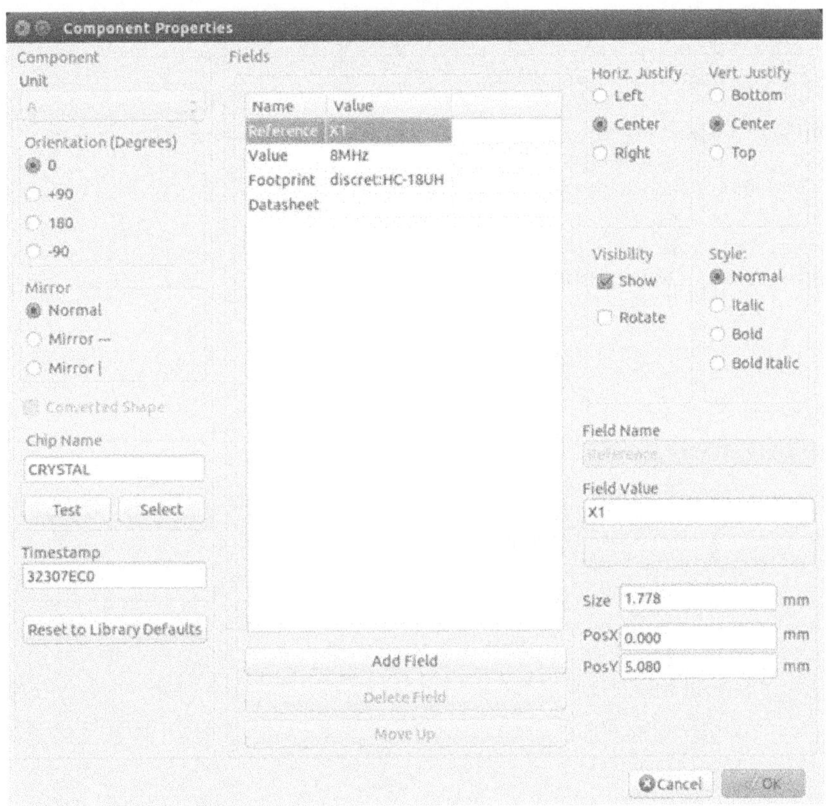

Each field can be visible or hidden, and displayed horizontally or vertically. The displayed position is always indicated for a normally displayed component (no rotation or mirroring) and is relative to the anchor point of the component.

The option "Reset to Library Defaults" sets the component to the original orientation, and resets the options, size and position of each field. However, texts fields are not modified because this could break the schematic.

5.5 Wires, Buses, Labels, Power ports

5.5.1 Introduction

All these drawing elements can also be placed with the tools on the vertical right toolbar.

These elements are:

- **Wires:** most connections between components.
- **Buses:** to graphically join bus labels
- **Polylines:** for graphic presentation.
- **Junctions:** to create connections between crossing wires or buses.
- **Bus entries:** to show connections between wires and buses. Graphical only!
- **Labels:** for labeling or creating connections.
- **Global labels:** for connections between sheets.
- **Texts:** for comments and annotations.
- **"No Connect" flags:** to terminate a pin that does not need any connection.
- **Hierarchical sheets**, and their connection pins.

5.5.2 Connections (Wires and Labels)

There are two ways to establish connection:

- Pin to pin wires.
- Labels.

The following figure shows the two methods:

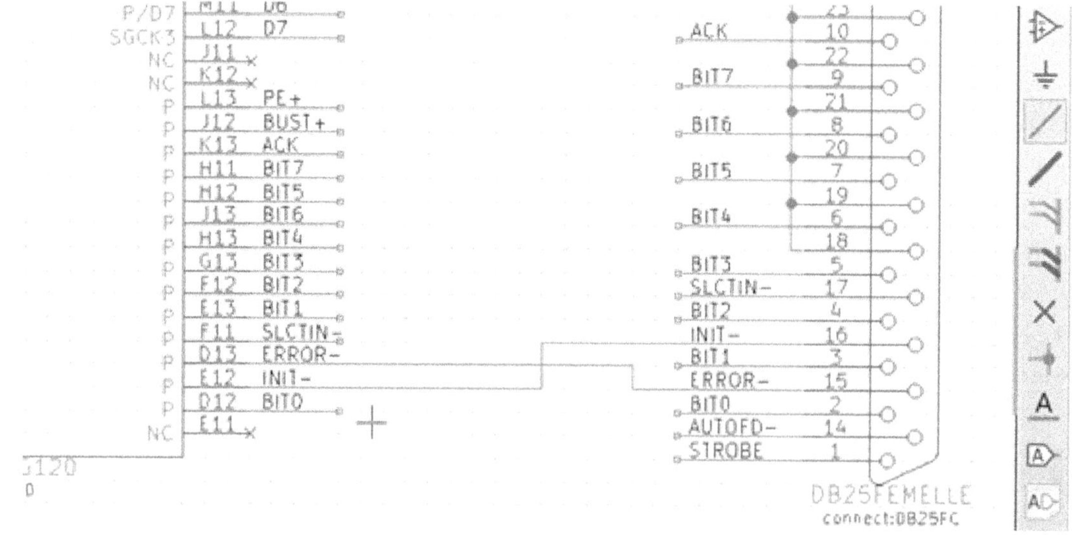

Note 1:

The point of "contact" of a label is the lower left corner of the first letter of the label. This point is displayed with a small square when not connected.

This point must thus be in contact with the wire, or be superimposed at the end of a pin so that the label is seen as connected.

Note 2:

To establish a connection, a segment of wire must be connected by its ends to an another segment or to a pin.

If there is overlapping (if a wire passes over a pin, but without being connected to the pin end) there is no connection.

Note 3:

Wires that cross are not implicitly connected. It is necessary to join them with a junction dot if a connection is desired.

The previous figure (wires connected to DB25FEMALE pins 22, 21, 20, 19) shows such a case of connection using a junction symbol.

Note 4:

If two different labels are placed on the same wire, they are connected together and become equivalent: all the other elements connected to one or the other labels are then connected to all of them.

5.5.3 Connections (Buses)

In the following schematic, many pins are connected to buses.

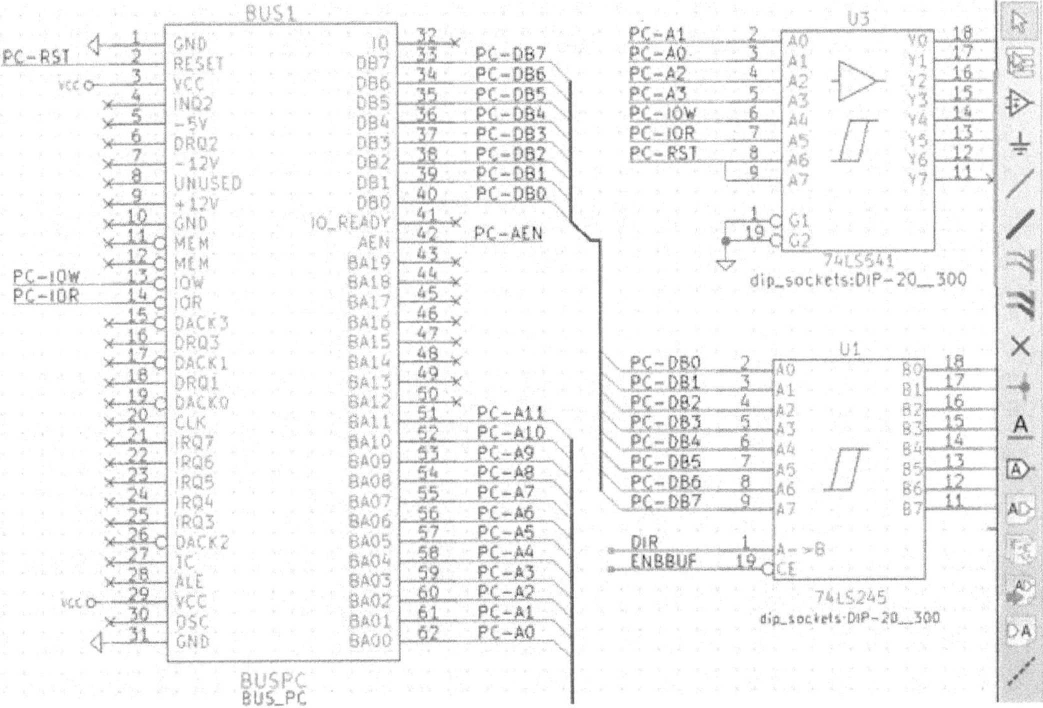

5.5.3.1 Bus members

From the schematic point of view, a bus is a collection of signals, starting with a common prefix, and ending with a number. For example, PCA0, PCA1, and PCA2 are members of the PCA bus.

The complete bus is named PCA[N..m], where N and m are the first and the last wire number of this bus. Thus if PCA has 20 members from 0 to 19, the complete bus is noted PCA[0..19]. A collection of signals like PCA0, PCA1, PCA2, WRITE, READ cannot be contained in a bus.

5.5.3.2 Connections between bus members

Pins connected between the same members of a bus must be connected by labels. It is not possible to connect a pin directly to a bus; this type of connection will be ignored by Eeschema.

In the example above, connections are made by the labels placed on wires connected to the pins. Bus entries (wire segments at 45 degrees) to buses are graphical only, and are not necessary to form logical connections.

In fact, using the repetition command (*Insert* key), connections can be very quickly made in the following way, if component pins are aligned in increasing order (a common case in practice on components such as memories, microprocessors…):

- Place the first label (for example PCA0)
- Use the repetition command as much as needed to place members. Eeschema will automatically create the next labels (PCA1, PCA2…) vertically aligned, theoretically on the position of the other pins.
- Draw the wire under the first label. Then use the repetition command to place the other wires under the labels.
- If needed, place the bus entries by the same way (Place the first entry, then use the repetition command).

Note

In the Preferences/Options menu, you can set the repetition parameters:

- Vertical step.
- Horizontal step.
- Label increment (which can thus be incremented by 2, 3. or decremented).

5.5.3.3 Global connections between buses

You may need connections between buses, in order to link two buses having different names, or in the case of a hierarchy, to create connections between different sheets. You can make these connections in the following way.

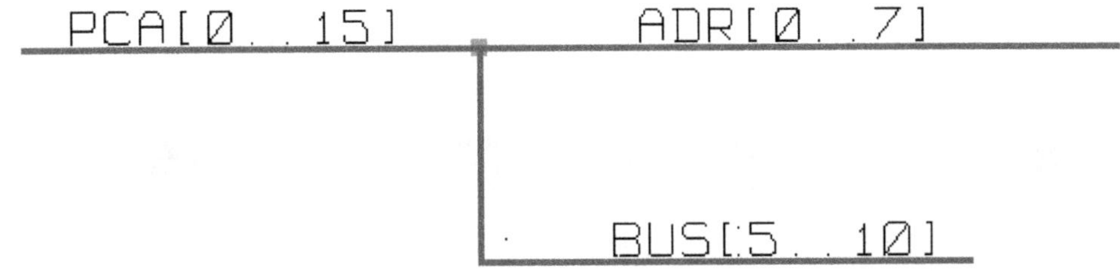

Buses PCA [0..15], ADR [0..7] and BUS [5..10] are connected together (note the junction here because the vertical bus wire joins the middle of the horizontal bus segment).

More precisely, the corresponding members are connected together : PCA0, ADR0 are connected, (as same as PCA1 and ADR1 ···PCA7 and ADR7).

Furthermore, PCA5, BUS5 and ADR5 are connected (just as PCA6, BUS6 and ADR6 like PCA7, BUS7 and ADR7).

PCA8 and BUS8 are also connected (just as PCA9 and BUS9, PCA10 and BUS10)

5.5.4 Power ports connection

When the power pins of the components are visible, they must be connected, as for any other signal.

Components such as gates and flip-flops may have invisible power pins. Care must be taken with these because:

- You cannot connect wires, because of their invisibility.
- You do not know their names.

And moreover, it would be a bad idea to make them visible and to connect them like the other pins, because the schematic would become unreadable and not in accordance with usual conventions.

Note

If you want to enforce the display of these invisible power pins, you must check the option "Show invisible power pins" in the Preferences/Options dialog box of the main menu, or the icon on the left (options) toolbar.

Eeschema automatically connects invisible power pins of the same name to the power net of that name. It may be necessary to join power nets of different names (for example, "GND" in TTL components and "VSS" in MOS components); use power ports for this.

It is not recommended to use labels for power connection. These only have a "local" connection scope, and would not connect the invisible power pins.

The figure below shows an example of power port connections.

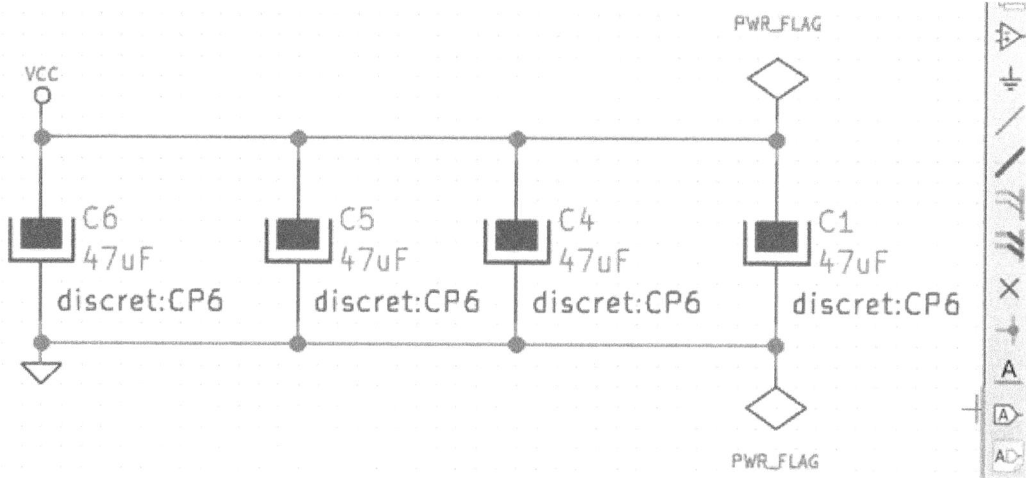

In this example, ground (GND) is connected to power port VSS, and power port VCC is connected to VDD.

Two PWR_FLAG symbols are visible. They indicate that the two power ports VCC and GND are really connected to a power source. Without these two flags, the ERC tool would diagnose: *Warning: power port not powered.*

All these symbols are components of the schematic library "power" .

5.5.5 "No Connect" flag

These symbols are very useful to avoid undesired ERC warnings. The electric rules check ensures that no connection has been accidentally left unconnected.

If pins must really remain unconnected, it is necessary to place a "No Connect" flag (tool X) on these pins. These symbols do not have any influence on the generated netlists.

5.6 Drawing Complements

5.6.1 Text Comments

It can be useful (to aid in understanding the schematic) to place annotations such as text fields and frames. Text fields (tool T) and Polyline (tool) are intended for this use, contrary to labels and wires, which are connection elements.

Here you can find an example of a frame with a textual comment.

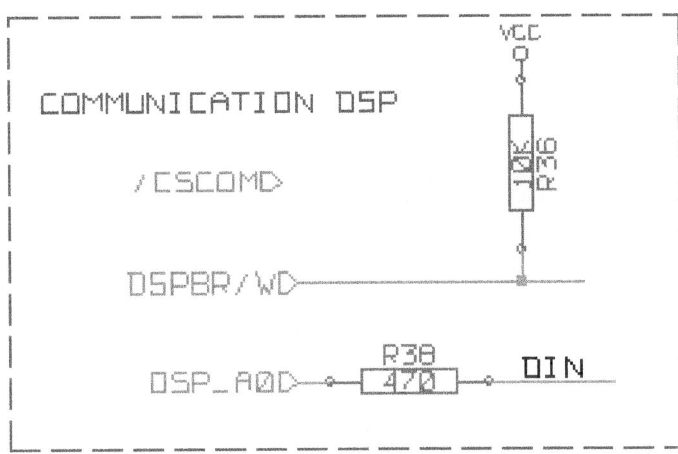

5.6.2 Sheet title block

The title block is edited with the tool .

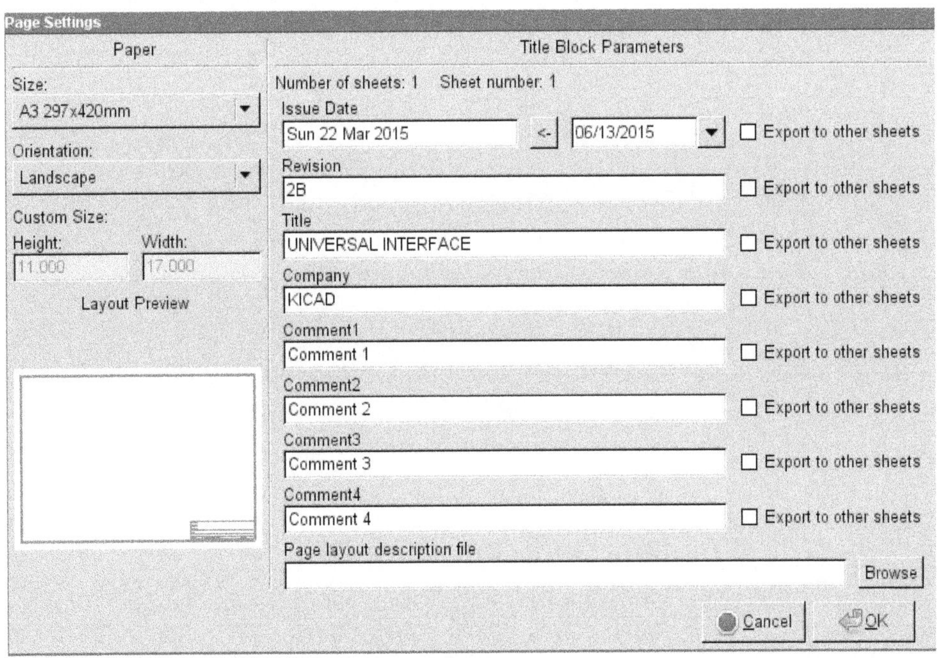

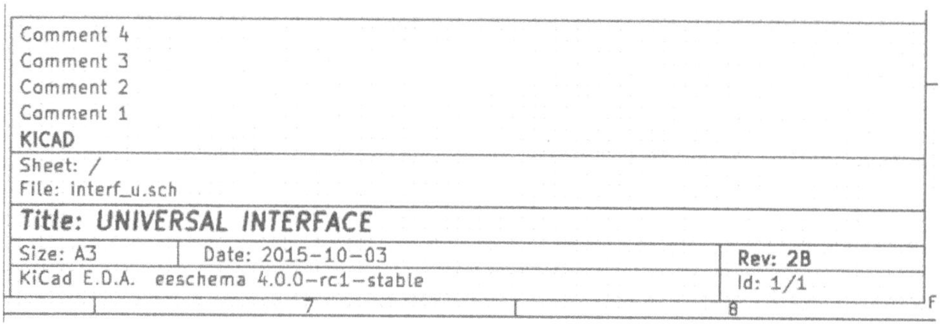

Comment 4
Comment 3
Comment 2
Comment 1
KICAD
Sheet: /
File: interf_u.sch
Title: UNIVERSAL INTERFACE
Size: A3 Date: 2015-10-03 Rev: 2B
KiCad E.D.A. eeschema 4.0.0-rc1-stable Id: 1/1

The sheet number (Sheet X/Y) is automatically updated.

5.7 Rescuing cached components

By default, Eeschema loads component symbols out of the libraries according to the set paths. This can cause a problem when loading a very old project: if the symbols in the library have changed since they were used in the project, the ones in the project would be automatically replaced with the new versions. The new versions might not line up correctly or might be oriented differently, leading to a broken schematic.

However, when a project is saved, a cache library is saved along with it. This allows the project to be distributed without the full libraries. If you load a project where symbols are present both in its cache and in the system libraries, Eeschema will scan the libraries for conflicts. Any conflicts found will be listed in the following dialog:

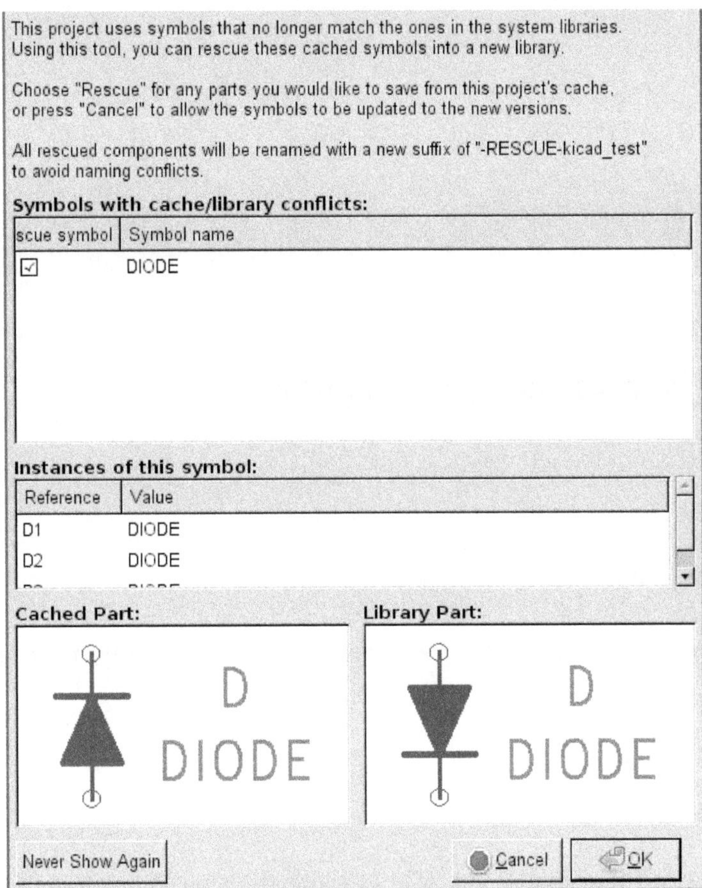

You can see in this example that the project originally used a diode with the cathode facing up, but the library now contains one with the cathode facing down. This change could ruin the project! Pressing OK here will cause the old symbol to be saved into a special "rescue" library, and all the components using that symbol will be renamed to avoid naming conflicts.

If you press Cancel, no rescues will be made, so Eeschema will load all the new components by default. Because no changes were made, you can still go back and run the rescue function again: choose "Rescue Cached Components" in the Tools menu to call up the dialog again.

If you would prefer not to see this dialog, you can press "Never Show Again". The default will be to do nothing and allow the new components to be loaded. This option can be changed back in the Component Libraries preferences.

Chapter 6

Hierarchical schematics

6.1 Introduction

A hierarchical representation is generally a good solution for projects bigger than a few sheets. If you want to manage this kind of project, it will be necessary to:

- Use large sheets, which results in printing and handling problems.
- Use several sheets, which leads you to a hierarchy structure.

The complete schematic then consists in a main schematic sheet, called root sheet, and sub-sheets constituting the hierarchy. Moreover, a skillful subdividing of the design into separate sheets often improves on its readability.

From the root sheet, you must be able to find all sub-sheets. Hierarchical schematics management is very easy with Eeschema, thanks to an integrated "hierarchy navigator" accessible via the icon of the top toolbar.

There are two types of hierarchy that can exist simultaneously: the first one has just been evoked and is of general use. The second consists in creating components in the library that appear like traditional components in the schematic, but which actually correspond to a schematic which describes their internal structure.

This second type is used to develop integrated circuits, because in this case you have to use function libraries in the schematic you are drawing.

Eeschema currently doesn′ t treat this second case.

A hierarchy can be:

- simple: a given sheet is used only once
- complex: a given sheet is used more than once (multiples instances)
- flat: which is a simple hierarchy, but connections between sheets are not drawn.

Eeschema can deal with all these hierarchies.

The creation of a hierarchical schematic is easy, the whole hierarchy is handled starting from the root schematic, as if you had only one schematic.

The two important steps to understand are:

- How to create a sub-sheet.
- How to build electric connections between sub-sheets.

6.2 Navigation in the Hierarchy

Navigation among sub-sheets It is very easy thanks to the navigator tool accessible via the button on the top toolbar.

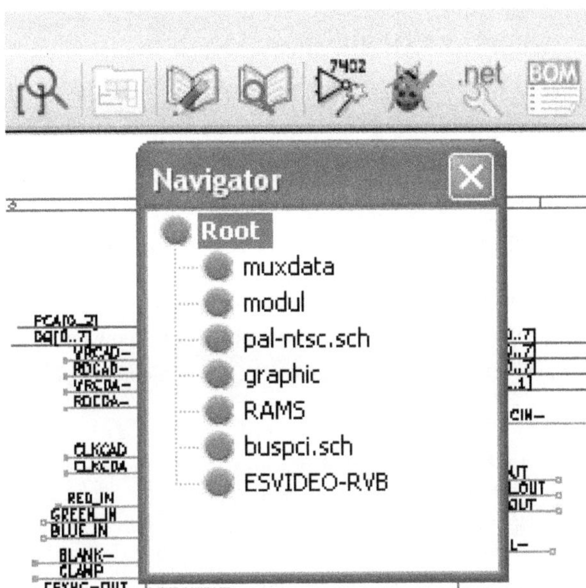

Each sheet is reachable by clicking on its name. For quick access, right click on a sheet name, and choose to Enter Sheet.

You can quickly reach the root sheet, or a sub-sheet thanks to the tool of the right toolbar. After the navigation tool has been selected:

- Click on a sheet name to select the sheet.
- Click elsewhere to select the Root sheet.

6.3 Local, hierarchical and global labels

6.3.1 Properties

Local labels, tool , are connecting signals only within a sheet. Hierarchical labels (tool) are connecting signals only within a sheet and to a hierarchical pin placed in the parent sheet.

Global labels (tool) are connecting signals across all the hierarchy. Power pins (type *power in* and *power out*) invisible are like global labels because they are seen as connected between them across all the hierarchy.

Note

Within a hierarchy (simple or complex) one can use both hierarchical labels and/or global labels.

6.4 Hierarchy creation of headlines

You have to:

- Place in the root sheet a hierarchy symbol called "sheet symbol".
- Enter into the new schematic (sub-sheet) with the navigator and draw it, like any other schematic.
- Draw the electric connections between the two schematics by placing Global Labels (HLabels) in the new schematic (sub-sheet), and labels having the same name in the root sheet, known as SheetLabels. These SheetLabels will be connected to the sheet symbol of the root sheet to the other elements of the schematic like standard component pins.

6.5 Sheet symbol

Draw a rectangle defined by two diagonal points symbolizing the sub-sheet.

The size of this rectangle must allow you to place later particular labels, hierarchy pins, corresponding to the global labels (HLabels) in the sub-sheet.

These labels are similar to usual component pins. Select the tool .

Click to place the upper left corner of the rectangle. Click again to place the lower right corner, having a large enough rectangle.

You will then be prompted to type a file name and a sheet name for this sub-sheet (in order to reach the corresponding schematic, using the hierarchy navigator).

You must give at least a file name. If there is no sheet name, the file name will be used as sheet name (usual way to do that).

6.6 Connections - hierarchical pins

You will create here points of connection (hierarchy pins) for the symbol which has been just created.

These points of connection are similar to normal component pins, with however the possibility to connect a complete bus with only one point of connection.

There are two ways to do this:

- Place the different pins before drawing the sub-sheet (manual placement).
- Place the different pins after drawing the sub-sheet, and the global labels (semi-automatic placement).

The second solution is quite preferable.

Manual placement:

- To select the tool .
- Click on the hierarchy symbol where you want to place this pin.

See below an example of the creation of the hierarchical pin called "CONNEXION".

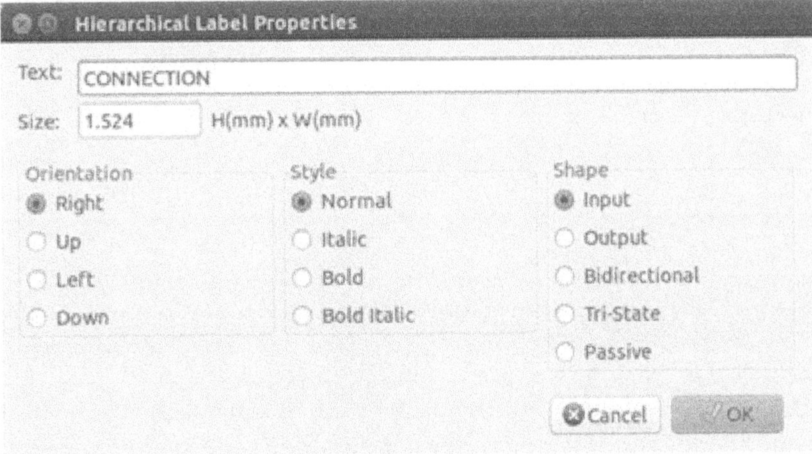

You can define its graphical attributes, and size or later, by editing this pin sheet (Right click and select Edit in the PopUp menu).

Various pin symbols are available:

- Input
- Output
- Bidirectional
- Tri-State
- Passive

These pin symbols are only graphic enhancements, and have no other role.

Automatic placement:

- Select the tool 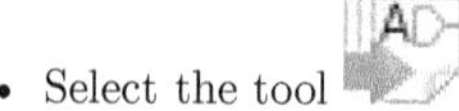.
- Click on the hierarchy symbol from where you want to import the pins corresponding to global labels placed in the corresponding schematic. A hierarchical pin appears, if a new global label exists, i.e. not corresponding to an already placed pin.
- Click where you want to place this pin.

All necessary pins can thus be placed quickly and without error. Their aspect is in accordance with corresponding global labels.

6.7 Connections - hierarchical labels

Each pin of the sheet symbol just created, must correspond to a label called hierarchical Label in the sub-sheet. Hierarchical labels are similar to labels, but they provide connections between sub-sheet and root sheet. The graphical representation of the two complementary labels (pin and HLabel) is similar. Hierarchical labels creation is made with the tool .

See below a root sheet example:

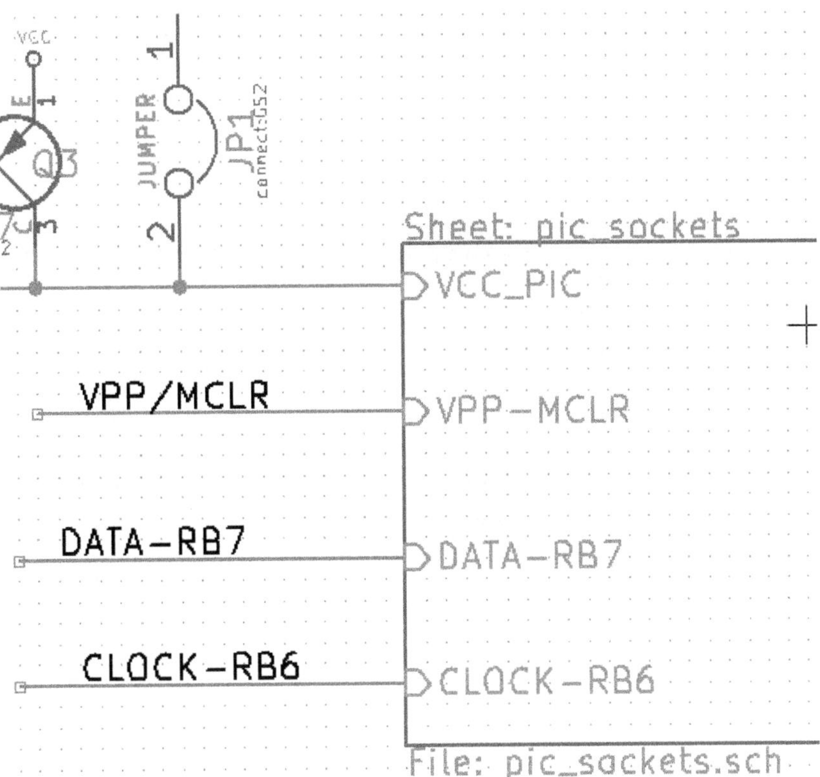

Notice pin VCC_PIC, connected to connector JP1.

Here are the corresponding connections in the sub-sheet :

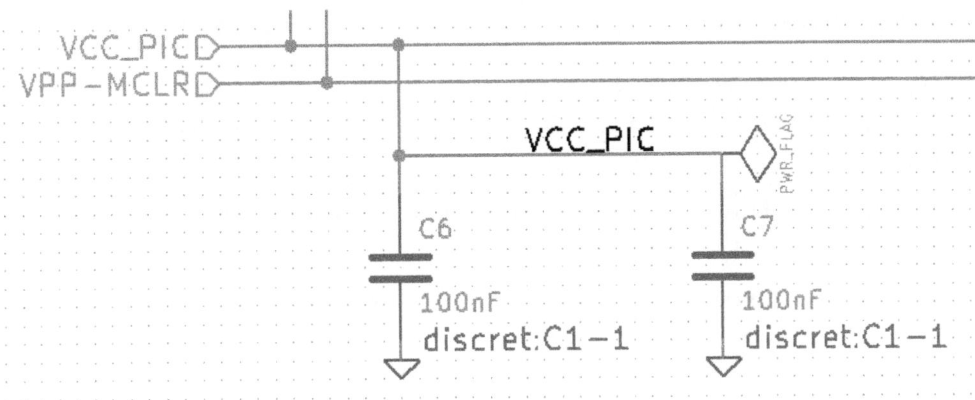

You find again, the two corresponding hierarchical labels, providing connection between the two hierarchical sheets.

Note

You can use hierarchical labels and hierarchy pins to connect two buses, according to the syntax (Bus [N. .m]) previously described.

6.7.1 Labels, hierarchical labels, global labels and invisible power pins

Here are some comments on various ways to provide connections, other than wire connections.

6.7.1.1 Simple labels

Simple labels have a local capacity of connection, i.e. limited to the schematic sheet where they are placed. This is due to the fact that :

- Each sheet has a sheet number.
- This sheet number is associated to a label.

Thus, if you place the label "TOTO" in sheet n° 3, in fact the true label is "TOTO_3". If you also place a label "TOTO" in sheet n° 1 (root sheet) you place in fact a label called "TOTO_1", different from "TOTO_3". This is always true, even if there is only one sheet.

6.7.1.2 Hierarchical labels

What is said for the simple labels is also true for hierarchical labels.

Thus in the same sheet, a HLabel "TOTO" is considered to be connected to a local label "TOTO", but not connected to a HLabel or label called "TOTO" in another sheet.

However a HLabel is considered to be connected to the corresponding SheetLabel symbol in the hierarchical symbol placed in the root sheet.

6.7.1.3 Invisible power pins

It was seen that invisible power pins were connected together if they have the same name. Thus all the power pins declared "Invisible Power Pins" and named VCC are connected and form the equipotential VCC, whatever the sheet they are placed on.

This means that if you place a VCC label in a sub-sheet, it will not be connected to VCC pins, because this label is actually VCC_n, where n is the sheet number.

If you want this label VCC to be really connected to the equipotential VCC, it will have to be explicitly connected to an invisible power pin, thanks to a VCC power port.

6.7.2 Global labels

Global labels that have an identical name are connected across the whole hierarchy.

(power labels like vcc ···are global labels)

6.8 Complex Hierarchy

Here is an example. The same schematic is used twice (two instances). The two sheets share the same schematic because the file name is the same for the two sheets (“other_sheet.sch”). But the sheet names must be different.

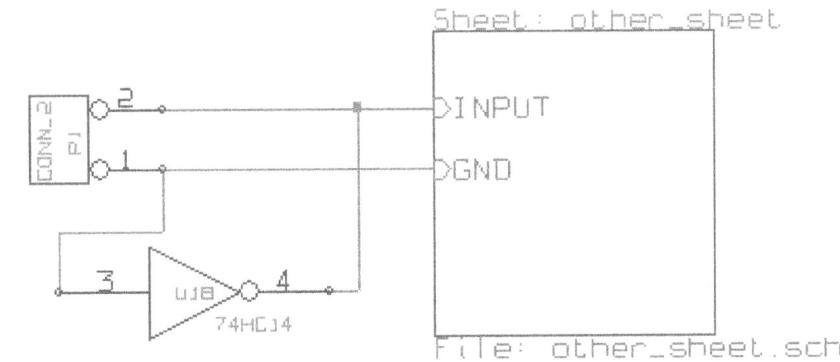

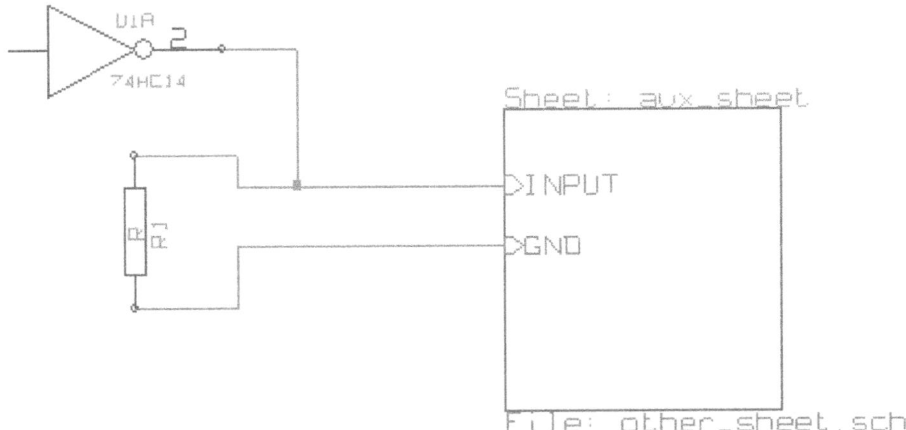

6.9 Flat hierarchy

You can create a project using many sheets, without creating connections between these sheets (flat hierarchy) if the next rules are respected:

- You must create a root sheet containing the other sheets, which acts as a link between others sheets.
- No explicit connections are needed.
- All connections between sheets will use global labels instead of hierarchical labels.

Here is an example of a root sheet.

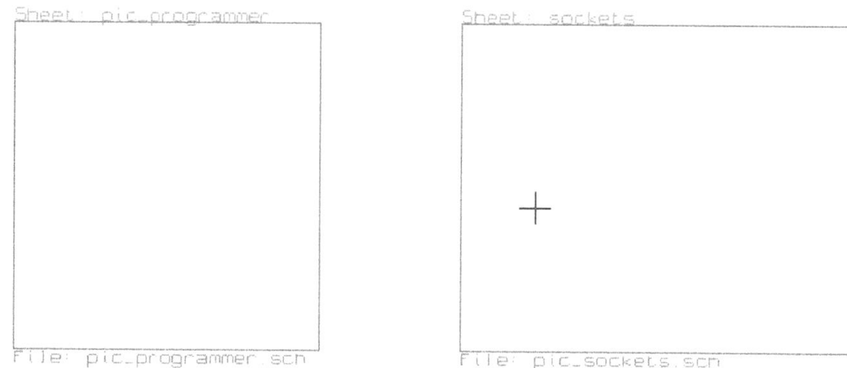

Here is the two pages, connected by global labels.

Here is the pic_programmer.sch.

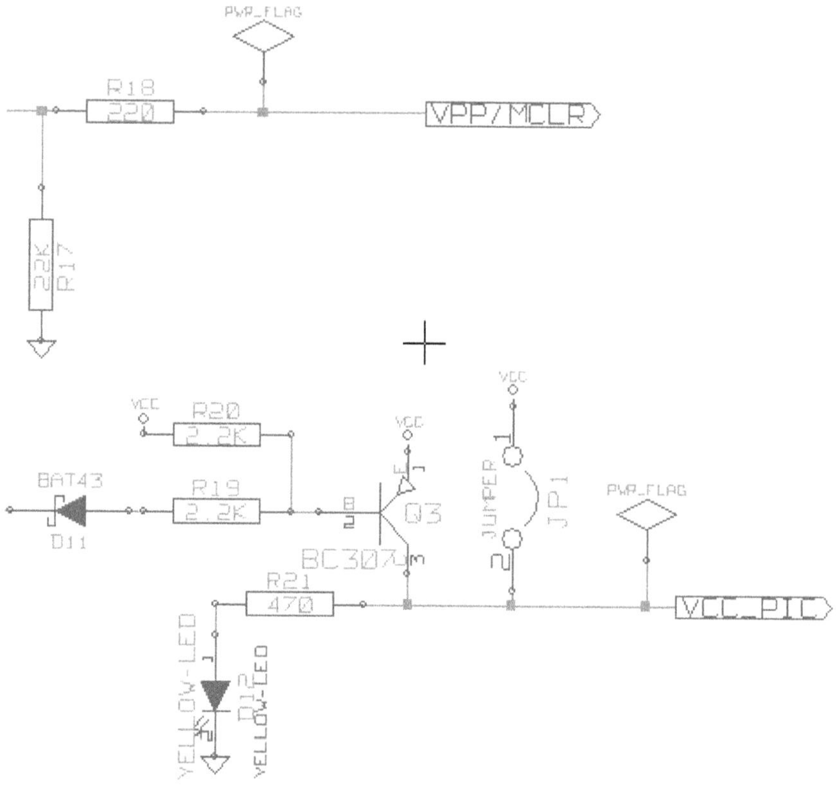

Here is the pic_sockets.sch.

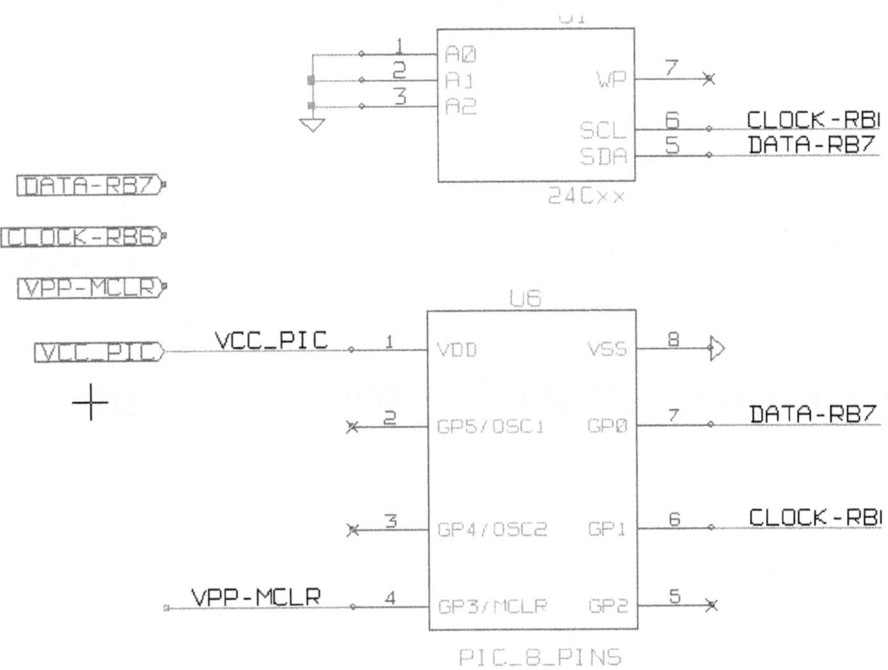

Look at global labels.

Chapter 7

Automatic classification Annotation

7.1 Introduction

The automatic classification annotation tool allows you to automatically assign a designator to components in your schematic. For multi-parts components, assign a multi-part suffix to minimize the number of these packages. The automatic classification annotation tool is accessible via the icon U?A 123. Here you find its main window.

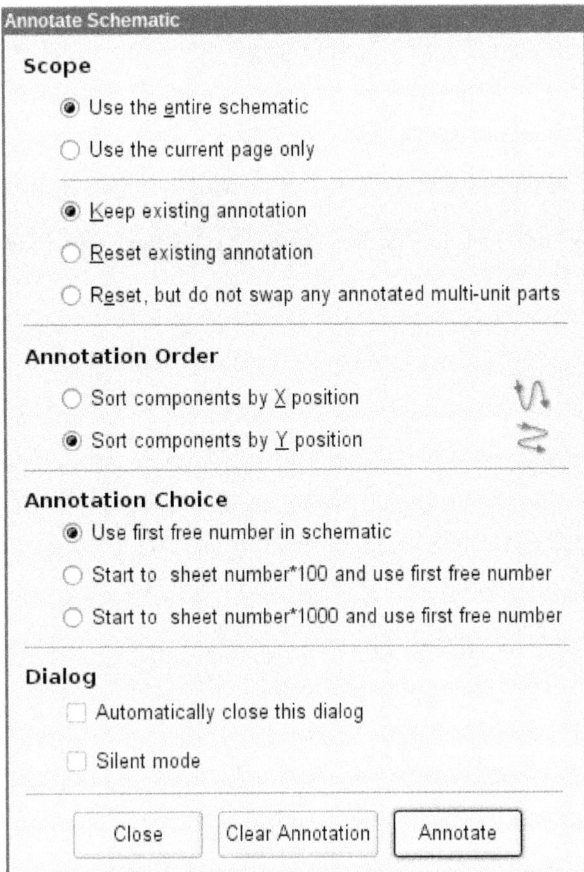

Various possibilities are available:

- Annotate all the components (reset existing annotation option)
- Annotate all the components, but do not swap any previously annotated multi-unit parts.
- Annotate new components only (i.e. those whose reference finishes by? like IC?) (keep existing annotation option).
- Annotate the whole hierarchy (use the entire schematic option).
- Annotate the current sheet only (use current page only option).

The "Reset, but do not swap any annotated multi-unit parts" option keeps all existing associations between multi-unit parts. That is, if you have U2A and U2B, they may be reannotated to U1A and U1B respectively, but they will never be reannotated to U1A and U2A, nor to U2B and U2A. This is useful if you want to ensure that pin groupings are maintained, if you have already decided by yourself which subunits are best placed where.

The annotation order choice gives the method used to set the reference number inside each sheet of the hierarchy.

Except for particular cases, an automatic annotation applies to the whole project (all sheets) and to the new components, if you don' t want to modify previous annotations.

The Annotation Choice gives the method used to calculate reference Id:

- Use first free number in schematic: components are annotated from 1 (for each reference prefix). If a previous annotation exists, not yet in use numbers will be used.
- Start to sheet number*100 and use first free number: annotation start from 101 for the sheet 1, from 201 for the sheet 2, etc. If there are more than 99 items having the same reference prefix (U, R) inside the sheet 1, the annotation tool uses the number 200 and more, and annotation for sheet 2 will start from the next free number.
- Start to sheet number*1000 and use first free number. Annotation start from 1001 for the sheet 1, from 2001 for the sheet 2.

7.2 Some examples

7.2.1 Annotation order

This example shows 5 elements placed, but not annotated.

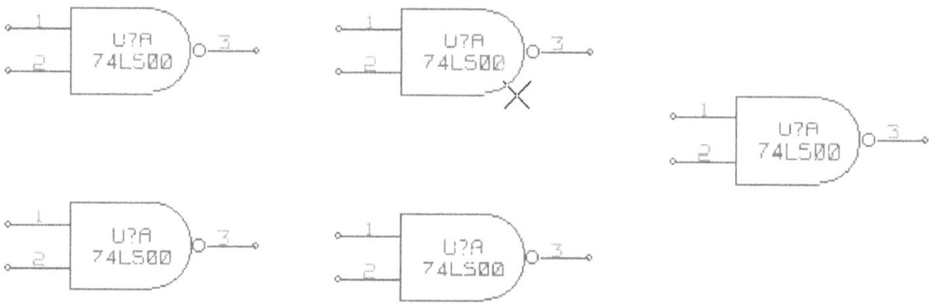

After the annotation tool Is executed, the following result is obtained.

Sort by X position.

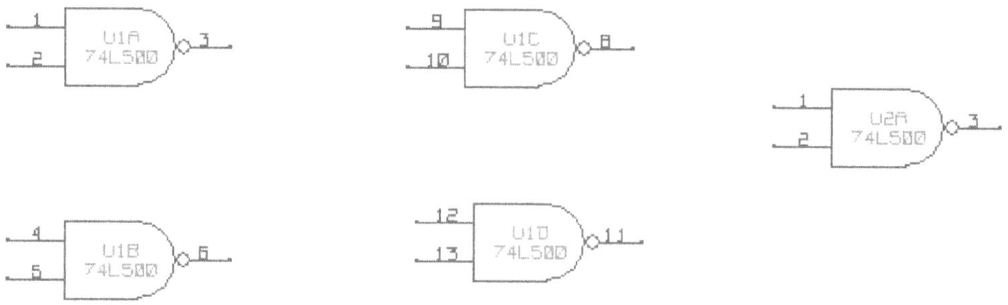

Sort by Y position.

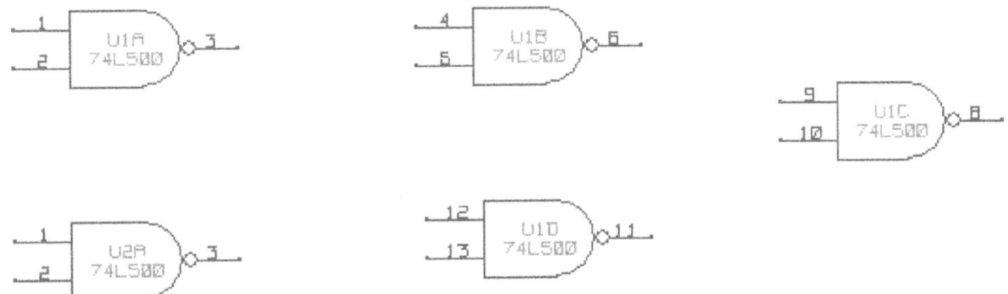

You can see that four 74LS00 gates were distributed in U1 package, and that the fifth 74LS00 has been assigned to the next, U2.

7.2.2 Annotation Choice

Here is an annotation in sheet 2 where the option use first free number in schematic was set.

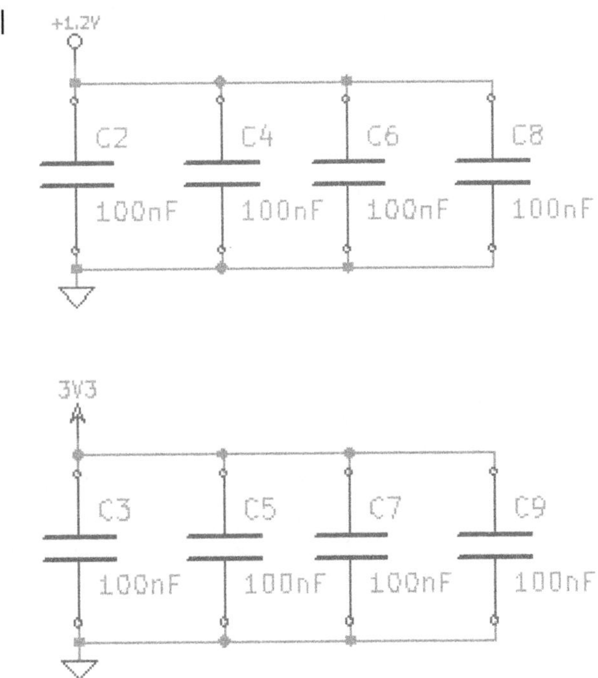

Option start to sheet number*100 and use first free number give the following result.

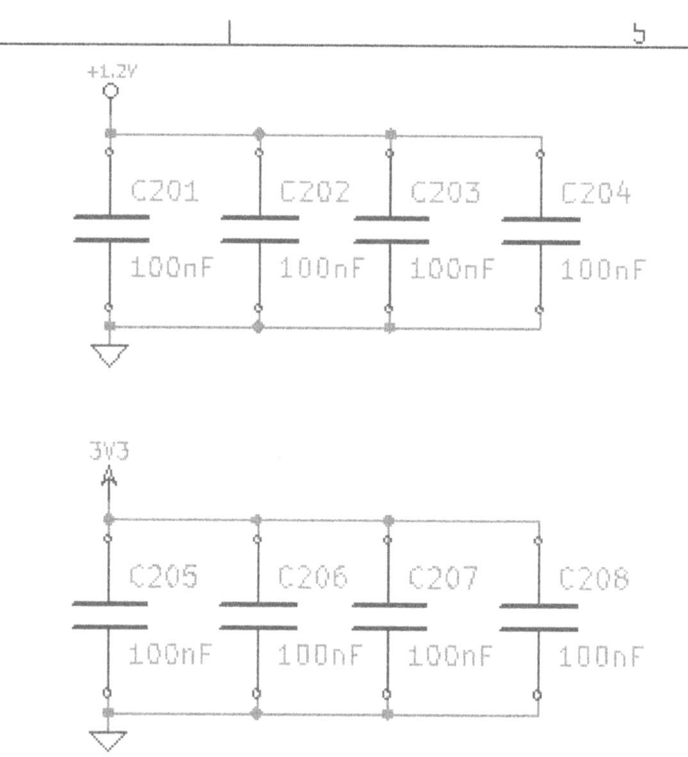

The option start to sheet number*1000 and use first free number gives the following result.

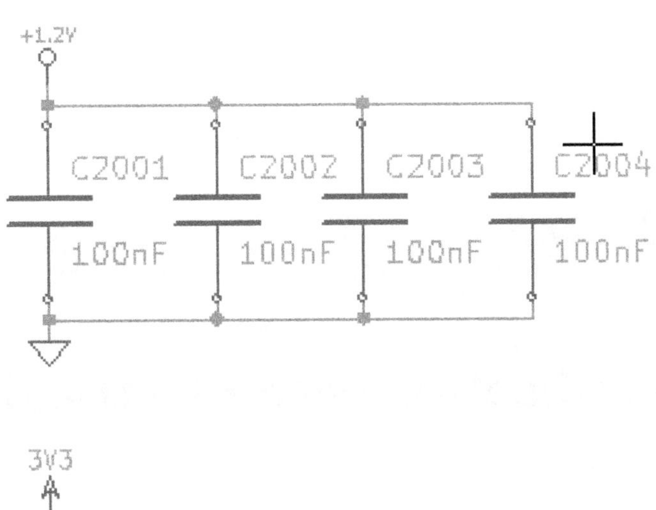
+1.2V
C2001
100nF
C2002
100nF
C2003
100nF
C2004
100nF

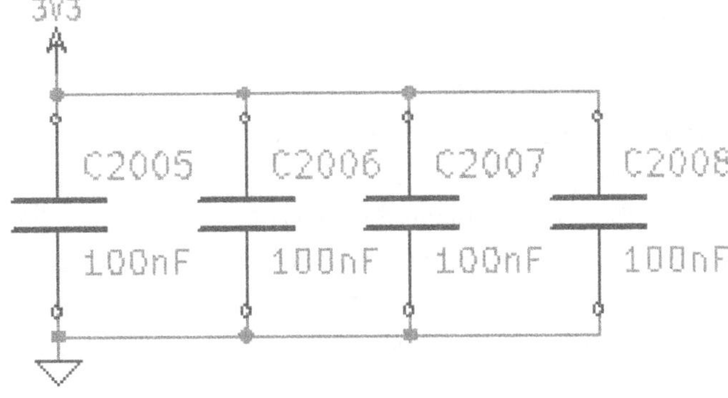
3V3
C2005
100nF
C2006
100nF
C2007
100nF
C2008
100nF

Chapter 8

Design verification with Electrical Rules Check

8.1 Introduction

The Electrical Rules Check (ERC) tool performs an automatic check of your schematic. The ERC checks for any errors in your sheet, such as unconnected pins, unconnected hierarchical symbols, shorted outputs, etc. Naturally, an automatic check is not infallible, and the software that makes it possible to detect all design errors is not yet 100% complete. Such a check is very useful, because it allows you to detect many oversights and small errors.

In fact all detected errors must be checked and then corrected before proceeding as normal. The quality of the ERC is directly related to the care taken in declaring electrical pin properties during library creation. ERC output is reported as "errors" or "warnings".

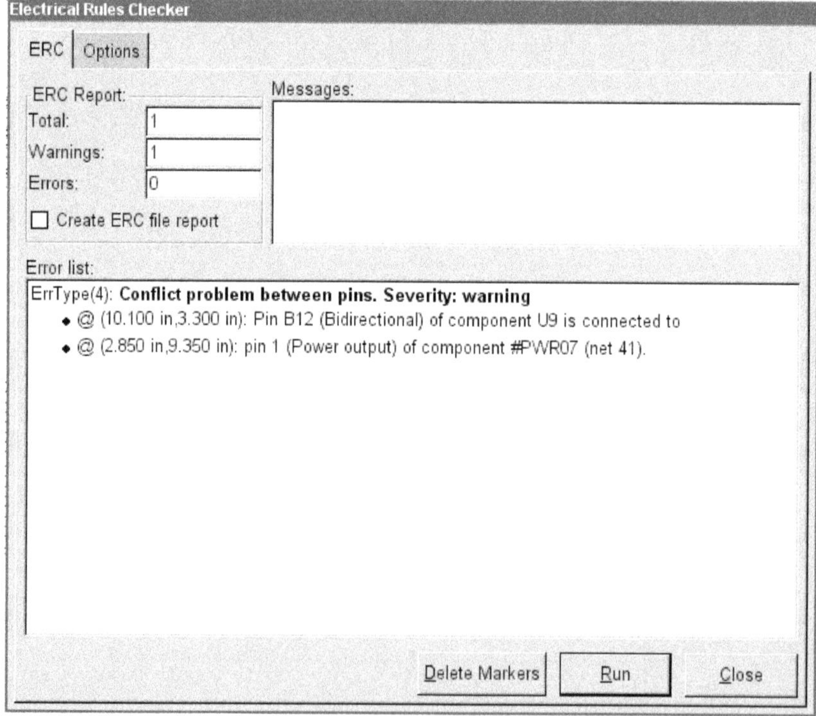

8.2 How to use ERC

ERC can be started by clicking on the icon  .

Warnings are placed on the schematic elements raising an ERC error (pins or labels).

Note

- In this dialog window, when clicking on an error message you can jump to the corresponding marker in the schematic.
- In the schematic right-click on a marker to access the corresponding diagnostic message.

You can also delete error markers from the dialog.

8.3 Example of ERC

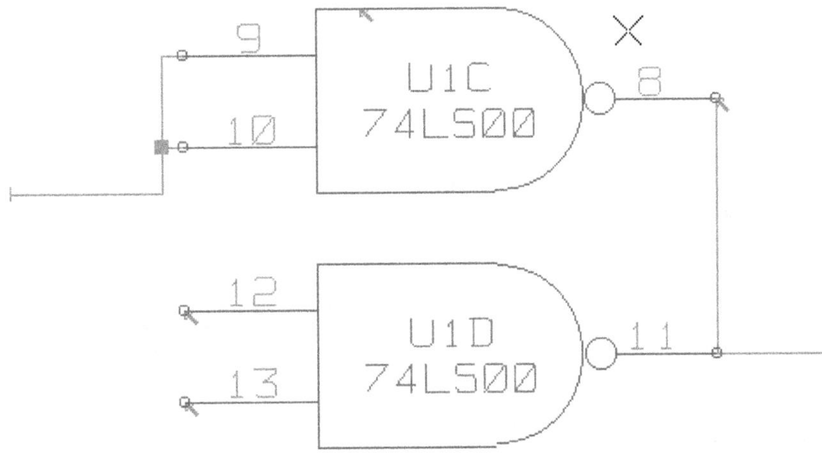

Here you can see four errors:

- Two outputs have been erroneously connected together (red arrow).
- Two inputs have been left unconnected (green arrow).
- There is an error on an invisible power port, power flag is missing (green arrow on the top).

8.4 Displaying diagnostics

By right-clicking on a marker the pop-up menu allows you to access the ERC marker diagnostic window.

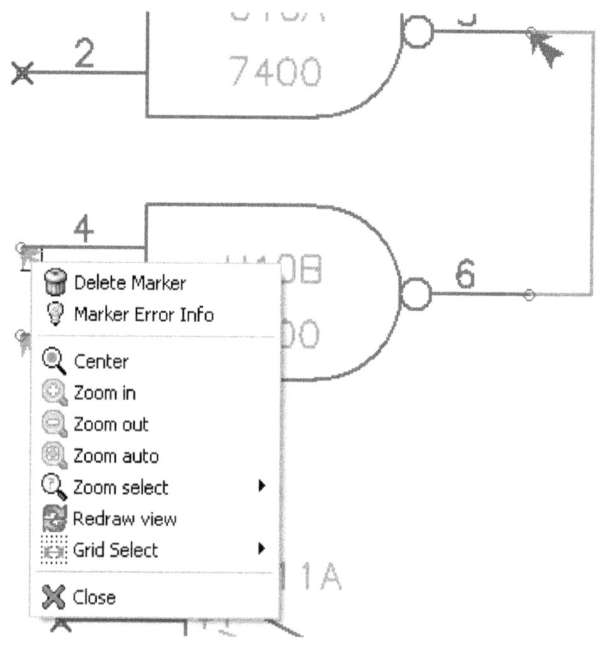

and when clicking on Marker Error Info you can get a description of the error.

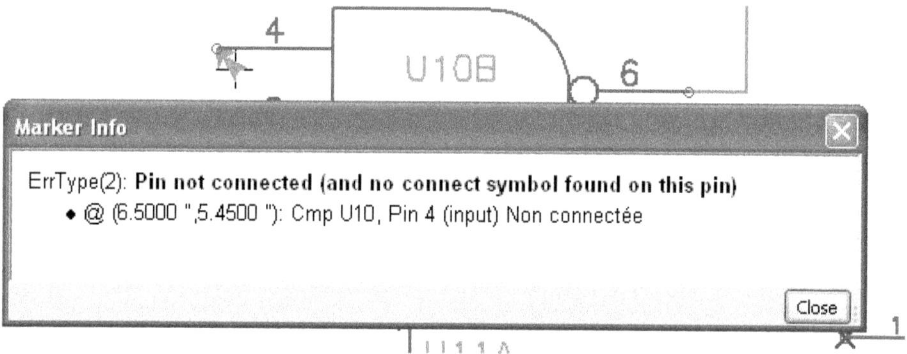

8.5 Power pins and Power flags

It is common to have an error or a warning on power pins, even though all seems normal. See example above. This happens because, in most designs, the power is provided by connectors that are not power sources (like regulator output, which is declared as Power out).

The ERC thus won' t detect any Power out pin to control this wire and will declare them not driven by a power source.

To avoid this warning you have to place a "PWR_FLAG" on such a power port. Take a look at the following example:

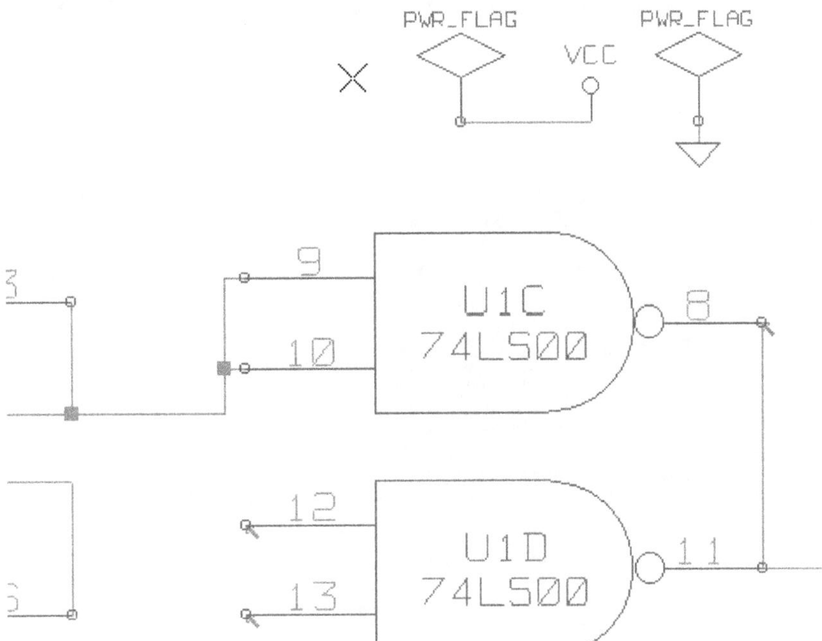

The error marker will then disappear.

Most of the time, a PWR_FLAG must be connected to GND, because usually regulators have outputs declared as power out, but ground pins are never power out (the normal attribute is power in), so grounds never appear connected to a power source without a pwr_flag.

8.6 Configuration

The Options panel allows you to configure connectivity rules to define electrical conditions for errors and warnings check.

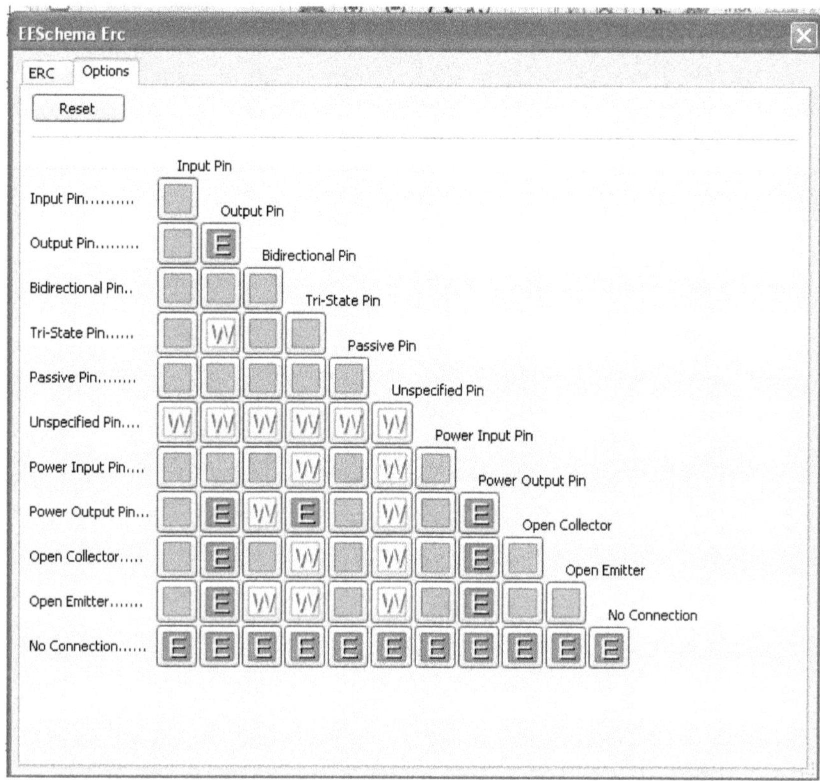

Rules can be changed by clicking on the desired square of the matrix, causing it to cycle through the choices: normal, warning, error.

8.7 ERC report file

An ERC report file can be generated and saved by checking the option Write ERC report. The file extension for ERC report files is .erc. Here is an example of ERC report file.

```
ERC control (4/1/1997-14:16:4)

***** Sheet 1 (INTERFACE UNIVERSAL)
ERC: Warning Pin input Unconnected @ 8.450, 2.350
ERC: Warning passive Pin Unconnected @ 8.450, 1.950
ERC: Warning: BiDir Pin connected to power Pin (Net 6) @ 10.100, 3.300
ERC: Warning: Power Pin connected to BiDir Pin (Net 6) @ 4.950, 1.400

>> Errors ERC: 4
```

Chapter 9

Create a Netlist

9.1 Overview

A netlist is a file which describes electrical connections between components. In the netlist file you can find:

- The list of the components
- The list of connections between components, called equi-potential nets.

Different netlist formats exist. Sometimes the components list and the equi-potential list are two separate files. This netlist is fundamental in the use of schematic capture software, because the netlist is the link with other electronic CAD software, like:

- PCB software.
- Schematic and PCB Simulators.
- CPLD (and other programmable IC′ s) compilers.

Eeschema supports several netlist formats.

- PCBNEW format (printed circuits).
- ORCAD PCB2 format (printed circuits).
- CADSTAR format (printed circuits).
- Spice format, for various simulators (the Spice format is also used by other simulators).

9.2 Netlist formats

Select the tool NET to open the netlist creation dialog box.

Pcbnew selected

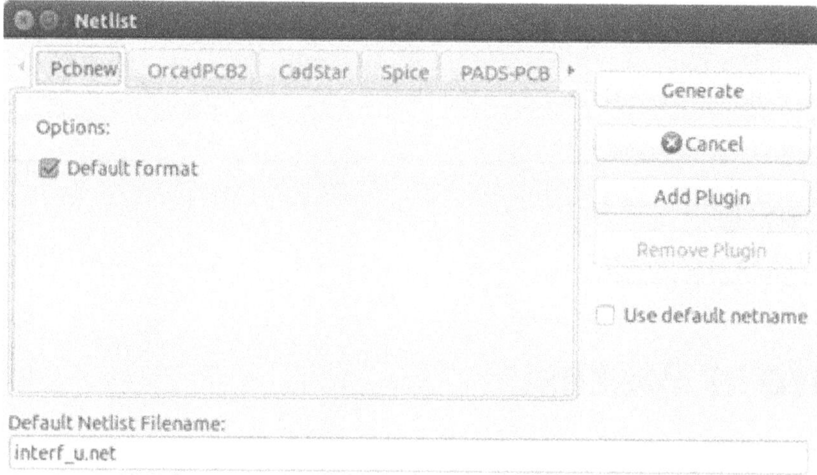

Spice selected

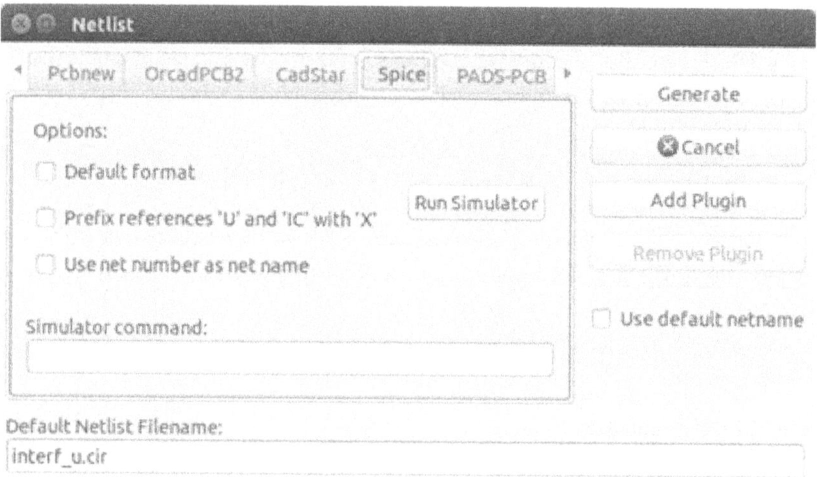

Using the different tabs you can select the desired format. In Spice format you can generate netlists with either equi-potential names (it is more legible) or net numbers (old Spice versions accept numbers only). By clicking the Netlist button, you will be asked for a netlist file name.

Note

With big projects, the netlist generation can take up to several minutes.

9.3 Netlist examples

You can see below a schematic design using the PSPICE library:

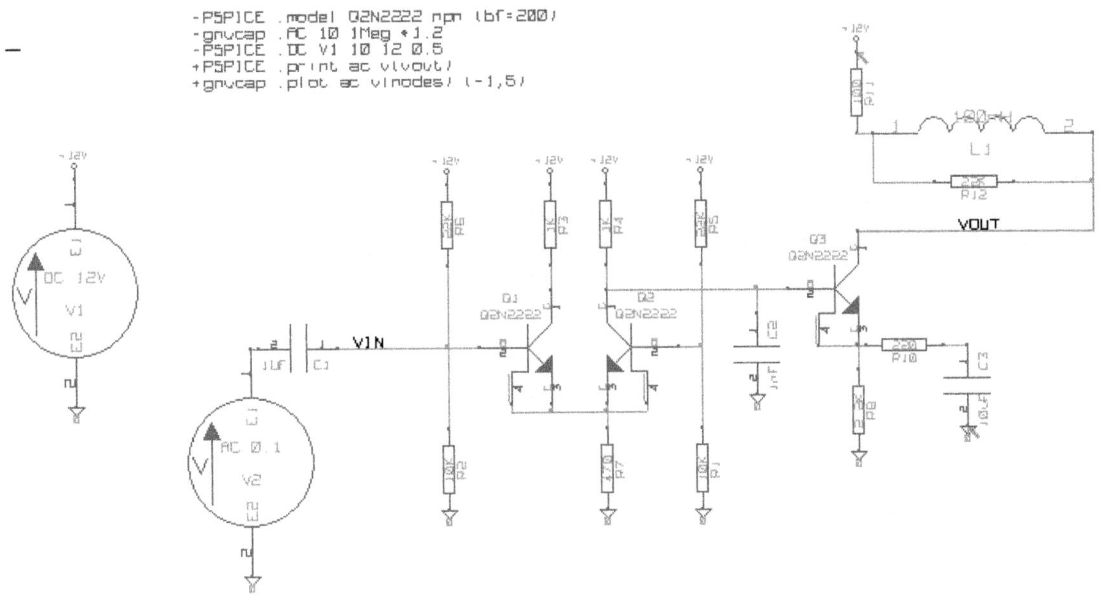

Example of a PCBNEW netlist file:

```
# Eeschema Netlist Version 1.0 generee le 21/1/1997-16:51:15
(
(32E35B76 $noname C2 1NF {Lib=C}
(1 0)
(2 VOUT_1)
)
(32CFC454 $noname V2 AC_0.1 {Lib=VSOURCE}
(1 N-000003)
(2 0)
)
(32CFC413 $noname C1 1UF {Lib=C}
(1 INPUT_1)
(2 N-000003)
)
(32CFC337 $noname V1 DC_12V {Lib=VSOURCE}
(1 +12V)
(2 0)
)
(32CFC293 $noname R2 10K {Lib=R}
(1 INPUT_1)
(2 0)
)
(32CFC288 $noname R6 22K {Lib=R}
(1 +12V)
(2 INPUT_1)
)
(32CFC27F $noname R5 22K {Lib=R}
```

```
(1 +12V)
(2 N-000008)
)
(32CFC277 $noname R1 10K {Lib=R}
(1 N-000008)
(2 0)
)
(32CFC25A $noname R7 470 {Lib=R}
(1 EMET_1)
(2 0)
)
(32CFC254 $noname R4 1K {Lib=R}
(1 +12V)
(2 VOUT_1)
)
(32CFC24C $noname R3 1K {Lib=R}
(1 +12V)
(2 N-000006)
)
(32CFC230 $noname Q2 Q2N2222 {Lib=NPN}
(1 VOUT_1)
(2 N-000008)
(3 EMET_1)
)
(32CFC227 $noname Q1 Q2N2222 {Lib=NPN}
(1 N-000006)
(2 INPUT_1)
(3 EMET_1)
)
)
# End
```

In PSPICE format, the netlist is as follows:

```
* Eeschema Netlist Version 1.1 (Spice format) creation date: 18/6/2008-08:38:03

.model Q2N2222 npn (bf=200)
.AC 10 1Meg \*1.2
.DC V1 10 12 0.5


R12   /VOUT N-000003 22K
R11   +12V N-000003 100
L1   N-000003 /VOUT 100mH
R10   N-000005 N-000004 220
C3   N-000005 0 10uF
C2   N-000009 0 1nF
R8   N-000004 0 2.2K
```

```
Q3    /VOUT N-000009 N-000004 N-000004 Q2N2222
V2    N-000008 0 AC 0.1
C1    /VIN N-000008 1UF
V1    +12V 0 DC 12V
R2    /VIN 0 10K
R6    +12V /VIN 22K
R5    +12V N-000012 22K
R1    N-000012 0 10K
R7    N-000007 0 470
R4    +12V N-000009 1K
R3    +12V N-000010 1K
Q2    N-000009 N-000012 N-000007 N-000007 Q2N2222
Q1    N-000010 /VIN N-000007 N-000007 Q2N2222

.print ac v(vout)
.plot ac v(nodes) (-1,5)

.end
```

9.4 Notes on Netlists

9.4.1 Netlist name precautions

Many software tools that use netlists do not accept spaces in the component names, pins, equi-potential nets or others. Systematically avoid spaces in labels, or names and value fields of components or their pins.

In the same way, special characters other than letters and numbers can cause problems. Note that this limitation is not related to Eeschema, but to the netlist formats that can then become untranslatable to software that uses netlist files.

9.4.2 PSPICE netlists

For the Pspice simulator, you have to include some command lines in the netlist itself (.PROBE, .AC, etc.).

Any text line included in the schematic diagram starting with the keyword **-pspice** or **-gnucap** will be inserted (without the keyword) at the top of the netlist.

Any text line included in the schematic diagram starting with the keyword **+pspice** or **+gnucap** will be inserted (without the keyword) at the end of the netlist.

Here is a sample using many one-line texts and one multi-line text:

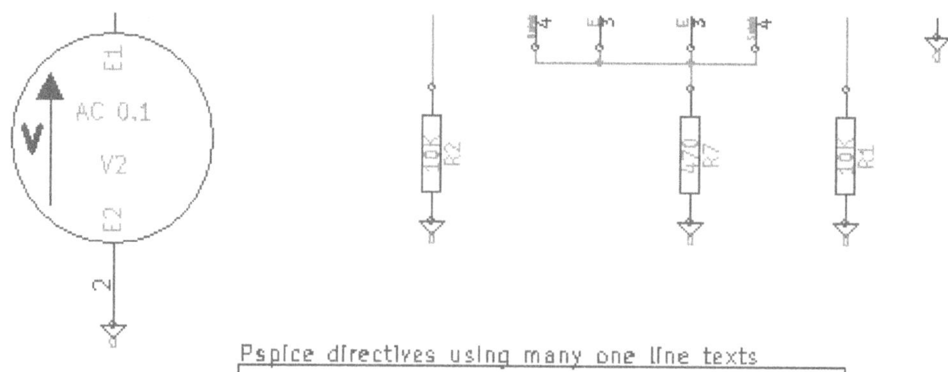

Pspice directives using many one line texts

```
-PSPICE .model Q2N2222 npn (bf=200)
-gnucap .AC dec 10 1Meg *1.2
-PSPICE .DC V1 10 12 0.5
+PSPICE .print ac v(vout)
+gnucap .plot ac v(nodes) (-1,5)
```

Pspice directives using one multiline text:

```
+PSPICE .model NPN NPN
.model PNP PNP
.lib C:\Program Files\LTC\LTspiceIV\lib\cmp\standard.bjt
.backanno
```

For example, if you type the following text (do not use a label!):

```
-PSPICE .PROBE
```

a line .PROBE will be inserted in the netlist.

In the previous example three lines were inserted at the beginning of the netlist and two at the end with this technique.

If you are using multiline texts, **+pspice** or **+gnucap** keywords are needed only once:

```
+PSPICE .model NPN NPN
.model PNP PNP
.lib C:\Program Files\LTC\LTspiceIV\lib\cmp\standard.bjt
.backanno
```

creates the four lines:

```
.model NPN NPN
.model PNP PNP
.lib C:\Program Files\LTC\LTspiceIV\lib\cmp\standard.bjt
.backanno
```

Also note that the equipotential GND must be named 0 (zero) for Pspice.

9.5 Other formats

For other netlist formats you can add netlist converters in the form of plugins. These converters are automatically launched by Eeschema. Chapter 14 gives some explanations and examples of converters.

A converter is a text file (xsl format) but one can use other languages like Python. When using the xsl format, a tool (xsltproc.exe or xsltproc) read the intermediate file created by Eeschema, and the converter file to create the output file. In this case, the converter file (a sheet style) is very small and very easy to write.

9.5.1 Init the dialog window

You can add a new netlist plug-in via the Add Plugin button.

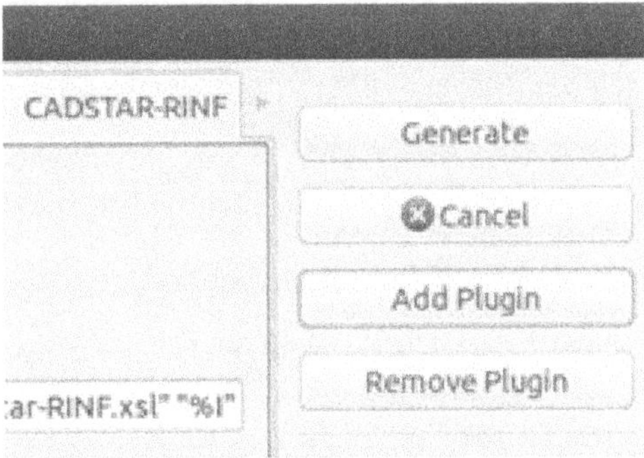

Here is the plug-in PadsPcb setup window:

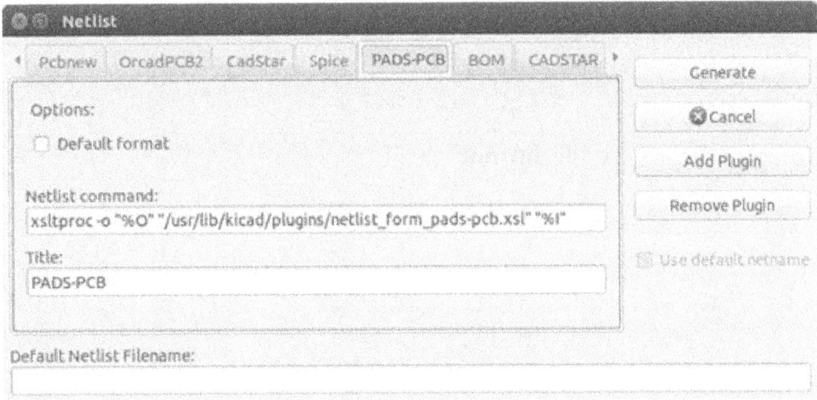

The setup will require:

- A title (for example, the name of the netlist format).
- The plug-in to launch.

When the netlist is generated:

1. Eeschema creates an intermediate file *.tmp, for example test.tmp.
2. Eeschema runs the plug-in, which reads test.tmp and creates test.net.

9.5.2 Command line format

Here is an example, using xsltproc.exe as a tool to convert .xsl files, and a file netlist_form_pads-pcb.xsl as converter sheet style:

f:/kicad/bin/xsltproc.exe -o %O.net f:/kicad/bin/plugins/netlist_form_pads-pcb.xsl %I

With:

f:/kicad/bin/xsltproc.exe	A tool to read and convert xsl file
-o %O.net	Output file: %O will define the output file.
f:/kicad/bin/plugins/netlist_form_pads-pcb.xsl	File name converter (a sheet style, xsl format).
%I	Will be replaced by the intermediate file created by Eeschema (*.tmp).

For a schematic named test.sch, the actual command line is:

f:/kicad/bin/xsltproc.exe -o test.net f:/kicad/bin/plugins/netlist_form_pads-pcb.xsl test.tmp.

9.5.3 Converter and sheet style (plug-in)

This is a very simple piece of software, because its purpose is only to convert an input text file (the intermediate text file) to another text file. Moreover, from the intermediate text file, you can create a BOM list.

When using xsltproc as the converter tool only the sheet style will be generated.

9.5.4 Intermediate netlist file format

See Chapter 14 for more explanations about xslproc, descriptions of the intermediate file format, and some examples of sheet style for converters.

Chapter 10

Plot and Print

10.1 Introduction

You can access both print and plot commands via the file menu.

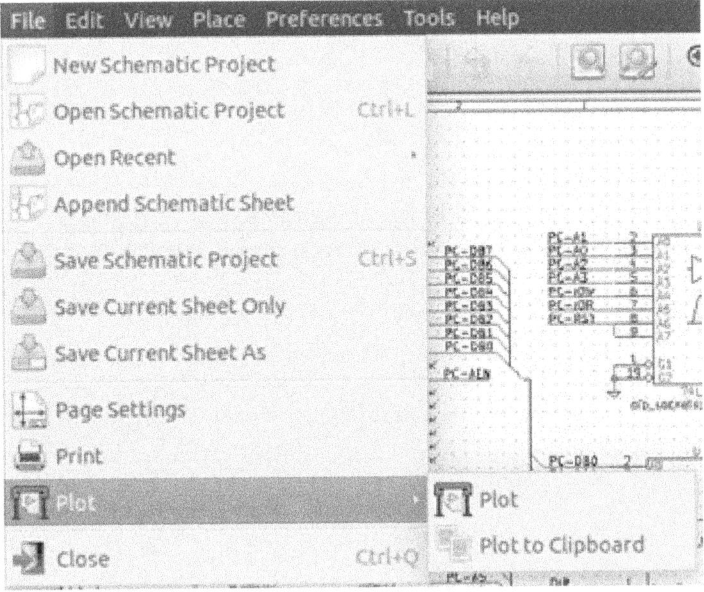

The suported output formats are Postscript, PDF, SVG, DXF and HPGL. You can also directly print to your printer.

10.2 Common printing commands

Plot Current Page
prints one file for the current sheet only.

Plot All Pages
allows you to plot the whole hierarchy (one print file is generated for each sheet).

10.3 Plot in Postscript

This command allows you to create PostScript files.

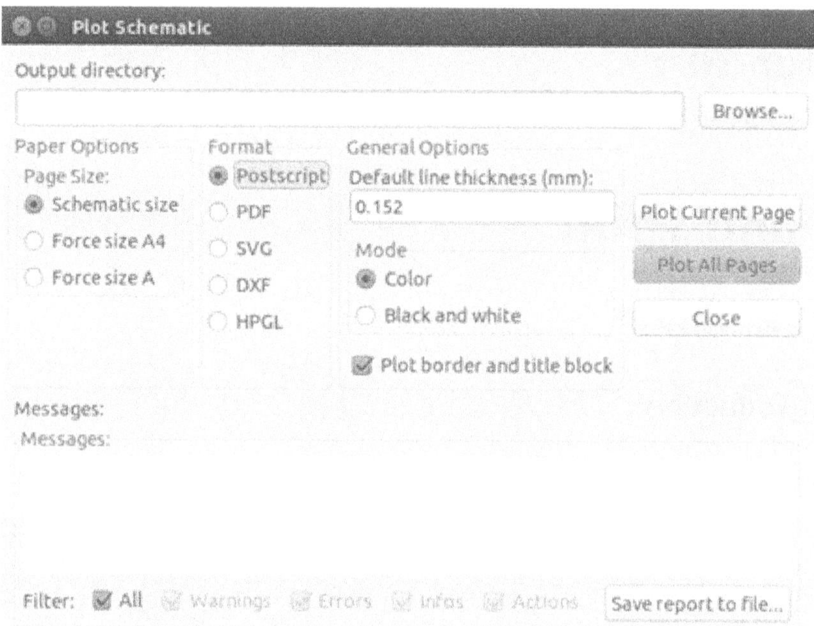

The file name is the sheet name with an extension .ps. You can disable the option "Plot border and title block". This is useful if you want to create a postscript file for encapsulation (format .eps) often used to insert a diagram in a word processing software. The message window displays the file names created.

10.4 Plot in PDF

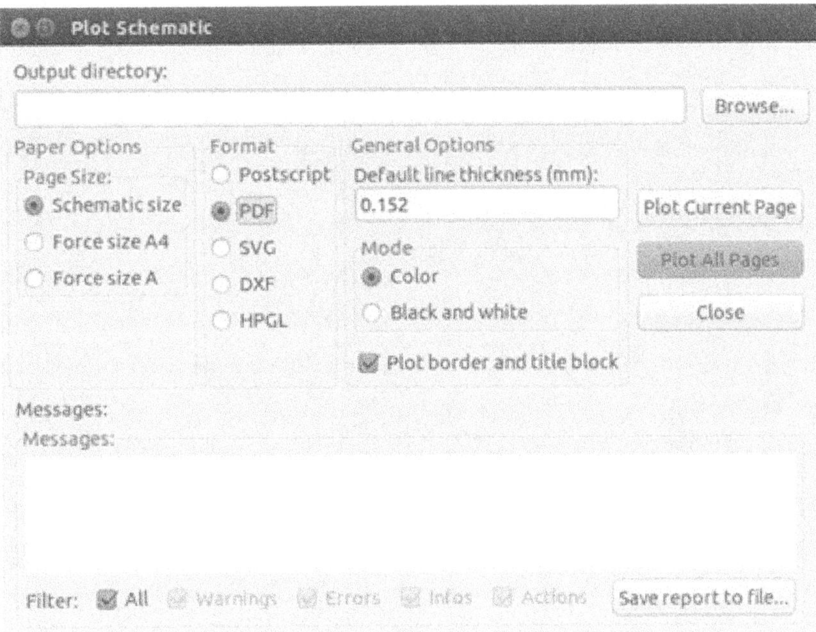

Allows you to create plot files using the format PDF. The file name is the sheet name with an extension .pdf.

10.5 Plot in SVG

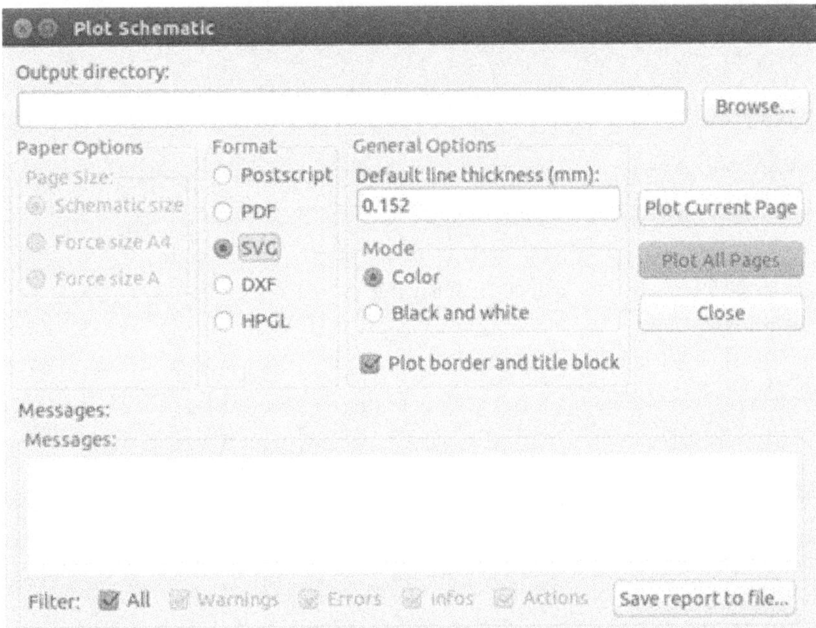

Allows you to create plot files using the vectored format SVG. The file name is the sheet name with an extension .svg.

10.6 Plot in DXF

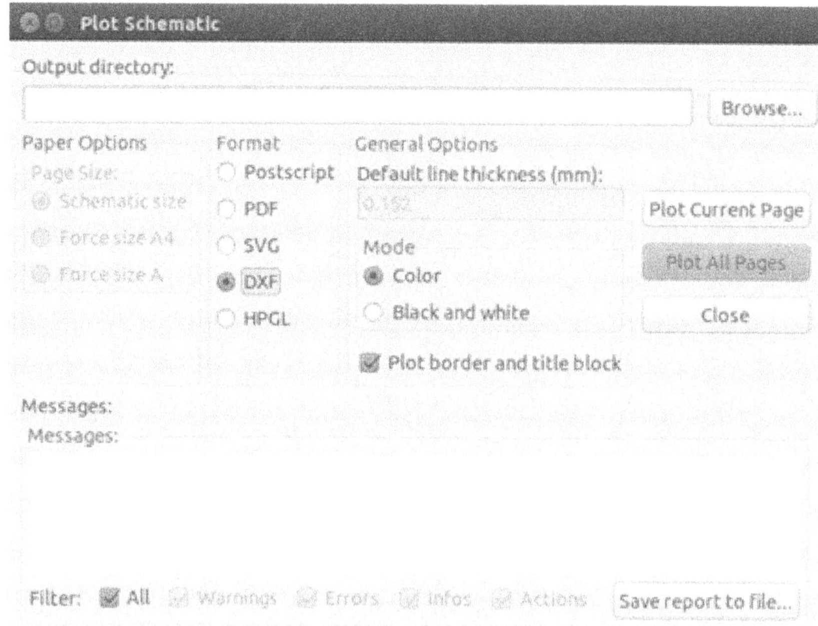

Allows you to create plot files using the format DXF. The file name is the sheet name with an extension .dxf.

10.7 Plot in HPGL

This command allows you to create an HPGL file. In this format you can define:

- Page size.
- Origin.
- Pen width (in mm).

The plotter setup dialog window looks like the following:

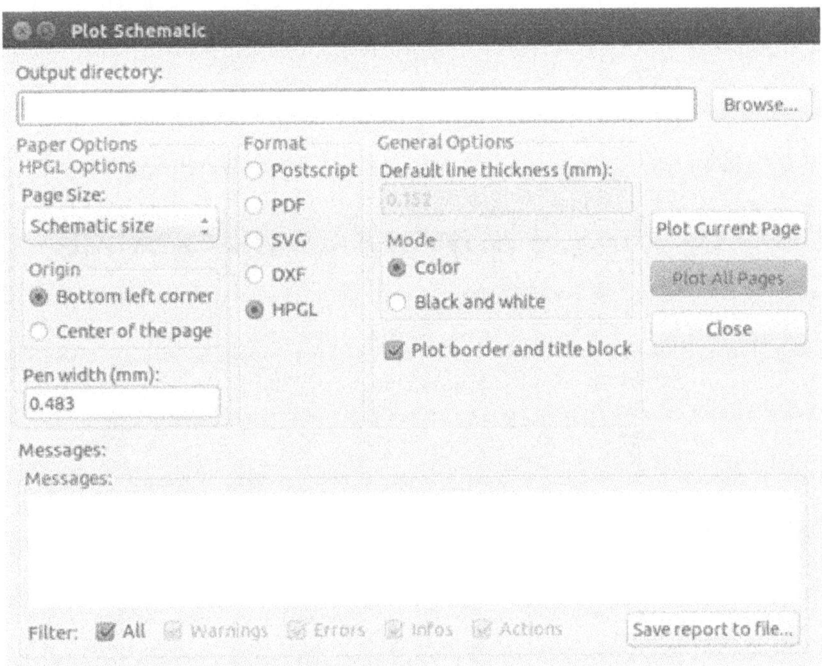

The output file name will be the sheet name plus the extension .plt.

10.7.1 Sheet size selection

Sheet size is normally checked. In this case, the sheet size defined in the title block menu will be used and the chosen scale will be 1. If a different sheet size is selected (A4 with A0, or A with E), the scale is automatically adjusted to fill the page.

10.7.2 Offset adjustments

For all standard dimensions, you can adjust the offsets to center the drawing as accurately as possible. Because plotters have an origin point at the center or at the lower left corner of the sheet, it is necessary to be able to introduce an offset in order to plot properly.

Generally speaking:

- For plotters having their origin point at the center of the sheet the offset must be negative and set at half of the sheet dimension.
- For plotters having their origin point at the lower left corner of the sheet the offset must be set to 0.

To set an offset:

- Select sheet size.
- Set offset X and offset Y.
- Click on accept offset.

10.8 Print on paper

This command, available via the icon , allows you to visualize and generate design files for the standard printer.

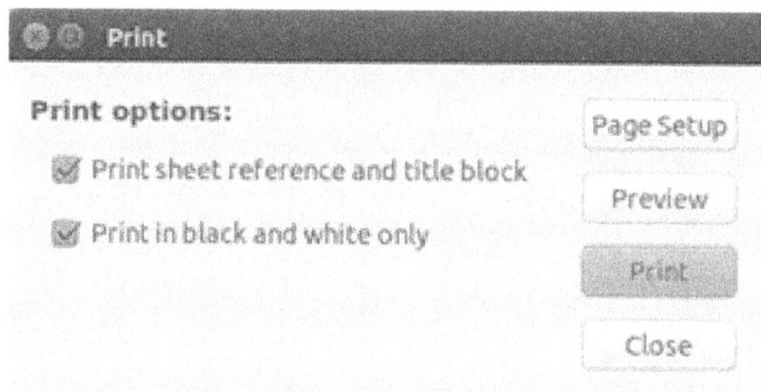

The "Print sheet reference and title block" option enables or disables sheet references and title block.

The "Print in black and white" option sets printing in monochrome. This option is generally necessary if you use a black and white laser printer, because colors are printed into half-tones that are often not so readable.

Chapter 11

Component Library Editor

11.1 General Information About Component Libraries

A component is a schematic element which contains a graphical representation, electrical connections, and fields defining the component. Components used in a schematic are stored in component libraries. Eeschema provides a component library editing tool that allows you to create libraries, add, delete or transfer components between libraries, export components to files, and import components from files. The library editing tool provides a simple way to manage component library files.

11.2 Component Library Overview

A component library is composed of one or more components. Generally the components are logically grouped by function, type, and/or manufacturer.

A component is composed of:

- Graphical items (lines, circles, arcs, text, etc) that provide the symbolic definition.
- Pins which have both graphic properties (line, clock, inverted, low level active, etc) and electrical properties (input, output, bidirectional, etc.) used by the Electrical Rules Check (ERC) tool.
- Fields such as references, values, corresponding footprint names for PCB design, etc.
- Aliases used to associate a common component such as a 7400 with all of its derivatives such as 74LS00, 74HC00, and 7437. All of these aliases share the same library component.

Proper component designing requires:

- Defining if the component is made up of one or more units.
- Defining if the component has an alternate body style also known as a De Morgan representation.
- Designing its symbolic representation using lines, rectangles, circles, polygons and text.

- Adding pins by carefully defining each pin' s graphical elements, name, number, and electrical property (input, output, tri-state, power port, etc.).
- Adding an alias if other components have the same symbol and pin out or removing one if the component has been created from another component.
- Adding optional fields such as the name of the footprint used by the PCB design software and/or defining their visibility.
- Documenting the component by adding a description string and links to data sheets, etc.
- Saving it in the desired library.

11.3 Component Library Editor Overview

The component library editor main window is shown below. It consists of three tool bars for quick access to common features and a component viewing/editing area. Not all commands are available on the tool bars but can be accessed using the menus.

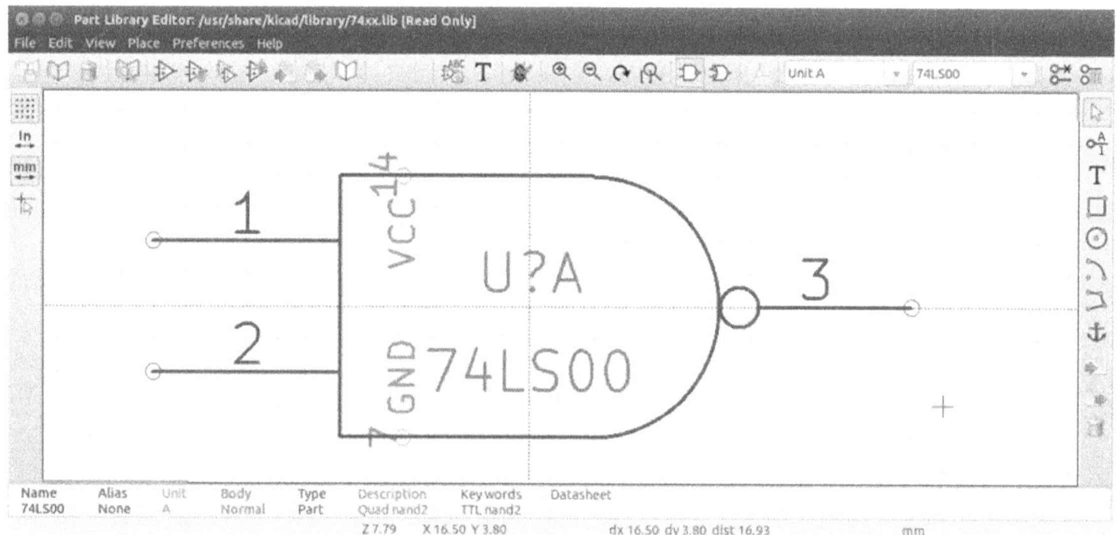

11.3.1 Main Toolbar

The main tool bar typically located at the top of the main window shown below consists of the library management tools, undo/redo commands, zoom commands, and component properties dialogs.

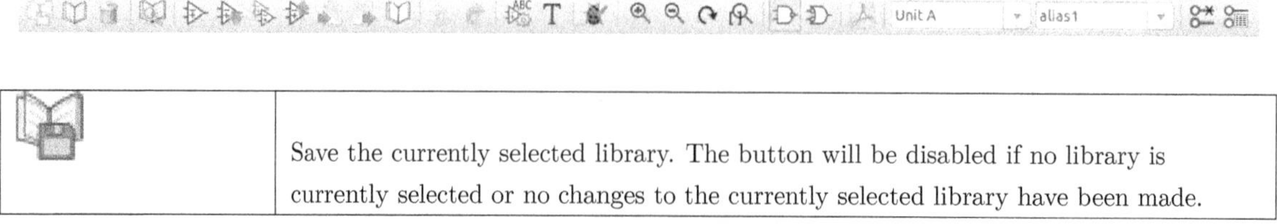

	Save the currently selected library. The button will be disabled if no library is currently selected or no changes to the currently selected library have been made.

	Select the library to edit.
	Delete a component from the currently selected library or any library defined by the project if no library is currently selected.
	Open the component library browser to select the library and component to edit.
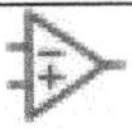	Create a new component.
	Load component from currently selected library for editing.
	Create a new component from the currently loaded component.
	Save the current component changes in memory. The library file is not changed.
	Import one component from a file.
	Export the current component to a file.
	Create a new library file containing the current component. Note: new libraries are not automatically added to the project.
	Undo last edit.
	Redo last undo.
	Edit the current component properties.
	Edit the fields of current component.
	Test the current component for design errors.
	Zoom in.
	Zoom out.
	Refresh display.
	Zoom to fit component in display.
	Select the normal body style. The button is disabled if the current component does not have an alternate body style.

	Select the alternate body style. The button is disabled if the current component does not have an alternate body style.
	Show the associated documentation. The button will be disabled if no documentation is defined for the current component.
Unit A	Select the unit to display. The drop down control will be disabled if the current component is not derived from multiple units.
74LS00	Select the alias. The drop down control will be disabled if the current component does not have any aliases.
	Pin editing: independent editing for pin shape and position for components with multiple units and alternate symbols.
	Show pin table.

11.3.2 Element Toolbar

The vertical toolbar typically located on the right hand side of the main window allows you to place all of the elements required to design a component. The table below defines each toolbar button.

	Select tool. Right-clicking with the select tool opens the context menu for the object under the cursor. Left-clicking with the select tool displays the attributes of the object under the cursor in the message panel at the bottom of the main window. Double-left-clicking with the select tool will open the properties dialog for the object under the cursor.
	Pin tool. Left-click to add a new pin.
	Graphical text tool. Left-click to add a new graphical text item.
	Rectangle tool. Left-click to begin drawing the first corner of a graphical rectangle. Left-click again to place the opposite corner of the rectangle.
	Circle tool. Left-click to begin drawing a new graphical circle from the center. Left-click again to define the radius of the cicle.
	Arc tool. Left-click to begin drawing a new graphical arc item from the center. Left-click again to define the first arc end point. Left-click again to define the second arc end point.
	Polygon tool. Left-click to begin drawing a new graphical polygon item in the current component. Left-click for each addition polygon line. Double-left-click to complete the polygon.

	Anchor tool. Left-click to set the anchor position of the component.
	Import a component from a file.
	Export the current component to a file.
	Delete tool. Left-click to delete an object from the current component.

11.3.3 Options Toolbar

The vertical tool bar typically located on the left hand side of the main window allows you to set some of the editor drawing options. The table below defines each tool bar button.

	Toggle grid visibility on and off.
In	Set units to inches.
mm	Set units to millimeters.
	Toggle full screen cursor on and off.

11.4 Library Selection and Maintenance

The selection of the current library is possible via the which shows you all available libraries and allows you to select one. When a component is loaded or saved, it will be put in this library. The library name of component is the contents of its value field.

Note

- You must load a library into Eeschema, in order to access its contents.
- The content of the current library can be saved after modification, by clicking on the on the main tool bar.
- A component can be removed from any library by clicking on the  .

11.4.1 Select and Save a Component

When you edit a component you are not really working on the component in its library but on a copy of it in the computer' s memory. Any edit action can be undone easily. A component may be loaded from a local library or from an existing component.

11.4.1.1 Component Selection

Clicking the on the main tool bar displays the list of the available components that you can select and load from the currently selected library.

Note

If a component is selected by its alias, the name of the loaded component is displayed on the window title bar instead of the selected alias. The list of component aliases is always loaded with each component and can be edited. You can create a new component by selecting an alias of the current component from the 74LS00. The first item in the alias list is the root name of the component.

Note

Alternatively, clicking the allows you to load a component which has been previously saved by the .

11.4.1.2 Save a Component

After modification, a component can be saved in the current library, in a new library, or exported to a backup file.

To save the modified component in the current library, click the . Please note that the update command only saves the component changes in the local memory. This way, you can make up your mind before you save the library.

To permanently save the component changes to the library file, click the which will overwrite the existing library file with the component changes.

If you want to create a new library containing the current component, click the . You will be asked to enter a new library name.

Note

New libraries are not automatically added to the current project.

You must add any new library you wish to use in a schematic to the list of project libraries in Eeschema using the component configuration dialog.

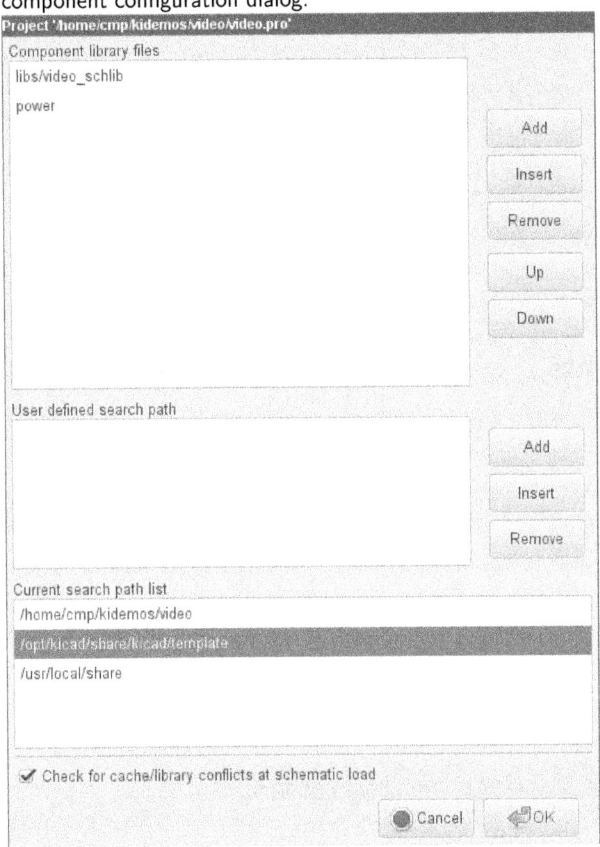

Click the to create a file containing only the current component. This file will be a standard library file which will contain only one component. This file can be used to import the component into another library. In fact, the create new library command and the export command are basically identical.

11.4.1.3 Transfer Components to Another Library

You can very easily copy a component from a source library into a destination library using the following commands:

- Select the source library by clicking the .
- Load the component to be transferred by clicking the . The component will be displayed in the editing area.
- Select the destination library by clicking the .

- Save the current component to the new library in the local memory by clicking the .
- Save the component in the current local library file by clicking the .

11.4.1.4 Discarding Component Changes

When you are working on a component, the edited component is only a working copy of the actual component in its library. This means that as long as you have not saved it, you can just reload it to discard all changes made. If you have already updated it in the local memory and you have not saved it to the library file, you can always quit and start again. Eeschema will undo all the changes.

11.5 Creating Library Components

11.5.1 Create a New Component

A new component can be created by clicking the . You will be asked for a component name (this name is used as default value for the value field in the schematic editor), the reference designator (U, IC, R···), the number of units per package (for example a 7400 is made of 4 units per package) and if an alternate body style (sometimes referred to as DeMorgan) is desired. If the reference designator field is left empty, it will default to "U". These properties can be changed later, but it is preferable to set them correctly at the creation of the component.

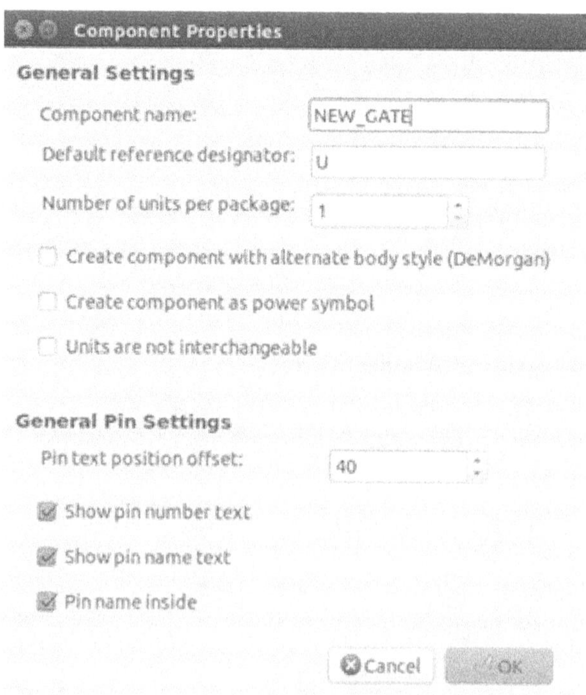

A new component will be created using the properties above and will appear in the editor as shown below.

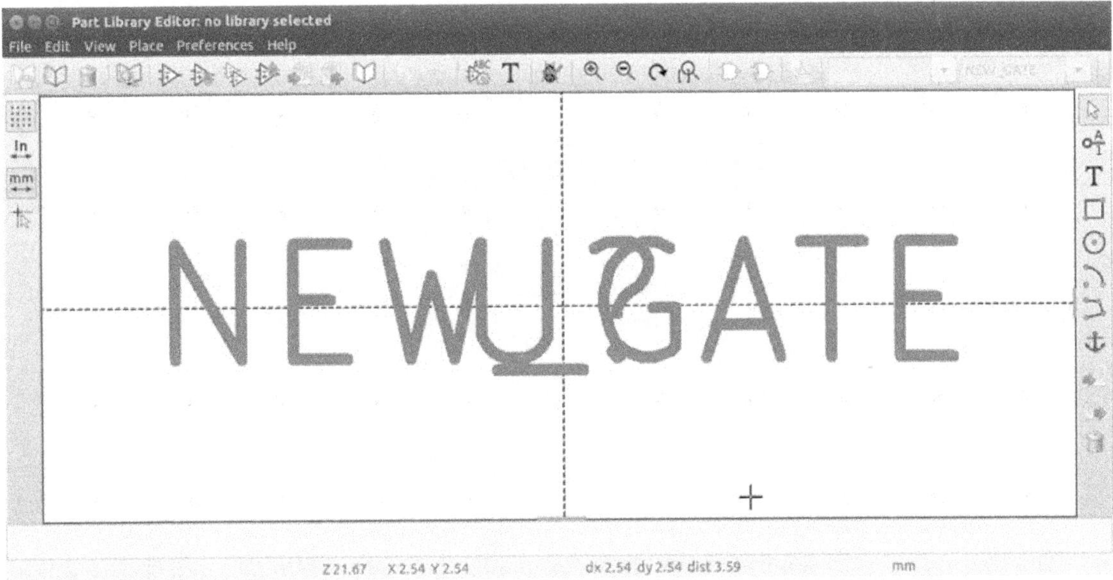

11.5.2 Create a Component from Another Component

Often, the component that you want to make is similar to one already in a component library. In this case it is easy to load and modify an existing component.

- Load the component which will be used as a starting point.
- Click on the or modify its name by right-clicking on the value field and editing the text. If you chose to duplicate the current component, you will be prompted for a new component name.
- If the model component has aliases, you will be prompted to remove aliases from the new component which conflict with the current library. If the answer is no the new component creation will be aborted. Component libraries cannot have any duplicate names or aliases.
- Edit the new component as required.
- Update the new component in the current library by clicking the or save to a new library by clicking the or if you want to save this new component in an other existing library select the other library by clicking on the and save the new component.
- Save the current library file to disk by clicking the .

11.5.3 Component Properties

Component properties should be carefully set during the component creation or alternatively they are inherited from the copied component. To change the component properties, click on the to show the dialog below.

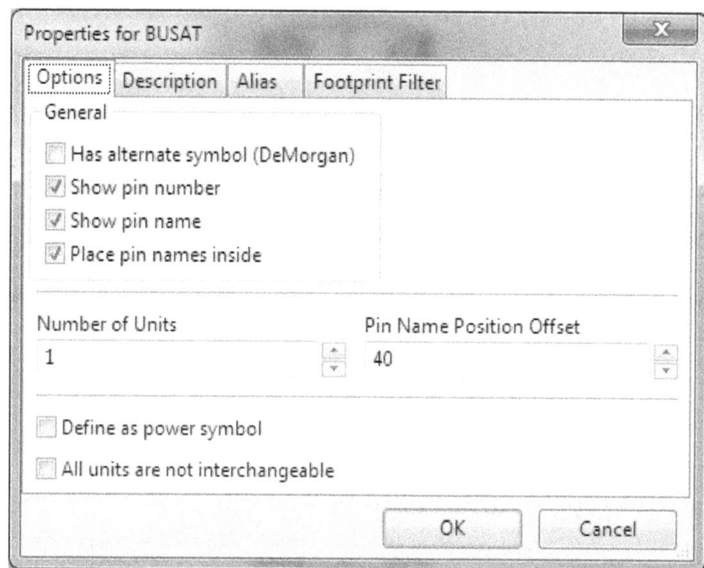

It is very important to correctly set the number of units per package and if the component has an alternate symbolic representation parameters correctly because when pins are edited or created the corresponding pins for each unit will created. If you change the number of units per package after pin creation and editing, there will be additional work introduced to add the new unit pins and symbols. Nevertheless, it is possible to modify these properies at any time.

The graphic options "Show pin number" and "Show pin name" define the visibility of the pin number and pin name text. This text will be visible if the corresponding options are checked. The option "Place pin names inside" defines the pin name position relative to the pin body. This text will be displayed inside the component outline if the option is checked. In this case the "Pin Name Position Offset" property defines the shift of the text away from the body end of the pin. A value from 30 to 40 (in 1/1000 inch) is reasonable.

The example below shows a component with the "Place pin name inside" option unchecked. Notice the position of the names and pin numbers.

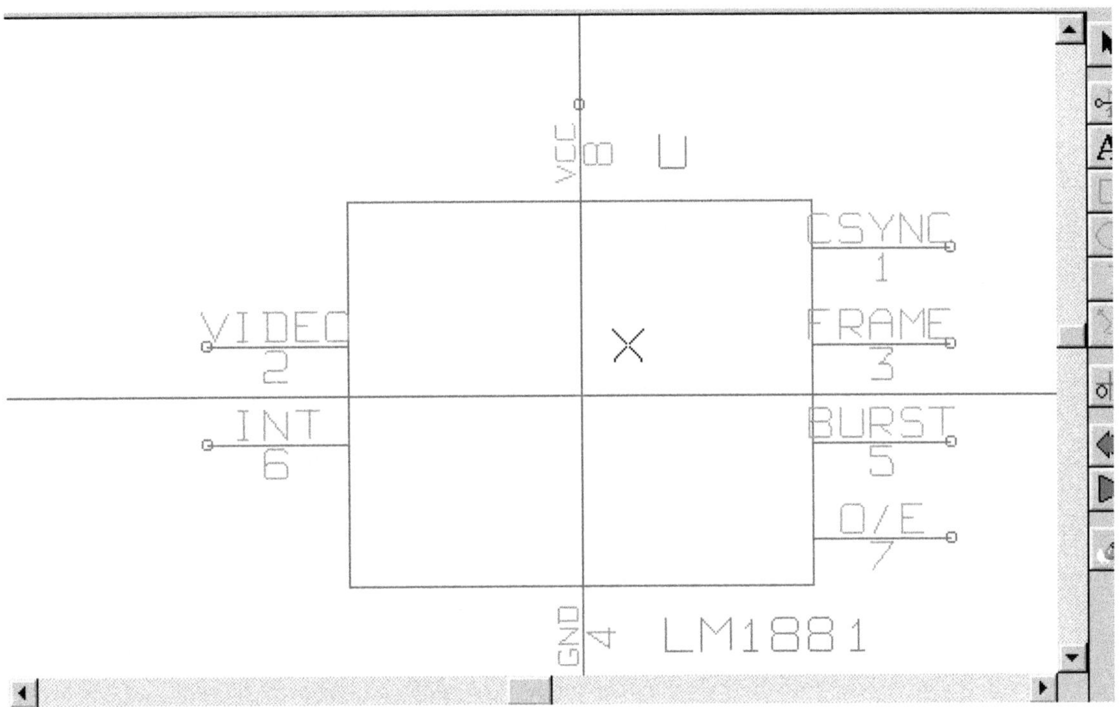

11.5.4 Components with Alternate Symbols

If the component has more than one symbolic repersentation, you will have to select the different symbols of the component in order to edit them. To edit the normal symbol, click the .

To edit the alternate symbol click on the . Use the 74LS00 shown below to select the unit you wish to edit.

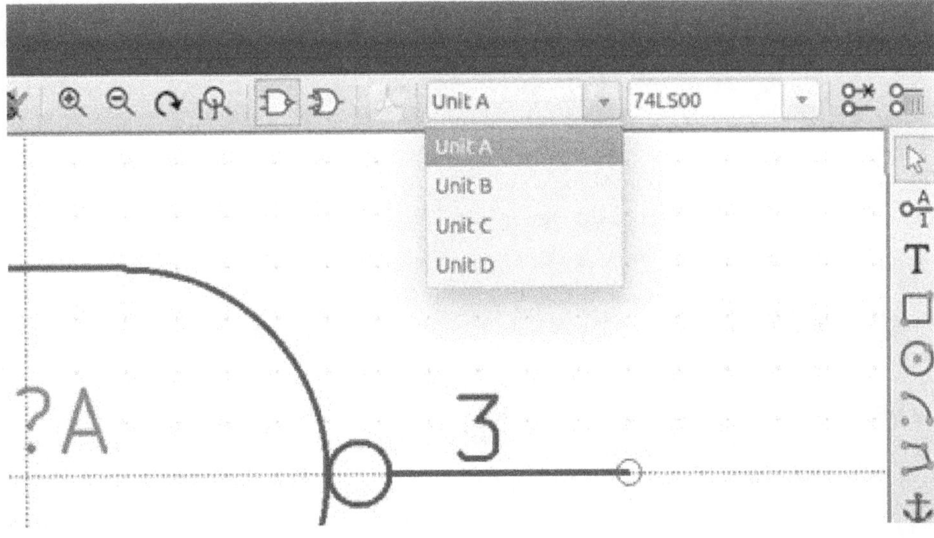

11.6 Graphical Elements

Graphical elements create the symbolic representation of a component and contain no electrical connection information. Their design is possible using the following tools:

- Lines and polygons defined by start and end points.
- Rectangles defined by two diagonal corners.
- Circles defined by the center and radius.
- Arcs defined by the starting and ending point of the arc and its center. An arc goes from 0° to 180°.

The vertical toolbar on the right hand side of the main window allows you to place all of the graphical elements required to design a component′ s symbolic representation.

11.6.1 Graphical Element Membership

Each graphic element (line, arc, circle, etc.) can be defined as common to all units and/or body styles or specific to a given unit and/or body style. Element options can be quickly accessed by right-clicking on the element to display the context menu for the selected element. Below is the context menu for a line element.

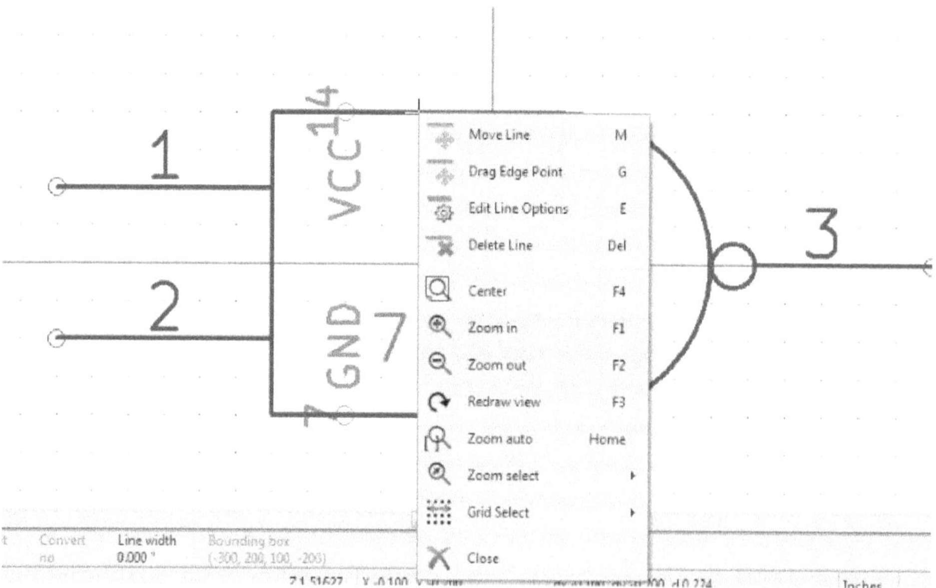

You can also double-left-click on an element to modify its properties. Below is the properties dialog for a polygon element.

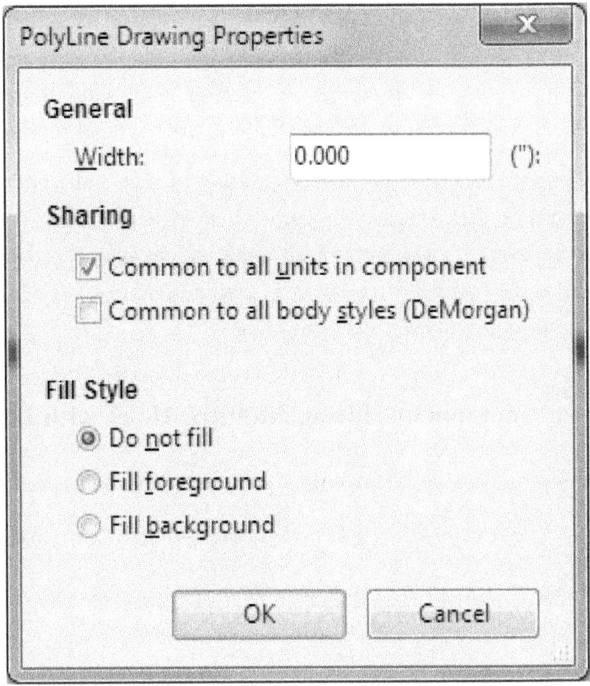

The properties of a graphic element are:

- Line width which defines the width of the element' s line in the current drawing units.
- The "Common to all units in component" setting defines if the graphical element is drawn for each unit in component with more than one unit per package or if the graphical element is only drawn for the current unit.
- The "Common by all body styles (DeMorgan)" setting defines if the graphical element is drawn for each symbolic representation in components with an alternate body style or if the graphical element is only drawn for the current body style.
- The fill style setting determines if the symbol defined by the graphical element is to be drawn unfilled, background filled, or foreground filled.

11.6.2 Graphical Text Elements

The T allows for the creation of graphical text. Graphical text is always readable, even when the component is mirrored. Please note that graphical text items are not fields.

11.7 Multiple Units per Component and Alternate Body Styles

Components can have two symbolic representations (a standard symbol and an alternate symbol often referred to as "DeMorgan") and/or have more than one unit per package (logic gates for example). Some components can have more than one unit per package each with different symbols and pin configurations.

Consider for instance a relay with two switches which can be designed as a component with three different units: a coil, switch 1, and switch 2. Designing a component with multiple units per package and/or alternate body styles is very flexible. A pin or a body symbol item can be common to all units or specific to a given unit or they can be common to both symbolic representation so are specific to a given symbol representation.

By default, pins are specific to each symbolic representation of each unit, because the pin number is specific to a unit, and the shape depends on the symbolic representation. When a pin is common to each unit or each symbolic representation, you need to create it only once for all units and all symbolic representations (this is usually the case for power pins). This is also the case for the body style graphic shapes and text, which may be common to each unit (but typically are specific to each symbolic representation).

11.7.1 Example of a Component Having Multiple Units with Different Symbols:

This is an example of a relay defined with three units per package, switch 1, switch 2, and the coil:

Option: pins are not linked. One can add or edit pins for each unit without any coupling with pins of other units.

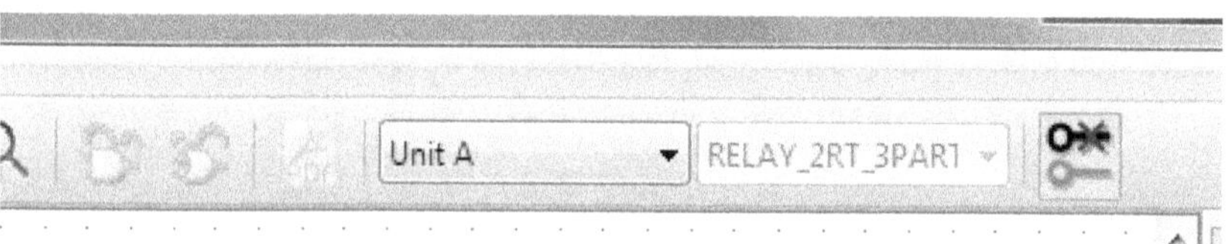

All units are not interchangeable must be selected.

Properties for RELAY_2RT_3PARTS

Options | Description | Alias | Footprint Filter

General

Has alternate symbol (DeMorgan)

Show pin number

Show pin name

Place pin names inside

Number of Units 3

Pin Name Position Offset 40

Define as power symbol

All units are not interchangeable

OK Cancel

Unit 1

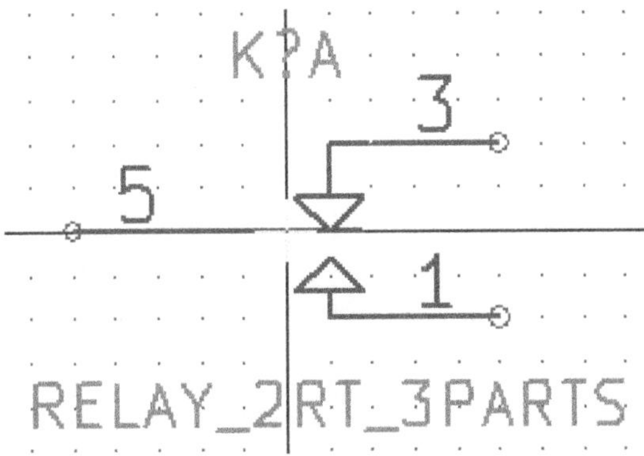

Unit 2

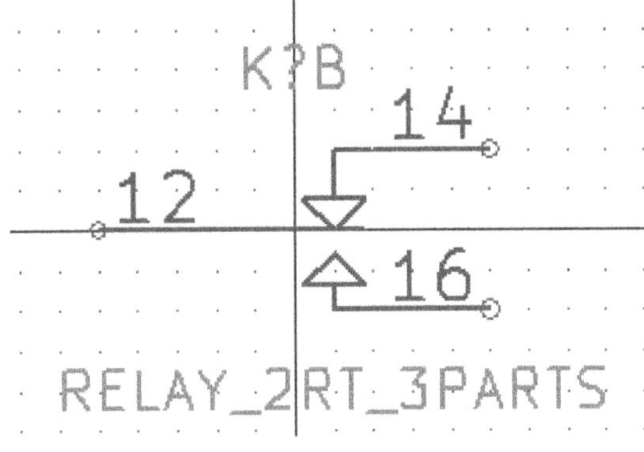

Unit 3

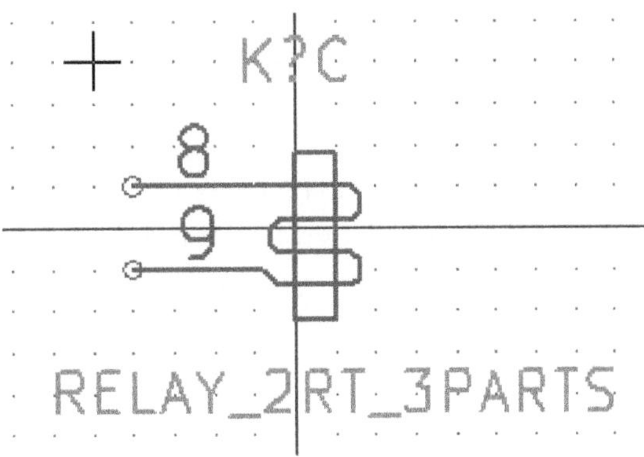

It does not have the same symbol and pin layout and therefore is not interchangeable with units 1 and 2.

11.7.1.1 Graphical Symbolic Elements

Shown below are properties for a graphic body element. From the relay example above, the three units have different symbolic representations. Therefore, each unit was created separately and the graphical body elements must have the "Common to all units in component" disabled.

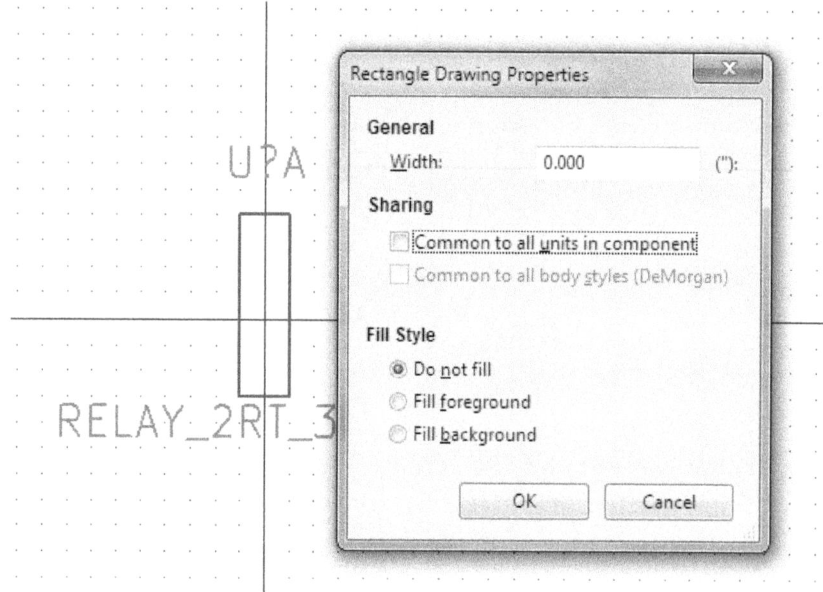

11.8 Pin Creation and Editing

You can click on the to create and insert a pin. The editing of all pin properties is done by double-clicking on the pin or right-clicking on the pin to open the pin context menu. Pins must be created carefully, because any error will have consequences on the PCB design. Any pin already placed can be edited, deleted, and/or moved.

11.8.1 Pin Overview

A pin is defined by its graphical representation, its name and its "number". The pin' s "number" is defined by a set of 4 letters and / or numbers. For the Electrical Rules Check (ERC) tool to be useful, the pin' s "electrical" type (input, output, tri-state…) must also be defined correctly. If this type is not defined properly, the schematic ERC check results may be invalid.

Important notes:

- Do not use spaces in pin names and numbers.
- To define a pin name with an inverted signal (overline) use the ~ (tilde) character. The next ~ character will turn off the overline. For example `\~FO~O` would display FO O.
- If the pin name is reduced to a single symbol, the pin is regarded as unnamed.
- Pin names starting with `#`, are reserved for power port symbols.
- A pin "number" consists of 1 to 4 letters and/ or numbers. 1,2,..9999 are valid numbers. A1, B3, Anod, Gnd, Wire, etc. are also valid.
- Duplicate pin "numbers" cannot exist in a component.

11.8.2 Pin Properties

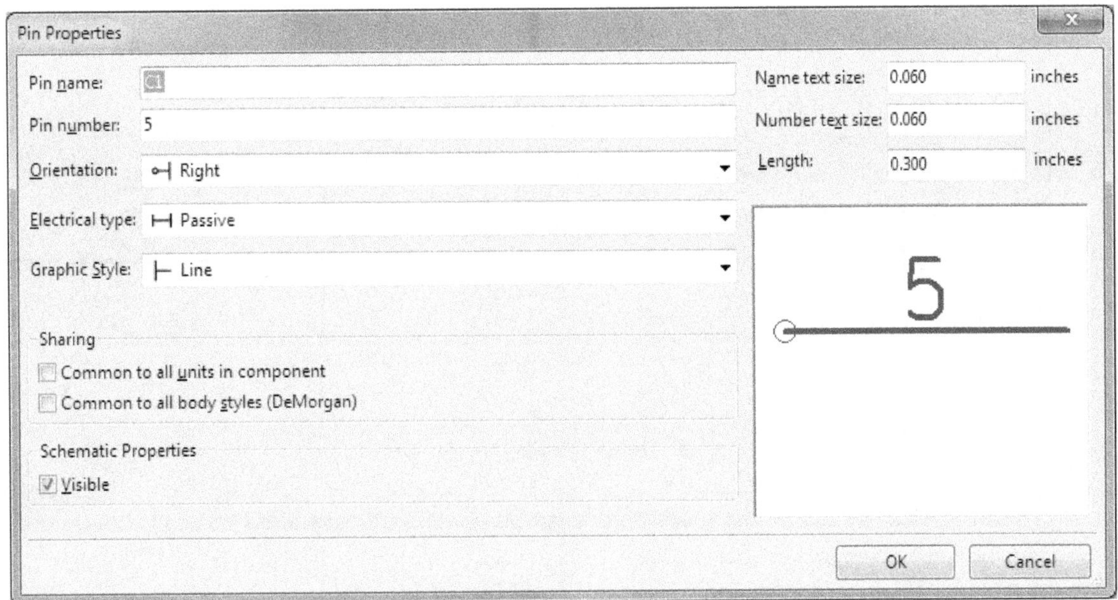

The pin properties dialog allows you to edit all of the characteristics of a pin. This dialog pops up automatically when you create a pin or when double-clicking on an existing pin. This dialog allows you to modify:

- Name and name' s text size.
- Number and number' s text size.
- Length.
- Electrical and graphical types.
- Unit and alternate representation membership.
- Visibility.

11.8.3 Pins Graphical Styles

Shown in the figure below are the different pin graphical styles. The choice of graphic styles does not have any influence on the pin' s electrical type.

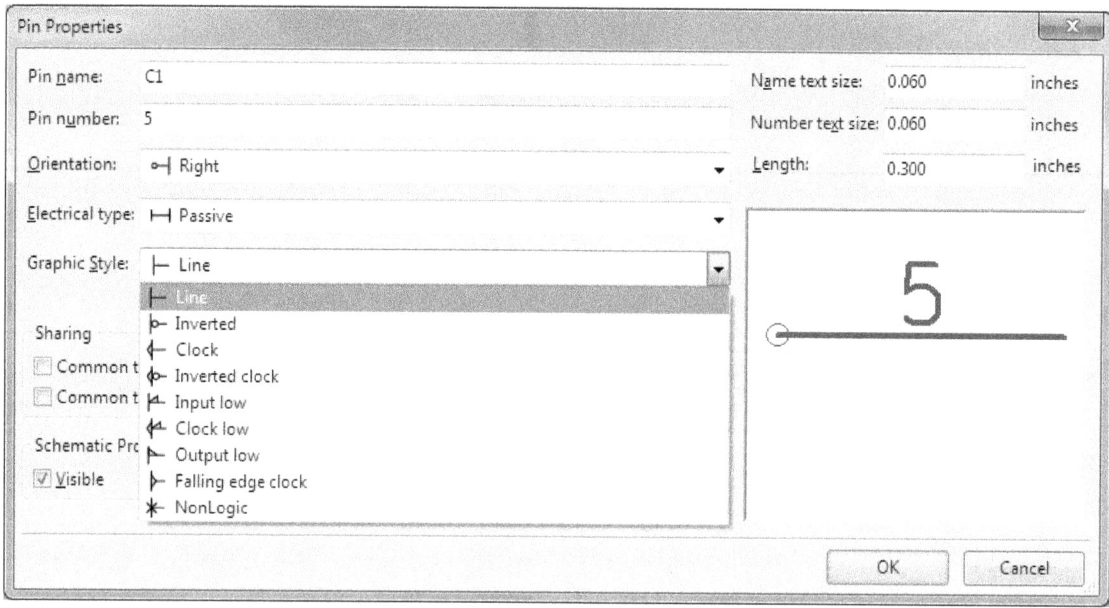

11.8.4 Pin Electrical Types

Choosing the correct electrical type is important for the schematic ERC tool. The electrical types defined are:

- Bidirectional which indicates bidirectional pins commutable between input and output (microprocessor data bus for example).
- Tri-state is the usual 3 states output.
- Passive is used for passive component pins, resistors, connectors, etc.
- Unspecified can be used when the ERC check doesn' t matter.
- Power input is used for the component' s power pins. Power pins are automatically connected to the other power input pins with the same name.
- Power output is used for regulator outputs.
- Open emitter and open collector types can be used for logic outputs defined as such.
- Not connected is used when a component has a pin that has no internal connection.

11.8.5 Pin Global Properties

You can modify the length or text size of the name and/or number of all the pins using the Global command entry of the pin context menu. Click on the parameter you want to modify and type the new value which will then be applied to all of the current component' s pins.

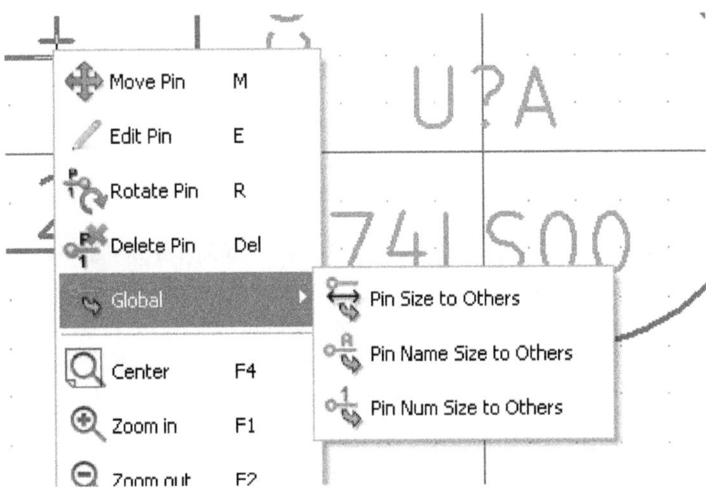

11.8.6 Defining Pins for Multiple Units and Alternate Symbolic Representations

Components with multiple units and/or graphical representations are particularly problematic when creating and editing pins. The majority of pins are specific to each unit (because their pin number is specific to each unit) and to each symbolic representation (because their form and position is specific to each symbolic representation). The creation and the editing of pins can be problematic for components with multiple units per package and alternate symbolic representations. The component library editor allows the simultaneous creation of pins. By default, changes made to a pin are made for all units of a multiple unit component and both representations for components with an alternate representation.

The only exception to this is the pin′ s graphical type and name. This dependency was established to allow for easier pin creation and editing in most of the cases. This dependency can be disabled by toggling the icon on the main tool bar. This will allow you to create pins for each unit and representation completely independently.

A component can have two symbolic representations (representation known as "DeMorgan") and can be made up of more than one unit as in the case of components with logic gates. For certain components, you may want several different graphic elements and pins. Like the relay sample shown in section 11.7.1, a relay can be represented by three distinct units: a coil, switch contact 1, and switch contact 2.

The management of the components with multiple units and components with alternate symbolic representations is flexible. A pin can be common or specific to different units. A pin can also be common to both symbolic representations or specific to each symbolic representation.

By default, pins are specific to each representation of each unit, because their number differs for each unit, and their design is different for each symbolic representation. When a pin is common to all units, it only has to drawn once such as in the case of power pins.

An example is the output pin 7400 quad dual input NAND gate. Since there are four units and two symbolic representations, there are eight separate output pins defined in the component definition. When creating a new 7400 component, unit A of the normal symbolic representation will be shown in the library editor. To edit the pin style in alternate symbolic representation, it must first be enabled by clicking the button on the tool bar. To edit the pin number for each unit, select the appropriate unit using the 

drop down control.

11.9 Component Fields

All library components are defined with four default fields. The reference designator, value, footprint assignment, and documentation file link fields are created whenever a component is created or copied. Only the reference designator and value fields are required. For existing fields, you can use the context menu commands by right-clicking on the pin. Components defined in libraries are typically defined with these four default fields. Additional fields such as vendor, part number, unit cost, etc. can be added to library components but generally this is done in the schematic editor so the additional fields can be applied to all of the components in the schematic.

11.9.1 Editing Component Fields

To edit an existing component field, right-click on the field text to show the field context menu shown below.

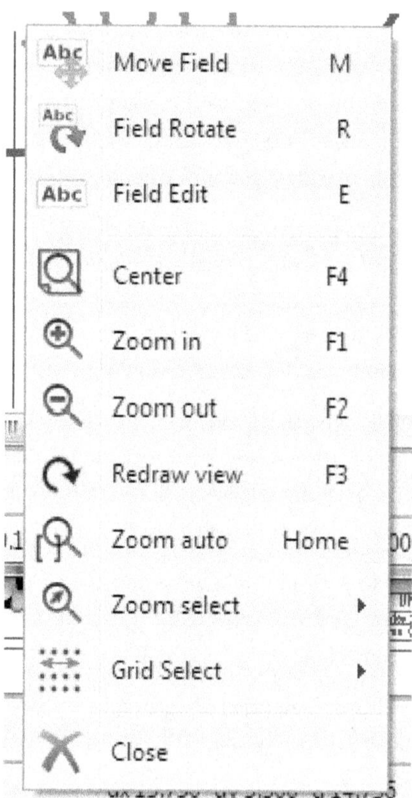

To edit undefined fields, add new fields, or delete optional fields T on the main tool bar to open the field properties dialog shown below.

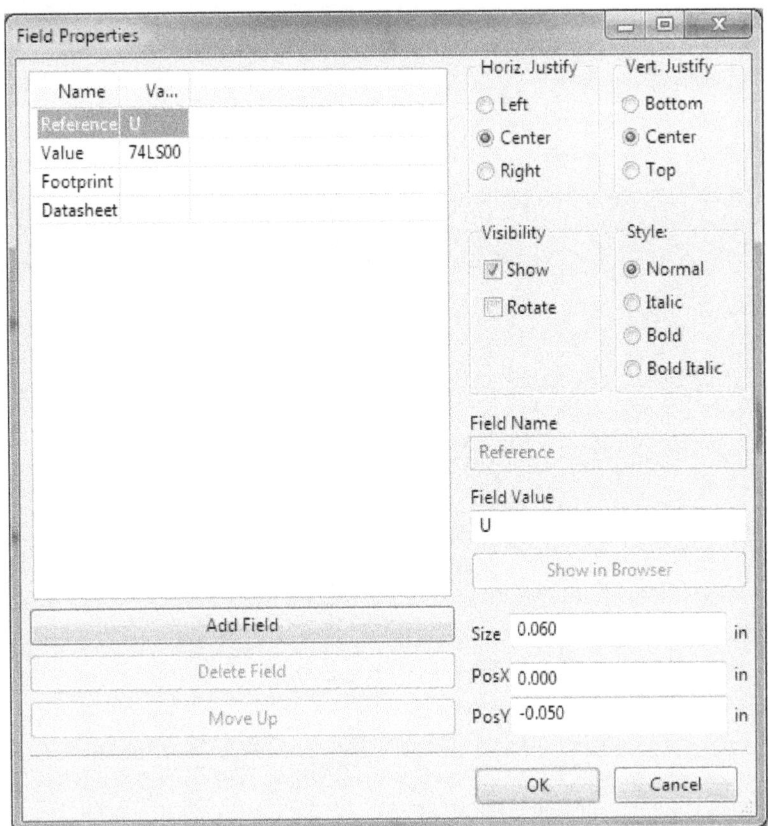

Fields are text sections associated with the component. Do not confuse them with the text belonging to the graphic representation of this component.

Important notes:

- Modifying value fields effectively creates a new component using the current component as the starting point for the new component. This new component has the name contained in the value field when you save it to the currently selected library.
- The field edit dialog above must be used to edit a field that is empty or has the invisible attribute enable.
- The footprint is defined as an absolute footprint using the LIBNAME:FPNAME format where LIBNAME is the name of the footprint library defined in the footprint library table (see the "Footprint Library Table" section in the Pcbnew "Reference Manual") and FPNAME is the name of the footprint in the library LIBNAME.

11.10 Power Symbols

Power symbols are created the same way as normal components. It may be useful to place them in a dedicated library such as power.lib. Power symbols consist of a graphical symbol and a pin of the type "Power Invisible". Power port symbols are handled like any other component by the schematic capture software. Some precautions are essential. Below is an example of a power +5V symbol.

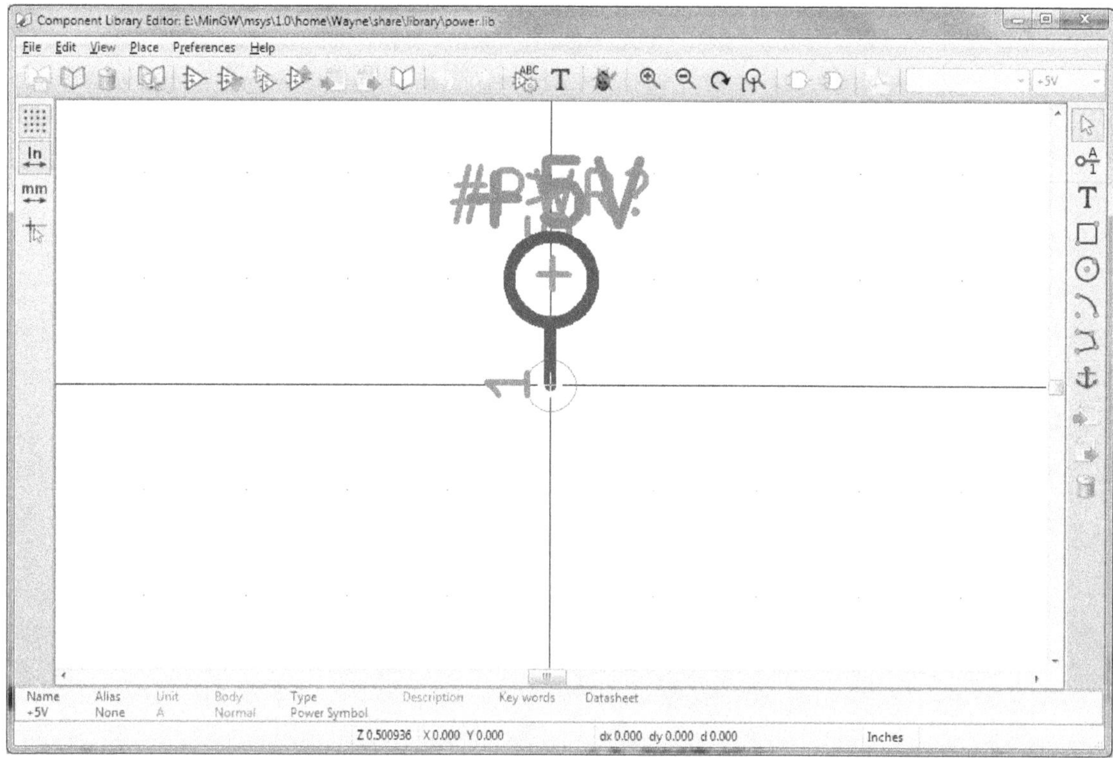

To create a power symbol, use the following steps:

- Add a pin of type "Power input" named +5V (important because this name will establish connection to the net +5V), with a pin number of 1 (number of no importance), a length of 0, and a "Line" "Graphic Style".
- Place a small circle and a segment from the pin to the circle as shown.
- The anchor of the symbol is on the pin.
- The component value is `+5V`.
- The component reference is `\#+5V`. The reference text is not important except the first character which must be `#` to indicate that the component is a power symbol. By convention, every component in which the reference field starts with a `#` will not appear in the component list or in the netlist and the reference is declared as invisible.

An easier method to create a new power port symbol is to use another symbol as a model:

- Load an existing power symbol.
- Edit the pin name with name of the new power symbol.
- Edit the value field to the same name as the pin, if you want to display the power port value.
- Save the new component.

Chapter 12

LibEdit - Complements

12.1 Overview

A component consist of the following elements

- A graphical representation (geometrical shapes, texts).
- Pins.
- Fields or associated text used by the post processors: netlist, components list.

Two fields are to be initialized: reference and value. The name of the design associated with the component, and the name of the associated footprint, the other fields are the free fields, they can generally remain empty, and could be filled during schematic capture.

However, managing the documentation associated with any component facilitates the research, use and maintenance of libraries. The associated documentation consists of

- A line of comment.
- A line of key words such as TTL CMOS NAND2, separated by spaces.
- An attached file name (for example an application note or a pdf file).

  The default directory for attached files:

  kicad/share/library/doc

  If not found:

  kicad/library/doc

  Under linux:

  /usr/local/kicad/share/library/doc

  /usr/share/kicad/library/doc

  /usr/local/share/kicad/library/doc

Key words allow you to selectively search for a component according to various selection criteria. Comments and key words are displayed in various menus, and particularly when you select a component from the library.

The component also has an anchoring point. A rotation or a mirror is made relative to this anchor point and during a placement this point is used as a reference position. It is thus useful to position this anchor accurately.

A component can have aliases, i.e. equivalent names. This allows you to considerably reduce the number of components that need to be created (for example, a 74LS00 can have aliases such as 74000, 74HC00, 74HCT00···).

Finally, the components are distributed in libraries (classified by topics, or manufacturer) in order to facilitate their management.

12.2 Position a component anchor

The anchor is at the coordinates (0,0) and it is shown by the blue axes displayed on your screen.

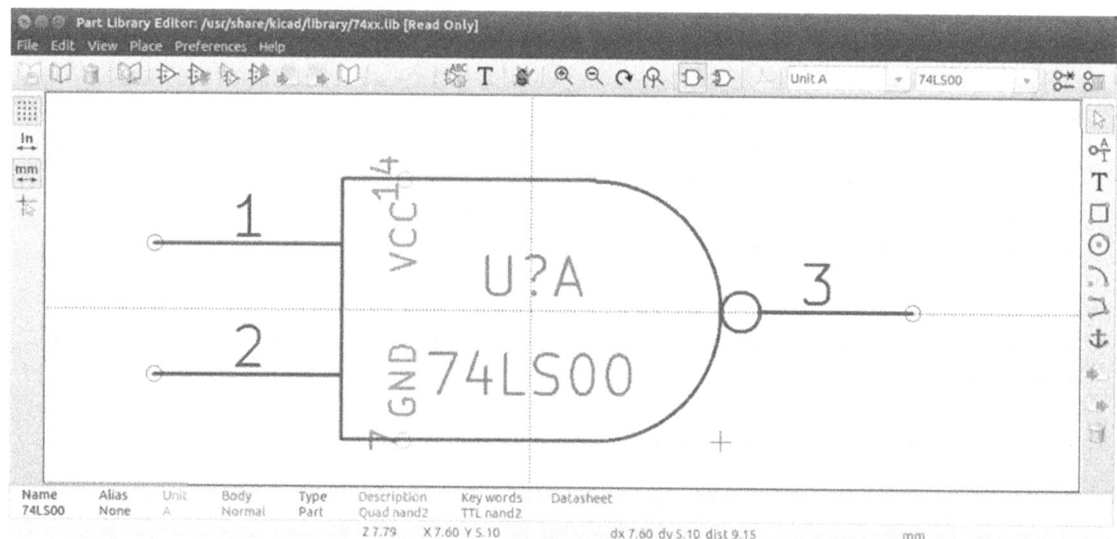

The anchor can be repositioned by selecting the icon and clicking on the new desired anchor position. The drawing will be automatically re-centered on the new anchor point.

12.3 Component aliases

An alias is another name corresponding to the same component in the library. Components with similar pin-out and representation can then be represented by only one component, having several aliases (e.g. 7400 with alias 74LS00, 74HC00, 74LS37).

The use of aliases allows you to build complete libraries quickly. In addition these libraries, being much more compact, are easily loaded by KiCad.

To modify the list of aliases, you have to select the main editing window via the icon and select the alias folder.

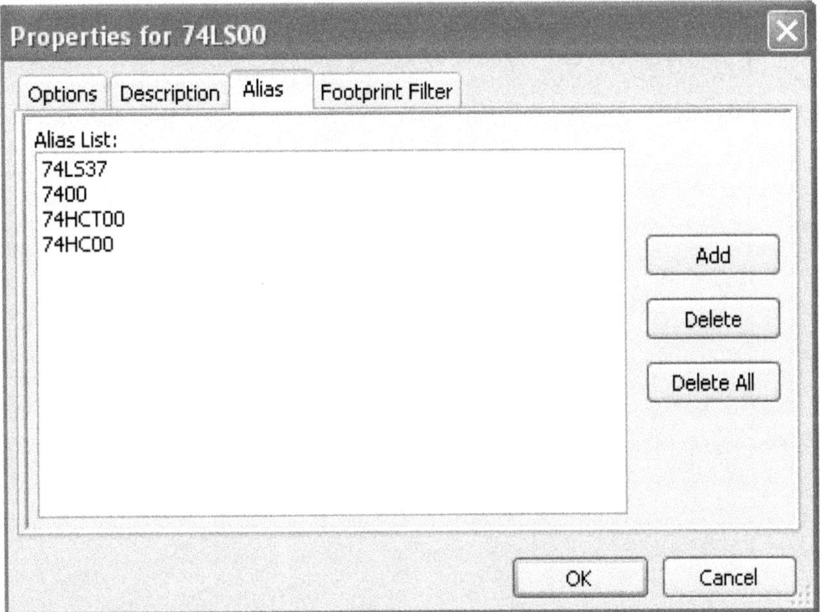

You can thus add or remove the desired alias. The current alias cannot obviously be removed since it is edited.

To remove all aliases, you have firstly to select the root component. The first component in the alias list in the window of selection of the main toolbar.

12.4 Component fields

The field editor is called via the icon T.

There are four special fields (texts attached to the component), and configurable user fields

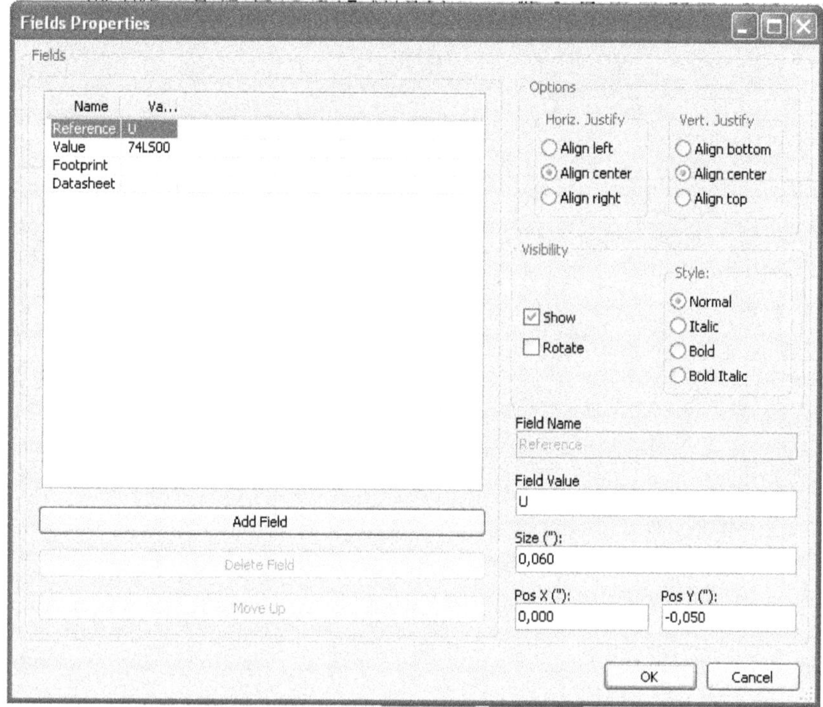

Special fields

- Reference.
- Value. It is the component name in the library and the default value field in schematic.
- Footprint. It is the footprint name used for the board. Not very useful when using CvPcb to setup the footprint list, but mandatory if CvPcb is not used.
- Sheet. It is a reserved field, not used at the time of writing.

12.5 Component documentation

To edit documentation information, it is necessary to call the main editing window of the component via the icon and to select the document folder.

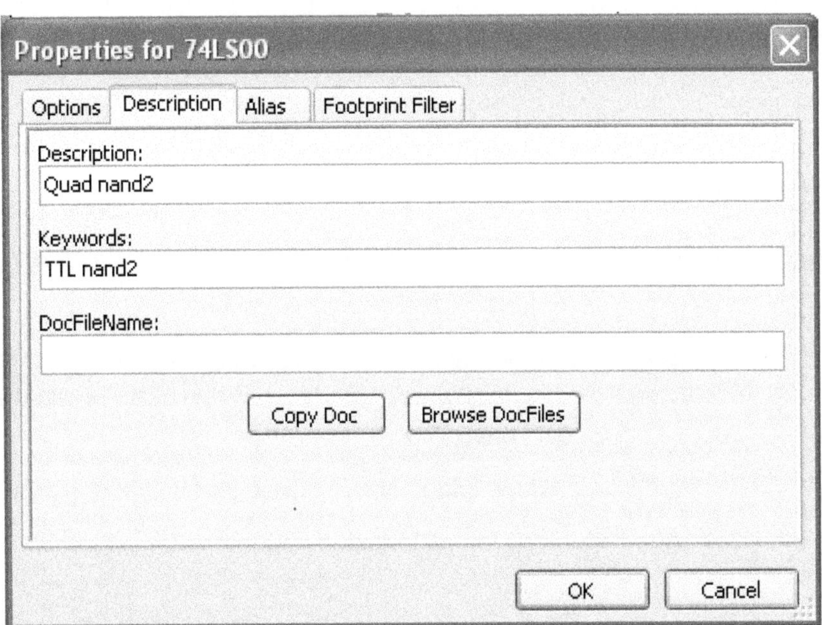

Be sure to select the right alias, or the root component, because this documentation is the only characteristic which differs between aliases. The "Copy Doc" button allows you to copy the documentation information from the root component towards the currently edited alias.

12.5.1 Component keywords

Keywords allow you to search in a selective way for a component according to specific selection criteria (function, technological family, etc.)

The Eeschema research tool is not case sensitive. The most current key words used in the libraries are

- CMOS TTL for the logic families
- AND2 NOR3 XOR2 INV···for the gates (AND2 = 2 inputs AND gate, NOR3 = 3 inputs NOR gate).
- JKFF DFF···for JK or D flip-flop.
- ADC, DAC, MUX···
- OpenCol for the gates with open collector output. Thus if in the schematic capture software, you search the component: by keys words NAND2 OpenCol Eeschema will display the list of components having these 2 key words.

12.5.2 Component documentation (Doc)

The line of comment (and keywords) is displayed in various menus, particularly when you select a component in the displayed components list of a library and in the ViewLib menu.

If this Doc. file exists, it is also accessible in the schematic capture software, in the pop-up menu displayed by right-clicking on the component.

12.5.3 Associated documentation file (DocFileName)

Indicates an attached file (documentation, application schematic) available (pdf file, schematic diagram, etc.).

12.5.4 Footprint filtering for CvPcb

You can enter a list of allowed footprints for the component. This list acts as a filter used by CvPcb to display only the allowed footprints. A void list does not filter anything.

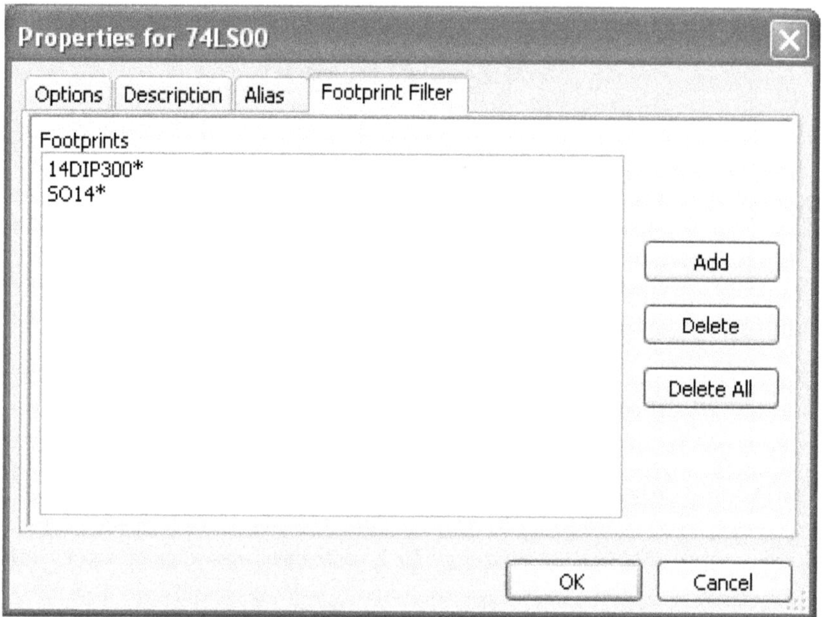

Wild-card characters are allowed.

S014* allows CvPcb to show all the footprints with a name starting by SO14.

For a resistor, R? shows all the footprints with a 2 letters name starting by R.

Here are samples: with and without filtering

With filtering

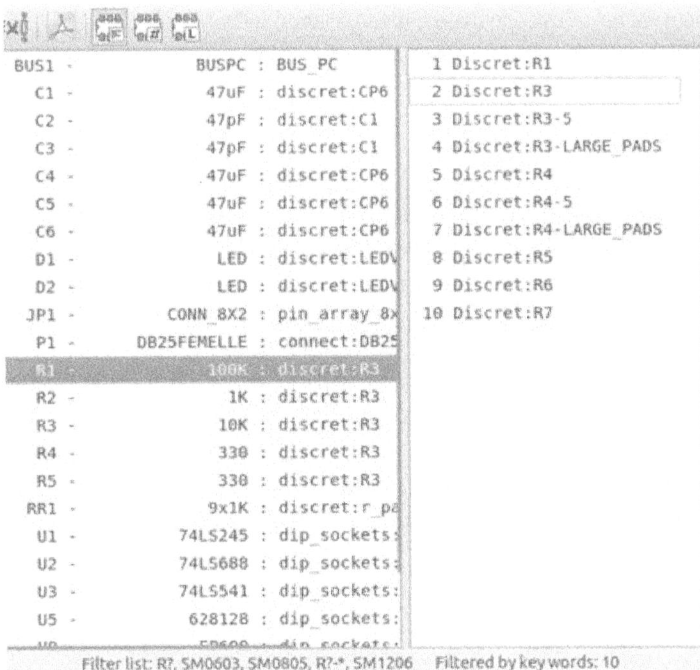

Without filtering

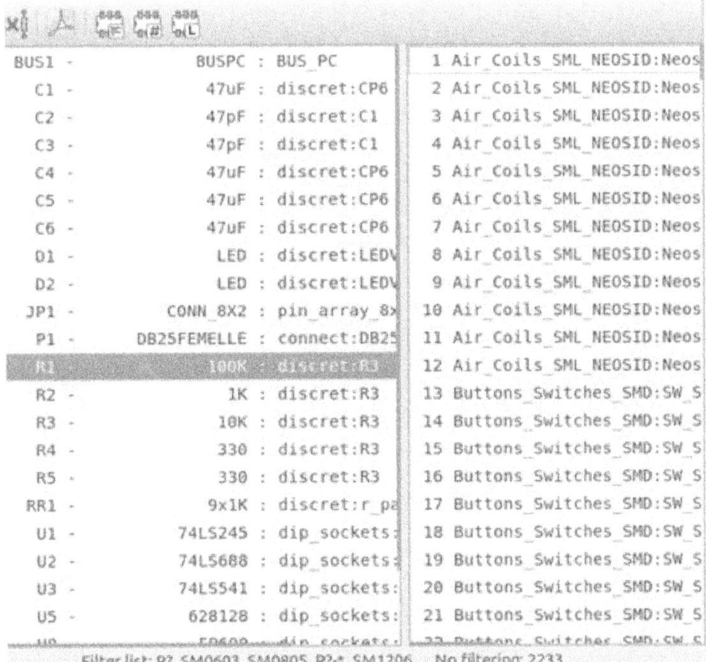

12.6 Symbol library

You can easily compile a graphic symbols library file containing frequently used symbols. This can be used for the creation of components (triangles, the shape of AND, OR, Exclusive OR gates, etc.) for saving and subsequent re-use.

These files are stored by default in the library directory and have a *.sym* extension. The symbols are not gathered in libraries like the components because they are generally not so many.

12.6.1 Export or create a symbol

A component can be exported as a symbol with the button . You can generally create only one graphic, also it will be a good idea to delete all pins, if they exist.

12.6.2 Import a symbol

Importing allows you to add graphics to a component you are editing. A symbol is imported with the button 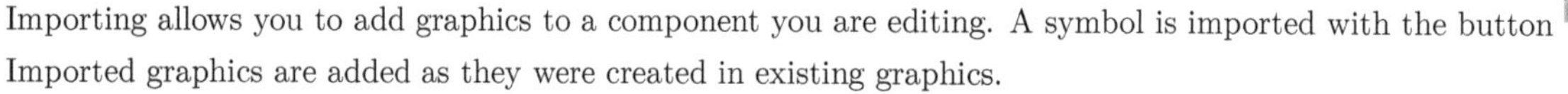. Imported graphics are added as they were created in existing graphics.

Chapter 13

Viewlib

13.1 Introduction

Viewlib allows you to quickly examine the content of libraries. Viewlib is called by the tool or by the "place component" tool available from the right-hand side toolbar.

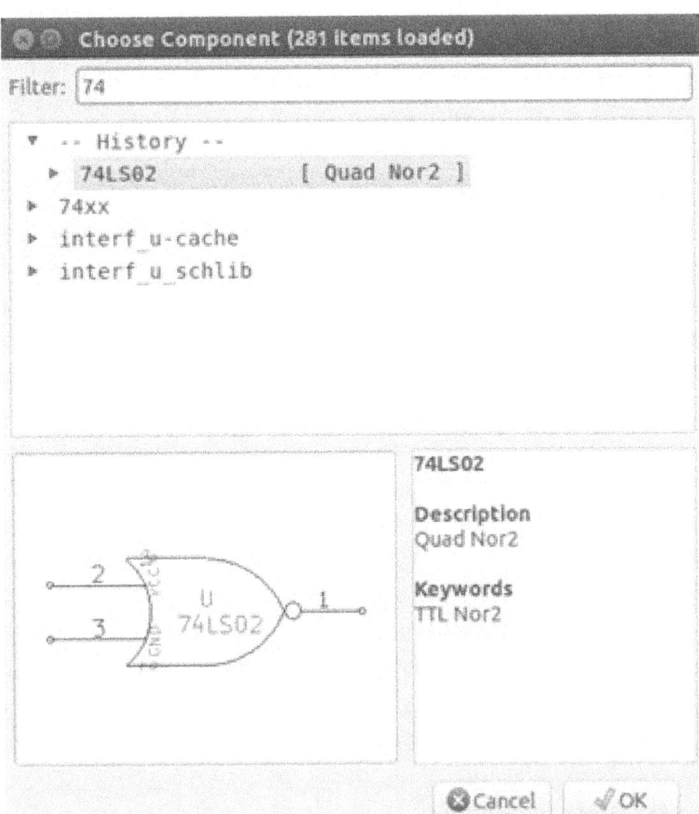

13.2 Viewlib - main screen

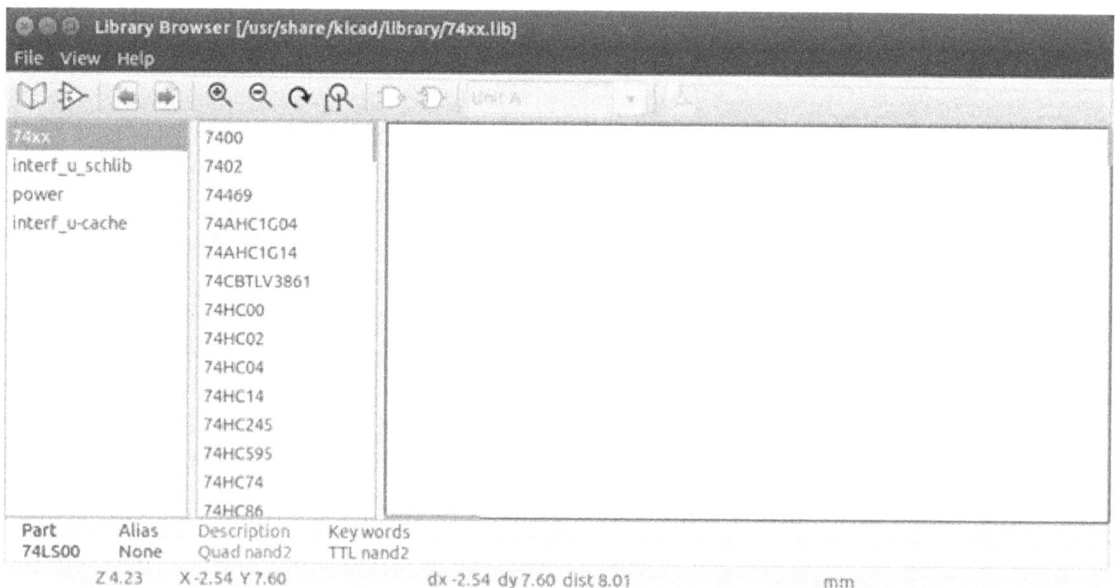

To examine the library content you need to select the wanted library from the list on the left-hand side. Available components will then appear in the second list which allow you to select a component.

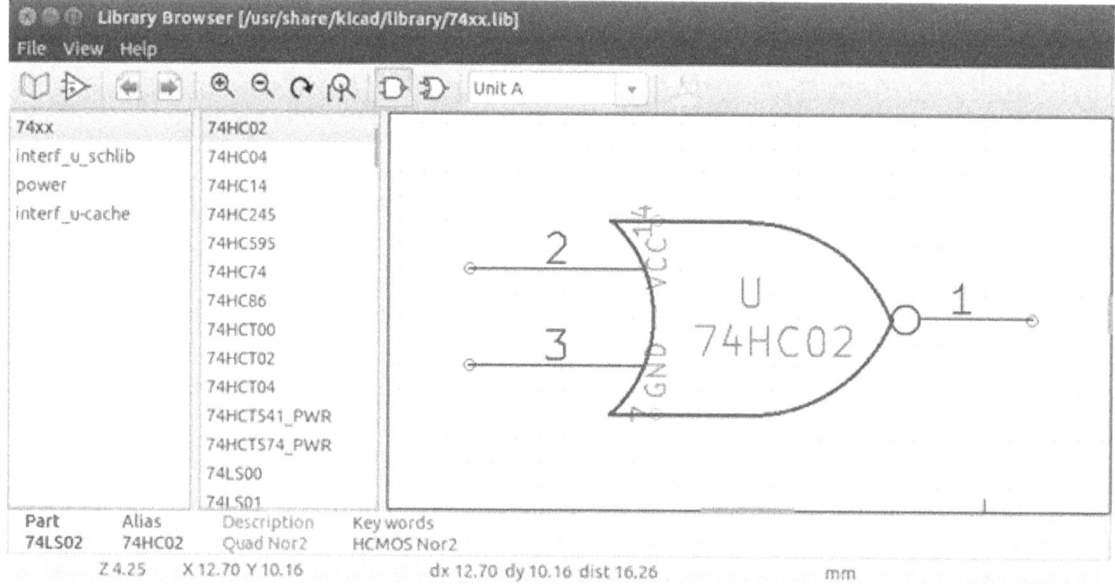

13.3 Viewlib top toolbar

The top tool bar in Viewlib is shown below.

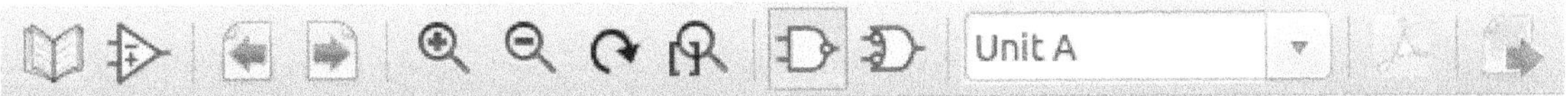

The available commands are.

	Selection of the desired library which can be also selected in the displayed list.
	Selection of the component which can be also selected in the displayed list.
	Display previous component.
	Display next component.
	Zoom tools.
	Selection of the representation (normal or converted) if exist.
Unit A	Selection of the part, only for multi-part components.
	If it exist, display the associated documents. Exists only when called by the place component dialog frame from Eeschema.
	Close Viewlib and place the selected component in Eeschema. This icon is only displayed when Viewlib has been called from Eeschema (click on a symbol in the component chooser).

Chapter 14

Creating Customized Netlists and BOM Files

14.1 Intermediate Netlist File

BOM files and netlist files can be converted from an Intermediate netlist file created by Eeschema.

This file uses XML syntax and is called the intermediate netlist. The intermediate netlist includes a large amount of data about your board and because of this, it can be used with post-processing to create a BOM or other reports.

Depending on the output (BOM or netlist), different subsets of the complete Intermediate Netlist file will be used in the post-processing.

14.1.1 Schematic sample

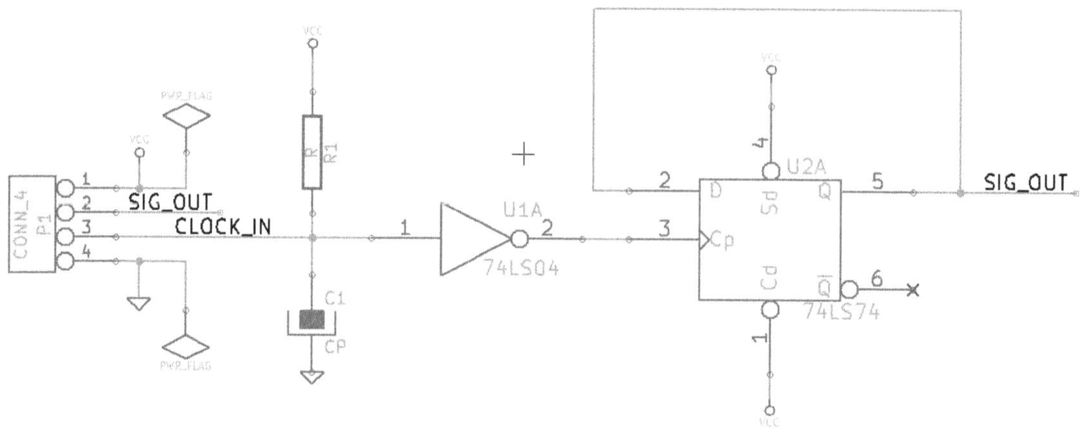

14.1.2 The Intermediate Netlist file sample

The corresponding intermediate netlist (using XML syntax) of the circuit above is shown below.

```
<?xml version="1.0" encoding="utf-8"?>
<export version="D">
  <design>
    <source>F:\kicad_aux\netlist_test\netlist_test.sch</source>
    <date>29/08/2010 20:35:21</date>
    <tool>eeschema (2010-08-28 BZR 2458)-unstable</tool>
  </design>
  <components>
    <comp ref="P1">
      <value>CONN_4</value>
      <libsource lib="conn" part="CONN_4"/>
      <sheetpath names="/" tstamps="/"/>
      <tstamp>4C6E2141</tstamp>
    </comp>
    <comp ref="U2">
      <value>74LS74</value>
      <libsource lib="74xx" part="74LS74"/>
      <sheetpath names="/" tstamps="/"/>
      <tstamp>4C6E20BA</tstamp>
    </comp>
    <comp ref="U1">
      <value>74LS04</value>
      <libsource lib="74xx" part="74LS04"/>
      <sheetpath names="/" tstamps="/"/>
      <tstamp>4C6E20A6</tstamp>
    </comp>
    <comp ref="C1">
      <value>CP</value>
      <libsource lib="device" part="CP"/>
      <sheetpath names="/" tstamps="/"/>
      <tstamp>4C6E2094</tstamp>
    </comp>
    <comp ref="R1">
      <value>R</value>
      <libsource lib="device" part="R"/>
      <sheetpath names="/" tstamps="/"/>
      <tstamp>4C6E208A</tstamp>
    </comp>
  </components>
  <libparts>
    <libpart lib="device" part="C">
      <description>Condensateur non polarise</description>
      <footprints>
        <fp>SM*</fp>
```

```
        <fp>C?</fp>
        <fp>C1-1</fp>
      </footprints>
      <fields>
        <field name="Reference">C</field>
        <field name="Value">C</field>
      </fields>
      <pins>
        <pin num="1" name="~" type="passive"/>
        <pin num="2" name="~" type="passive"/>
      </pins>
    </libpart>
    <libpart lib="device" part="R">
      <description>Resistance</description>
      <footprints>
        <fp>R?</fp>
        <fp>SM0603</fp>
        <fp>SM0805</fp>
        <fp>R?-*</fp>
        <fp>SM1206</fp>
      </footprints>
      <fields>
        <field name="Reference">R</field>
        <field name="Value">R</field>
      </fields>
      <pins>
        <pin num="1" name="~" type="passive"/>
        <pin num="2" name="~" type="passive"/>
      </pins>
    </libpart>
    <libpart lib="conn" part="CONN_4">
      <description>Symbole general de connecteur</description>
      <fields>
        <field name="Reference">P</field>
        <field name="Value">CONN_4</field>
      </fields>
      <pins>
        <pin num="1" name="P1" type="passive"/>
        <pin num="2" name="P2" type="passive"/>
        <pin num="3" name="P3" type="passive"/>
        <pin num="4" name="P4" type="passive"/>
      </pins>
    </libpart>
    <libpart lib="74xx" part="74LS04">
      <description>Hex Inverseur</description>
      <fields>
        <field name="Reference">U</field>
        <field name="Value">74LS04</field>
```

```
    </fields>
    <pins>
      <pin num="1" name="~" type="input"/>
      <pin num="2" name="~" type="output"/>
      <pin num="3" name="~" type="input"/>
      <pin num="4" name="~" type="output"/>
      <pin num="5" name="~" type="input"/>
      <pin num="6" name="~" type="output"/>
      <pin num="7" name="GND" type="power_in"/>
      <pin num="8" name="~" type="output"/>
      <pin num="9" name="~" type="input"/>
      <pin num="10" name="~" type="output"/>
      <pin num="11" name="~" type="input"/>
      <pin num="12" name="~" type="output"/>
      <pin num="13" name="~" type="input"/>
      <pin num="14" name="VCC" type="power_in"/>
    </pins>
  </libpart>
  <libpart lib="74xx" part="74LS74">
    <description>Dual D FlipFlop, Set &amp; Reset</description>
    <docs>74xx/74hc_hct74.pdf</docs>
    <fields>
      <field name="Reference">U</field>
      <field name="Value">74LS74</field>
    </fields>
    <pins>
      <pin num="1" name="Cd" type="input"/>
      <pin num="2" name="D" type="input"/>
      <pin num="3" name="Cp" type="input"/>
      <pin num="4" name="Sd" type="input"/>
      <pin num="5" name="Q" type="output"/>
      <pin num="6" name="~Q" type="output"/>
      <pin num="7" name="GND" type="power_in"/>
      <pin num="8" name="~Q" type="output"/>
      <pin num="9" name="Q" type="output"/>
      <pin num="10" name="Sd" type="input"/>
      <pin num="11" name="Cp" type="input"/>
      <pin num="12" name="D" type="input"/>
      <pin num="13" name="Cd" type="input"/>
      <pin num="14" name="VCC" type="power_in"/>
    </pins>
  </libpart>
</libparts>
<libraries>
  <library logical="device">
    <uri>F:\kicad\share\library\device.lib</uri>
  </library>
  <library logical="conn">
```

```
    <uri>F:\kicad\share\library\conn.lib</uri>
  </library>
  <library logical="74xx">
    <uri>F:\kicad\share\library\74xx.lib</uri>
  </library>
</libraries>
<nets>
  <net code="1" name="GND">
    <node ref="U1" pin="7"/>
    <node ref="C1" pin="2"/>
    <node ref="U2" pin="7"/>
    <node ref="P1" pin="4"/>
  </net>
  <net code="2" name="VCC">
    <node ref="R1" pin="1"/>
    <node ref="U1" pin="14"/>
    <node ref="U2" pin="4"/>
    <node ref="U2" pin="1"/>
    <node ref="U2" pin="14"/>
    <node ref="P1" pin="1"/>
  </net>
  <net code="3" name="">
    <node ref="U2" pin="6"/>
  </net>
  <net code="4" name="">
    <node ref="U1" pin="2"/>
    <node ref="U2" pin="3"/>
  </net>
  <net code="5" name="/SIG_OUT">
    <node ref="P1" pin="2"/>
    <node ref="U2" pin="5"/>
    <node ref="U2" pin="2"/>
  </net>
  <net code="6" name="/CLOCK_IN">
    <node ref="R1" pin="2"/>
    <node ref="C1" pin="1"/>
    <node ref="U1" pin="1"/>
    <node ref="P1" pin="3"/>
  </net>
</nets>
</export>
```

14.2 Conversion to a new netlist format

By applying a post-processing filter to the Intermediate netlist file you can generate foreign netlist files as well as BOM files. Because this conversion is a text to text transformation, this post-processing filter can be written using

Python, XSLT, or any other tool capable of taking XML as input.

XSLT itself is a an XML language very suitable for XML transformations. There is a free program called *xsltproc* that you can download and install. The xsltproc program can be used to read the Intermediate XML netlist input file, apply a style-sheet to transform the input, and save the results in an output file. Use of xsltproc requires a style-sheet file using XSLT conventions. The full conversion process is handled by Eeschema, after it is configured once to run xsltproc in a specific way.

14.3 XSLT approach

The document that describes XSL Transformations (XSLT) is available here:

http://www.w3.org/TR/xslt

14.3.1 Create a Pads-Pcb netlist file

The pads-pcb format is comprised of two sections.

- The footprint list.
- The Nets list: grouping pads references by nets.

Immediately below is a style-sheet which converts the Intermediate Netlist file to a pads-pcb netlist format:

```
<?xml version="1.0" encoding="ISO-8859-1"?>
<!--XSL style sheet to Eeschema Generic Netlist Format to PADS netlist format
    Copyright (C) 2010, SoftPLC Corporation.
    GPL v2.

    How to use:
        https://lists.launchpad.net/kicad-developers/msg05157.html
-->

<!DOCTYPE xsl:stylesheet [
  <!ENTITY nl  "&#xd;&#xa;"> <!--new line CR, LF -->
]>

<xsl:stylesheet version="1.0" xmlns:xsl="http://www.w3.org/1999/XSL/Transform">
<xsl:output method="text" omit-xml-declaration="yes" indent="no"/>

<xsl:template match="/export">
    <xsl:text>*PADS-PCB*&nl;*PART*&nl;</xsl:text>
    <xsl:apply-templates select="components/comp"/>
    <xsl:text>&nl;*NET*&nl;</xsl:text>
    <xsl:apply-templates select="nets/net"/>
    <xsl:text>*END*&nl;</xsl:text>
</xsl:template>
```

```
<!-- for each component -->
<xsl:template match="comp">
    <xsl:text> </xsl:text>
    <xsl:value-of select="@ref"/>
    <xsl:text> </xsl:text>
    <xsl:choose>
        <xsl:when test = "footprint != '' ">
            <xsl:apply-templates select="footprint"/>
        </xsl:when>
        <xsl:otherwise>
            <xsl:text>unknown</xsl:text>
        </xsl:otherwise>
    </xsl:choose>
    <xsl:text>&nl;</xsl:text>
</xsl:template>

<!-- for each net -->
<xsl:template match="net">
    <!-- nets are output only if there is more than one pin in net -->
    <xsl:if test="count(node)>1">
        <xsl:text>*SIGNAL* </xsl:text>
        <xsl:choose>
            <xsl:when test = "@name != '' ">
                <xsl:value-of select="@name"/>
            </xsl:when>
            <xsl:otherwise>
                <xsl:text>N-</xsl:text>
                <xsl:value-of select="@code"/>
            </xsl:otherwise>
        </xsl:choose>
        <xsl:text>&nl;</xsl:text>
        <xsl:apply-templates select="node"/>
    </xsl:if>
</xsl:template>

<!-- for each node -->
<xsl:template match="node">
    <xsl:text> </xsl:text>
    <xsl:value-of select="@ref"/>
    <xsl:text>.</xsl:text>
    <xsl:value-of select="@pin"/>
    <xsl:text>&nl;</xsl:text>
</xsl:template>

</xsl:stylesheet>
```

And here is the pads-pcb output file after running xsltproc:

```
*PADS-PCB*
*PART*
P1 unknown
U2 unknown
U1 unknown
C1 unknown
R1 unknown
*NET*
*SIGNAL* GND
U1.7
C1.2
U2.7
P1.4
*SIGNAL* VCC
R1.1
U1.14
U2.4
U2.1
U2.14
P1.1
*SIGNAL* N-4
U1.2
U2.3
*SIGNAL* /SIG_OUT
P1.2
U2.5
U2.2
*SIGNAL* /CLOCK_IN
R1.2
C1.1
U1.1
P1.3

*END*
```

The command line to make this conversion is:

```
kicad\\bin\\xsltproc.exe -o test.net kicad\\bin\\plugins\\netlist_form_pads-pcb.xsl test. ↩
    tmp
```

14.3.2 Create a Cadstar netlist file

The Cadstar format is comprised of two sections.

- The footprint list.
- The Nets list: grouping pads references by nets.

Here is the style-sheet file to make this specific conversion:

```
<?xml version="1.0" encoding="ISO-8859-1"?>
<!--XSL style sheet to Eeschema Generic Netlist Format to CADSTAR netlist format
    Copyright (C) 2010, Jean-Pierre Charras.
    Copyright (C) 2010, SoftPLC Corporation.
    GPL v2.

<!DOCTYPE xsl:stylesheet [
  <!ENTITY nl  "&#xd;&#xa;"> <!--new line CR, LF -->
]>

<xsl:stylesheet version="1.0" xmlns:xsl="http://www.w3.org/1999/XSL/Transform">
<xsl:output method="text" omit-xml-declaration="yes" indent="no"/>

<!-- Netlist header -->
<xsl:template match="/export">
    <xsl:text>.HEA&nl;</xsl:text>
    <xsl:apply-templates select="design/date"/>  <!-- Generate line .TIM <time> -->
    <xsl:apply-templates select="design/tool"/>  <!-- Generate line .APP <eeschema version> ↩
        -->
    <xsl:apply-templates select="components/comp"/>  <!-- Generate list of components -->
    <xsl:text>&nl;&nl;</xsl:text>
    <xsl:apply-templates select="nets/net"/>          <!-- Generate list of nets and  ↩
        connections -->
    <xsl:text>&nl;.END&nl;</xsl:text>
</xsl:template>

 <!-- Generate line .TIM 20/08/2010 10:45:33 -->
<xsl:template match="tool">
    <xsl:text>.APP "</xsl:text>
    <xsl:apply-templates/>
    <xsl:text>"&nl;</xsl:text>
</xsl:template>

 <!-- Generate line .APP "eeschema (2010-08-17 BZR 2450)-unstable" -->
<xsl:template match="date">
    <xsl:text>.TIM </xsl:text>
    <xsl:apply-templates/>
    <xsl:text>&nl;</xsl:text>
</xsl:template>

<!-- for each component -->
<xsl:template match="comp">
    <xsl:text>.ADD_COM </xsl:text>
    <xsl:value-of select="@ref"/>
    <xsl:text> </xsl:text>
    <xsl:choose>
```

```
        <xsl:when test = "value != '' ">
            <xsl:text>"</xsl:text> <xsl:apply-templates select="value"/> <xsl:text>"</xsl: ↩
                text>
        </xsl:when>
        <xsl:otherwise>
            <xsl:text>""</xsl:text>
        </xsl:otherwise>
    </xsl:choose>
    <xsl:text>&nl;</xsl:text>
</xsl:template>

<!-- for each net -->
<xsl:template match="net">
    <!-- nets are output only if there is more than one pin in net -->
    <xsl:if test="count(node)>1">
    <xsl:variable name="netname">
        <xsl:text>"</xsl:text>
        <xsl:choose>
            <xsl:when test = "@name != '' ">
                <xsl:value-of select="@name"/>
            </xsl:when>
            <xsl:otherwise>
                <xsl:text>N-</xsl:text>
                <xsl:value-of select="@code"/>
        </xsl:otherwise>
        </xsl:choose>
        <xsl:text>"&nl;</xsl:text>
        </xsl:variable>
        <xsl:apply-templates select="node" mode="first"/>
        <xsl:value-of select="$netname"/>
        <xsl:apply-templates select="node" mode="others"/>
    </xsl:if>
</xsl:template>

<!-- for each node -->
<xsl:template match="node" mode="first">
    <xsl:if test="position()=1">
       <xsl:text>.ADD_TER </xsl:text>
    <xsl:value-of select="@ref"/>
    <xsl:text>.</xsl:text>
    <xsl:value-of select="@pin"/>
    <xsl:text> </xsl:text>
    </xsl:if>
</xsl:template>

<xsl:template match="node" mode="others">
    <xsl:choose>
        <xsl:when test='position()=1'>
```

```
            </xsl:when>
            <xsl:when test='position()=2'>
                <xsl:text>.TER     </xsl:text>
            </xsl:when>
            <xsl:otherwise>
                <xsl:text>         </xsl:text>
            </xsl:otherwise>
        </xsl:choose>
        <xsl:if test="position()>1">
            <xsl:value-of select="@ref"/>
            <xsl:text>.</xsl:text>
            <xsl:value-of select="@pin"/>
            <xsl:text>&nl;</xsl:text>
        </xsl:if>
</xsl:template>

</xsl:stylesheet>
```

Here is the Cadstar output file.

```
.HEA
.TIM 21/08/2010 08:12:08
.APP "eeschema (2010-08-09 BZR 2439)-unstable"
.ADD_COM P1 "CONN_4"
.ADD_COM U2 "74LS74"
.ADD_COM U1 "74LS04"
.ADD_COM C1 "CP"
.ADD_COM R1 "R"


.ADD_TER U1.7 "GND"
.TER     C1.2
         U2.7
         P1.4
.ADD_TER R1.1 "VCC"
.TER     U1.14
         U2.4
         U2.1
         U2.14
         P1.1
.ADD_TER U1.2 "N-4"
.TER     U2.3
.ADD_TER P1.2 "/SIG_OUT"
.TER     U2.5
         U2.2
.ADD_TER R1.2 "/CLOCK_IN"
.TER     C1.1
         U1.1
```

```
        P1.3

.END
```

14.3.3 Create a OrcadPCB2 netlist file

This format has only one section which is the footprint list. Each footprint includes its list of pads with reference to a net.

Here is the style-sheet for this specific conversion:

```
<?xml version="1.0" encoding="ISO-8859-1"?>
<!--XSL style sheet to Eeschema Generic Netlist Format to CADSTAR netlist format
    Copyright (C) 2010, SoftPLC Corporation.
    GPL v2.

    How to use:
        https://lists.launchpad.net/kicad-developers/msg05157.html
-->

<!DOCTYPE xsl:stylesheet [
  <!ENTITY nl  "&#xd;&#xa;"> <!--new line CR, LF -->
]>

<xsl:stylesheet version="1.0" xmlns:xsl="http://www.w3.org/1999/XSL/Transform">
<xsl:output method="text" omit-xml-declaration="yes" indent="no"/>

<!--
    Netlist header
    Creates the entire netlist
    (can be seen as equivalent to main function in C
-->
<xsl:template match="/export">
    <xsl:text>( { Eeschema Netlist Version 1.1  </xsl:text>
    <!-- Generate line .TIM <time> -->
<xsl:apply-templates select="design/date"/>
<!-- Generate line eeschema version ... -->
<xsl:apply-templates select="design/tool"/>
<xsl:text>}&nl;</xsl:text>

<!-- Generate the list of components -->
<xsl:apply-templates select="components/comp"/>  <!-- Generate list of components -->

<!-- end of file -->
<xsl:text>)&nl;*&nl;</xsl:text>
</xsl:template>

<!--
```

```
    Generate id in header like "eeschema (2010-08-17 BZR 2450)-unstable"
-->
<xsl:template match="tool">
    <xsl:apply-templates/>
</xsl:template>

<!--
    Generate date in header like "20/08/2010 10:45:33"
-->
<xsl:template match="date">
    <xsl:apply-templates/>
    <xsl:text>&nl;</xsl:text>
</xsl:template>

<!--
    This template read each component
    (path = /export/components/comp)
    creates lines:
     ( 3EBF7DBD $noname U1 74LS125
      ... pin list ...
      )
    and calls "create_pin_list" template to build the pin list
-->
<xsl:template match="comp">
    <xsl:text> ( </xsl:text>
    <xsl:choose>
        <xsl:when test = "tstamp != '' ">
            <xsl:apply-templates select="tstamp"/>
        </xsl:when>
        <xsl:otherwise>
            <xsl:text>00000000</xsl:text>
        </xsl:otherwise>
    </xsl:choose>
    <xsl:text> </xsl:text>
    <xsl:choose>
        <xsl:when test = "footprint != '' ">
            <xsl:apply-templates select="footprint"/>
        </xsl:when>
        <xsl:otherwise>
            <xsl:text>$noname</xsl:text>
        </xsl:otherwise>
    </xsl:choose>
    <xsl:text> </xsl:text>
    <xsl:value-of select="@ref"/>
    <xsl:text> </xsl:text>
    <xsl:choose>
        <xsl:when test = "value != '' ">
            <xsl:apply-templates select="value"/>
```

```
        </xsl:when>
        <xsl:otherwise>
            <xsl:text>"~"</xsl:text>
        </xsl:otherwise>
    </xsl:choose>
    <xsl:text>&nl;</xsl:text>
    <xsl:call-template name="Search_pin_list" >
        <xsl:with-param name="cmplib_id" select="libsource/@part"/>
        <xsl:with-param name="cmp_ref" select="@ref"/>
    </xsl:call-template>
    <xsl:text> )&nl;</xsl:text>
</xsl:template>

<!--
    This template search for a given lib component description in list
    lib component descriptions are in /export/libparts,
    and each description start at ./libpart
    We search here for the list of pins of the given component
    This template has 2 parameters:
        "cmplib_id" (reference in libparts)
        "cmp_ref"   (schematic reference of the given component)
-->
<xsl:template name="Search_pin_list" >
    <xsl:param name="cmplib_id" select="0" />
    <xsl:param name="cmp_ref" select="0" />
        <xsl:for-each select="/export/libparts/libpart">
            <xsl:if test = "@part = $cmplib_id ">
                <xsl:apply-templates name="build_pin_list" select="pins/pin">
                    <xsl:with-param name="cmp_ref" select="$cmp_ref"/>
                </xsl:apply-templates>
            </xsl:if>
        </xsl:for-each>
</xsl:template>


<!--
    This template writes the pin list of a component
    from the pin list of the library description
    The pin list from library description is something like
          <pins>
            <pin num="1" type="passive"/>
            <pin num="2" type="passive"/>
          </pins>
    Output pin list is ( <pin num> <net name> )
    something like
            ( 1 VCC )
            ( 2 GND )
-->
```

```
<xsl:template name="build_pin_list" match="pin">
    <xsl:param name="cmp_ref" select="0" />

    <!-- write pin numner and separator -->
    <xsl:text> ( </xsl:text>
    <xsl:value-of select="@num"/>
    <xsl:text> </xsl:text>

    <!-- search net name in nets section and write it: -->
    <xsl:variable name="pinNum" select="@num" />
    <xsl:for-each select="/export/nets/net">
        <!-- net name is output only if there is more than one pin in net
             else use "?" as net name, so count items in this net
        -->
        <xsl:variable name="pinCnt" select="count(node)" />
        <xsl:apply-templates name="Search_pin_netname" select="node">
            <xsl:with-param name="cmp_ref" select="$cmp_ref"/>
            <xsl:with-param name="pin_cnt_in_net" select="$pinCnt"/>
            <xsl:with-param name="pin_num"> <xsl:value-of select="$pinNum"/>
            </xsl:with-param>
        </xsl:apply-templates>
    </xsl:for-each>

    <!-- close line -->
    <xsl:text> )&nl;</xsl:text>
</xsl:template>

<!--
    This template writes the pin netname of a given pin of a given component
    from the nets list
    The nets list description is something like
      <nets>
        <net code="1" name="GND">
          <node ref="J1" pin="20"/>
              <node ref="C2" pin="2"/>
        </net>
        <net code="2" name="">
          <node ref="U2" pin="11"/>
        </net>
    </nets>
    This template has 2 parameters:
        "cmp_ref"   (schematic reference of the given component)
        "pin_num"   (pin number)
-->

<xsl:template name="Search_pin_netname" match="node">
    <xsl:param name="cmp_ref" select="0" />
    <xsl:param name="pin_num" select="0" />
```

```
    <xsl:param name="pin_cnt_in_net" select="0" />

    <xsl:if test = "@ref = $cmp_ref ">
        <xsl:if test = "@pin = $pin_num">
        <!-- net name is output only if there is more than one pin in net
             else use "?" as net name
        -->
            <xsl:if test = "$pin_cnt_in_net>1">
                <xsl:choose>
                    <!-- if a net has a name, use it,
                        else build a name from its net code
                    -->
                    <xsl:when test = "../@name != '' ">
                        <xsl:value-of select="../@name"/>
                    </xsl:when>
                    <xsl:otherwise>
                        <xsl:text>$N-0</xsl:text><xsl:value-of select="../@code"/>
                    </xsl:otherwise>
                </xsl:choose>
            </xsl:if>
            <xsl:if test = "$pin_cnt_in_net &lt;2">
                <xsl:text>?</xsl:text>
            </xsl:if>
        </xsl:if>
    </xsl:if>

</xsl:template>

</xsl:stylesheet>
```

Here is the OrcadPCB2 output file.

```
( { Eeschema Netlist Version 1.1  29/08/2010 21:07:51
eeschema (2010-08-28 BZR 2458)-unstable}
 ( 4C6E2141 $noname P1 CONN_4
  (  1 VCC )
  (  2 /SIG_OUT )
  (  3 /CLOCK_IN )
  (  4 GND )
 )
 ( 4C6E20BA $noname U2 74LS74
  (  1 VCC )
  (  2 /SIG_OUT )
  (  3 N-04 )
  (  4 VCC )
  (  5 /SIG_OUT )
  (  6 ? )
  (  7 GND )
```

```
  ( 14 VCC )
 )
 ( 4C6E20A6 $noname U1 74LS04
  ( 1 /CLOCK_IN )
  ( 2 N-04 )
  ( 7 GND )
  ( 14 VCC )
 )
 ( 4C6E2094 $noname C1 CP
  ( 1 /CLOCK_IN )
  ( 2 GND )
 )
 ( 4C6E208A $noname R1 R
  ( 1 VCC )
  ( 2 /CLOCK_IN )
 )
)
*
```

14.3.4 Eeschema plugins interface

Intermediate Netlist converters can be automatically launched within Eeschema.

14.3.4.1 Init the Dialog window

One can add a new netlist plug-in user interface tab by clicking on the Add Plugin button.

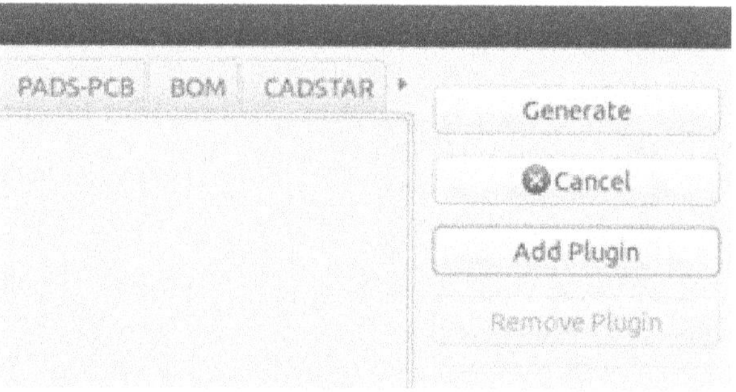

Here is what the configuration data for the PadsPcb tab looks like:

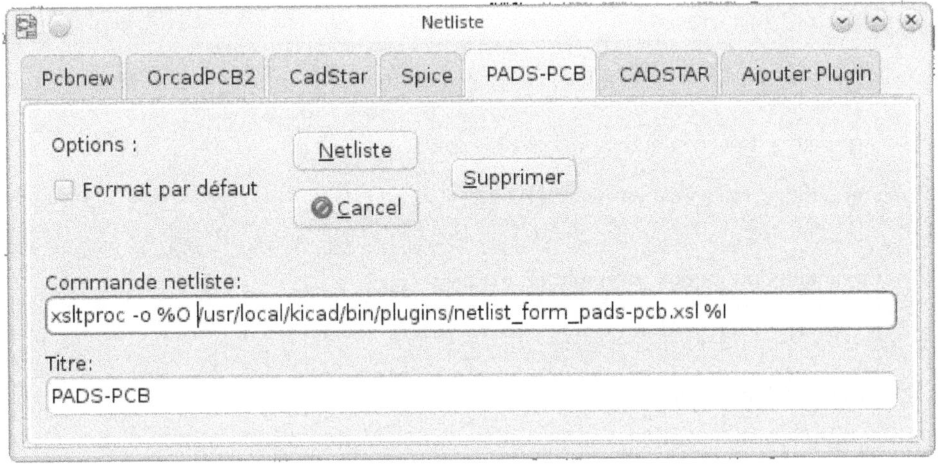

14.3.4.2 Plugin Configuration Parameters

The Eeschema plug-in configuration dialog requires the following information:

- The title: for instance, the name of the netlist format.
- The command line to launch the converter.

Once you click on the netlist button the following will happen:

1. Eeschema creates an intermediate netlist file *.xml, for instance test.xml.
2. Eeschema runs the plug-in by reading test.xml and creates test.net.

14.3.4.3 Generate netlist files with the command line

Assuming we are using the program *xsltproc.exe* to apply the sheet style to the intermediate file, *xsltproc.exe* is executed with the following command:

xsltproc.exe -o <output filename> < style-sheet filename> <input XML file to convert>

In KiCad under Windows the command line is the following:

f:/kicad/bin/xsltproc.exe -o "%O" f:/kicad/bin/plugins/netlist_form_pads-pcb.xsl "%I"

Under Linux the command becomes as follows:

xsltproc -o "%O" /usr/local/kicad/bin/plugins/netlist_form_pads-pcb.xsl "%I"

Where *netlist_form_pads-pcb.xsl* is the style-sheet that you are applying. Do not forget the double quotes around the file names, this allows them to have spaces after the substitution by Eeschema.

The command line format accepts parameters for filenames:

The supported formatting parameters are.

- %B base filename and path of selected output file, minus path and extension.

- %I complete filename and path of the temporary input file (the intermediate net file).
- %O complete filename and path of the user chosen output file.

%I will be replaced by the actual intermediate file name

%O will be replaced by the actual output file name.

14.3.4.4 Command line format: example for xsltproc

The command line format for xsltproc is the following:

<path of xsltproc> xsltproc <xsltproc parameters>

under Windows:

f:/kicad/bin/xsltproc.exe -o "%O" f:/kicad/bin/plugins/netlist_form_pads-pcb.xsl "%I"

under Linux:

xsltproc -o "%O" /usr/local/kicad/bin/plugins/netlist_form_pads-pcb.xsl "%I"

The above examples assume xsltproc is installed on your PC under Windows and all files located in kicad/bin.

14.3.5 Bill of Materials Generation

Because the intermediate netlist file contains all information about used components, a BOM can be extracted from it. Here is the plug-in setup window (on Linux) to create a customized Bill Of Materials (BOM) file:

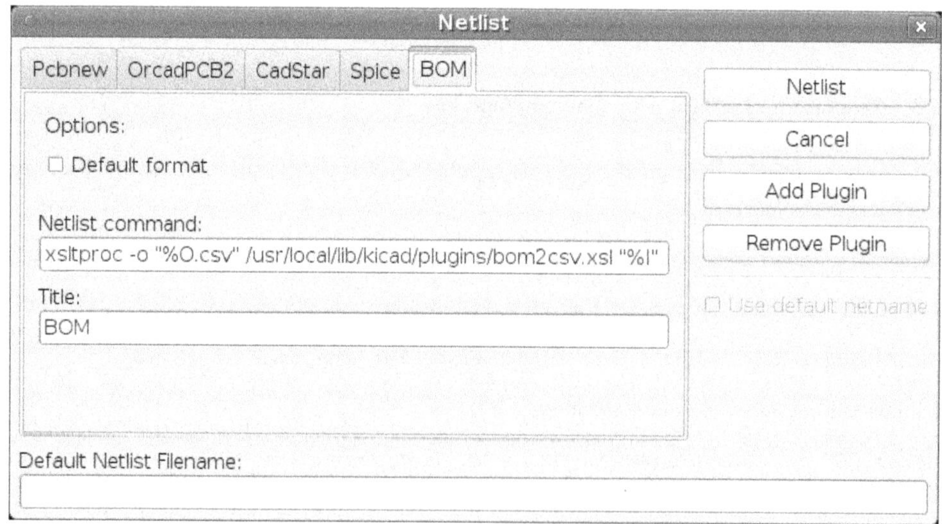

The path to the style sheet bom2csv.xsl is system dependent. The currently best XSLT style-sheet for BOM generation at this time is called *bom2csv.xsl*. You are free to modify it according to your needs, and if you develop something generally useful, ask that it become part of the KiCad project.

14.4 Command line format: example for python scripts

The command line format for python is something like:

python <script file name> <input filename> <output filename>

under Windows:

python *.exe f:/kicad/python/my_python_script.py "%I" "%O"

under Linux:

python /usr/local/kicad/python/my_python_script.py "%I" "%O"

Assuming python is installed on your PC.

14.5 Intermediate Netlist structure

This sample gives an idea of the netlist file format.

```
<?xml version="1.0" encoding="utf-8"?>
<export version="D">
  <design>
    <source>F:\kicad_aux\netlist_test\netlist_test.sch</source>
    <date>29/08/2010 21:07:51</date>
    <tool>eeschema (2010-08-28 BZR 2458)-unstable</tool>
  </design>
  <components>
    <comp ref="P1">
      <value>CONN_4</value>
      <libsource lib="conn" part="CONN_4"/>
      <sheetpath names="/" tstamps="/"/>
      <tstamp>4C6E2141</tstamp>
    </comp>
    <comp ref="U2">
      <value>74LS74</value>
      <libsource lib="74xx" part="74LS74"/>
      <sheetpath names="/" tstamps="/"/>
      <tstamp>4C6E20BA</tstamp>
    </comp>
    <comp ref="U1">
      <value>74LS04</value>
      <libsource lib="74xx" part="74LS04"/>
      <sheetpath names="/" tstamps="/"/>
      <tstamp>4C6E20A6</tstamp>
    </comp>
    <comp ref="C1">
      <value>CP</value>
      <libsource lib="device" part="CP"/>
      <sheetpath names="/" tstamps="/"/>
```

```
      <tstamp>4C6E2094</tstamp>
    <comp ref="R1">
      <value>R</value>
      <libsource lib="device" part="R"/>
      <sheetpath names="/" tstamps="/"/>
      <tstamp>4C6E208A</tstamp>
    </comp>
  </components>
  <libparts/>
  <libraries/>
  <nets>
    <net code="1" name="GND">
      <node ref="U1" pin="7"/>
      <node ref="C1" pin="2"/>
      <node ref="U2" pin="7"/>
      <node ref="P1" pin="4"/>
    </net>
    <net code="2" name="VCC">
      <node ref="R1" pin="1"/>
      <node ref="U1" pin="14"/>
      <node ref="U2" pin="4"/>
      <node ref="U2" pin="1"/>
      <node ref="U2" pin="14"/>
      <node ref="P1" pin="1"/>
    </net>
    <net code="3" name="">
      <node ref="U2" pin="6"/>
    </net>
    <net code="4" name="">
      <node ref="U1" pin="2"/>
      <node ref="U2" pin="3"/>
    </net>
    <net code="5" name="/SIG_OUT">
      <node ref="P1" pin="2"/>
      <node ref="U2" pin="5"/>
      <node ref="U2" pin="2"/>
    </net>
    <net code="6" name="/CLOCK_IN">
      <node ref="R1" pin="2"/>
      <node ref="C1" pin="1"/>
      <node ref="U1" pin="1"/>
      <node ref="P1" pin="3"/>
    </net>
  </nets>
</export>
```

14.5.1 General netlist file structure

The intermediate Netlist accounts for five sections.

- The header section.
- The components section.
- The lib parts section.
- The libraries section.
- The nets section.

The file content has the delimiter <export>

```
<export version="D">
...
</export>
```

14.5.2 The header section

The header has the delimiter <design>

```
<design>
<source>F:\kicad_aux\netlist_test\netlist_test.sch</source>
<date>21/08/2010 08:12:08</date>
<tool>eeschema (2010-08-09 BZR 2439)-unstable</tool>
</design>
```

This section can be considered a comment section.

14.5.3 The components section

The component section has the delimiter <components>

```
<components>
<comp ref="P1">
<value>CONN_4</value>
<libsource lib="conn" part="CONN_4"/>
<sheetpath names="/" tstamps="/"/>
<tstamp>4C6E2141</tstamp>
</comp>
</components>
```

This section contains the list of components in your schematic. Each component is described like this:

```
<comp ref="P1">
<value>CONN_4</value>
<libsource lib="conn" part="CONN_4"/>
<sheetpath names="/" tstamps="/"/>
<tstamp>4C6E2141</tstamp>
</comp>
```

libsource	name of the lib where this component was found.
part	component name inside this library.
sheetpath	path of the sheet inside the hierarchy: identify the sheet within the full schematic hierarchy.
tstamps (time stamps)	time stamp of the schematic file.
tstamp (time stamp)	time stamp of the component.

14.5.3.1 Note about time stamps for components

To identify a component in a netlist and therefore on a board, the timestamp reference is used as unique for each component. However KiCad provides an auxiliary way to identify a component which is the corresponding footprint on the board. This allows the re-annotation of components in a schematic project and does not loose the link between the component and its footprint.

A time stamp is an unique identifier for each component or sheet in a schematic project. However, in complex hierarchies, the same sheet is used more than once, so this sheet contains components having the same time stamp.

A given sheet inside a complex hierarchy has an unique identifier: its sheetpath. A given component (inside a complex hierarchy) has an unique identifier: the sheetpath + its tstamp

14.5.4 The libparts section

The libparts section has the delimiter <libparts>, and the content of this section is defined in the schematic libraries. The libparts section contains

- The allowed footprints names (names use jokers) delimiter <fp>.
- The fields defined in the library delimiter <fields>.
- The list of pins delimiter <pins>.

```
<libparts>
<libpart lib="device" part="CP">
  <description>Condensateur polarise</description>
  <footprints>
    <fp>CP*</fp>
    <fp>SM*</fp>
  </footprints>
  <fields>
```

```
    <field name="Reference">C</field>
    <field name="Valeur">CP</field>
  </fields>
  <pins>
    <pin num="1" name="1" type="passive"/>
    <pin num="2" name="2" type="passive"/>
  </pins>
</libpart>
</libparts>
```

Lines like <pin num=”1” type=”passive”/> give also the electrical pin type. Possible electrical pin types are

Input	Usual input pin
Output	Usual output
Bidirectional	Input or Output
Tri-state	Bus input/output
Passive	Usual ends of passive components
Unspecified	Unknown electrical type
Power input	Power input of a component
Power output	Power output like a regulator output
Open collector	Open collector often found in analog comparators
Open emitter	Open emitter sometimes found in logic
Not connected	Must be left open in schematic

14.5.5 The libraries section

The libraries section has the delimiter <libraries>. This section contains the list of schematic libraries used in the project.

```
<libraries>
  <library logical="device">
    <uri>F:\kicad\share\library\device.lib</uri>
  </library>
  <library logical="conn">
    <uri>F:\kicad\share\library\conn.lib</uri>
  </library>
</libraries>
```

14.5.6 The nets section

The nets section has the delimiter <nets>. This section contains the ”connectivity” of the schematic.

```
<nets>
  <net code="1" name="GND">
    <node ref="U1" pin="7"/>
    <node ref="C1" pin="2"/>
```

```
    <node ref="U2" pin="7"/>
    <node ref="P1" pin="4"/>
  </net>
  <net code="2" name="VCC">
    <node ref="R1" pin="1"/>
    <node ref="U1" pin="14"/>
    <node ref="U2" pin="4"/>
    <node ref="U2" pin="1"/>
    <node ref="U2" pin="14"/>
    <node ref="P1" pin="1"/>
  </net>
</nets>
```

This section lists all nets in the schematic.

A possible net contains the following.

```
<net code="1" name="GND">
  <node ref="U1" pin="7"/>
  <node ref="C1" pin="2"/>
  <node ref="U2" pin="7"/>
  <node ref="P1" pin="4"/>
</net>
```

net code	is an internal identifier for this net
name	is a name for this net
node	give a pin reference connected to this net

14.6 More about xsltproc

Refer to the page: *http://xmlsoft.org/XSLT/xsltproc.html*

14.6.1 Introduction

xsltproc is a command line tool for applying XSLT style-sheets to XML documents. While it was developed as part of the GNOME project, it can operate independently of the GNOME desktop.

xsltproc is invoked from the command line with the name of the style-sheet to be used followed by the name of the file or files to which the style-sheet is to be applied. It will use the standard input if a filename provided is - .

If a style-sheet is included in an XML document with a Style-sheet Processing Instruction, no style-sheet needs to be named in the command line. xsltproc will automatically detect the included style-sheet and use it. By default, the output is to *stdout*. You can specify a file for output using the -o option.

14.6.2 Synopsis

```
xsltproc [[-V] | [-v] | [-o *file* ] | [--timing] | [--repeat] |
[--debug] | [--novalid] | [--noout] | [--maxdepth *val* ] | [--html] |
[--param *name* *value* ] | [--stringparam *name* *value* ] | [--nonet] |
[--path *paths* ] | [--load-trace] | [--catalogs] | [--xinclude] |
[--profile] | [--dumpextensions] | [--nowrite] | [--nomkdir] |
[--writesubtree] | [--nodtdattr]] [ *stylesheet* ] [ *file1* ] [ *file2* ]
[ *....* ]
```

14.6.3 Command line options

-V or *--version*

Show the version of libxml and libxslt used.

-v or *--verbose*

Output each step taken by xsltproc in processing the stylesheet and the document.

-o or *--output file*

Direct output to the file named *file*. For multiple outputs, also known as "chunking", -o directory/ directs the output files to a specified directory. The directory must already exist.

--timing

Display the time used for parsing the stylesheet, parsing the document and applying the stylesheet and saving the result. Displayed in milliseconds.

--repeat

Run the transformation 20 times. Used for timing tests.

--debug

Output an XML tree of the transformed document for debugging purposes.

--novalid

Skip loading the document's DTD.

--noout

Do not output the result.

--maxdepth value

Adjust the maximum depth of the template stack before libxslt concludes it is in an infinite loop. The default is 500.

--html

The input document is an HTML file.

--param name value

Pass a parameter of name *name* and value *value* to the stylesheet. You may pass multiple name/value pairs up to a maximum of 32. If the value being passed is a string rather than a node identifier, use --stringparam instead.

--stringparam name value

Pass a paramenter of name *name* and value *value* where *value* is a string rather than a node identifier. (Note: The string must be utf-8.)

--nonet

Do not use the Internet to fetch DTD' s, entities or documents.

--path paths

Use the list (separated by space or colon) of filesystem paths specified by *paths* to load DTDs, entities or documents. Enclose space-separated lists by quotation marks.

--load-trace

Display to stderr all the documents loaded during the processing.

--catalogs

Use the SGML catalog specified in SGML_CATALOG_FILES to resolve the location of external entities. By default, xsltproc looks for the catalog specified in XML_CATALOG_FILES. If that is not specified, it uses /etc/xml/catalog.

--xinclude

Process the input document using the Xinclude specification. More details on this can be found in the Xinclude specification: http://www.w3.org/TR/xinclude/

--profile --norman

Output profiling information detailing the amount of time spent in each part of the stylesheet. This is useful in optimizing stylesheet performance.

--dumpextensions

Dumps the list of all registered extensions to stdout.

--nowrite

Refuses to write to any file or resource.

--nomkdir

Refuses to create directories.

--writesubtree path

Allow file write only within the *path* subtree.

--nodtdattr

Do not apply default attributes from the document' s DTD.

14.6.4 Xsltproc return values

xsltproc returns a status number that can be quite useful when calling it within a script.

0: normal

1: no argument

2: too many parameters

3: unknown option

4: failed to parse the stylesheet

5: error in the stylesheet

6: error in one of the documents

7: unsupported xsl:output method

8: string parameter contains both quote and double-quotes

9: internal processing error

10: processing was stopped by a terminating message

11: could not write the result to the output file

14.6.5 More Information about xsltproc

libxml web page: http://www.xmlsoft.org/

W3C XSLT page: http://www.w3.org/TR/xslt

Pcbnew

August 24, 2017

Contents

Reference manual

Copyright

Contributors

Jean-Pierre Charras, Fabrizio Tappero.

Feedback

Please direct any bug reports, suggestions or new versions to here:

- About KiCad document: https://github.com/KiCad/kicad-doc/issues
- About KiCad software: https://bugs.launchpad.net/kicad
- About KiCad software i18n: https://github.com/KiCad/kicad-i18n/issues

Publication date and software version

2014, march 17.

Chapter 1

Introduction to Pcbnew

1.1 Description

Pcbnew is a powerful printed circuit board software tool available for the Linux, Microsoft Windows and Apple OS X operating systems. Pcbnew is used in association with the schematic capture program Eeschema to create printed circuit boards.

Pcbnew manages libraries of footprints. Each footprint is a drawing of the physical component including its land pattern (the layout of pads on the circuit board). The required footprints are automatically loaded during the reading of the Netlist. Any changes to footprint selection or annotation can be changed in the schematic and updated in pcbnew by regenerating the netlist and reading it in pcbnew again.

Pcbnew provides a design rules check (DRC) tool which prevents track and pad clearance issues as well as preventing nets from being connected that aren' t connected in the netlist/schematic. When using the interactive router it continuously runs the design rules check and will help automatically route individual traces.

Pcbnew provides a rats nest display, a hairline connecting the pads of footprints which are connected on the schematic. These connections move dynamically as track and footprint movements are made.

Pcbnew has a simple but effective autorouter to assist in the production of the circuit board. An Export/Import in SPECCTRA dsn format allows the use of more advanced auto-routers.

Pcbnew provides options specifically provided for the production of ultra high frequency microwave circuits (such as pads of trapezoidal and complex form, automatic layout of coils on the printed circuit, etc).

1.2 Principal design features

The smallest unit in pcbnew is 1 nanometer. All dimensions are stored as integer nanometers.

Pcbnew can generate up to 32 layers of copper, 14 technical layers (silk screen, solder mask, component adhesive, solder paste and edge cuts) plus 4 auxiliary layers (drawings and comments) and manages in real time the hairline indication (rats nest) of missing tracks.

The display of the PCB elements (tracks, pads, text, drawings···) is customizable:

- In full or outline.
- With or without track clearance.

For complex circuits, the display of layers, zones, and components can be hidden in a selective way for clarity on screen. Nets of traces can be highlighted to provide high contrast as well.

Footprints can be rotated to any angle, with a resolution of 0.1 degree.

Pcbnew includes a Footprint Editor that allows editing of individual footprints that have been on a pcb or editing a footprint in a library.

The Footprint Editor provides many time saving tools such as:

- Fast pad numbering by simply dragging the mouse over pads in the order you want them numbered.
- Easy generation of rectangular and circular arrays of pads for LGA/BGA or circular footprints.
- Semi-automatic aligning of rows or columns of pads.

Footprint pads have a variety of properties that can be adjusted. The pads can be round, rectangular, oval or trapezoidal. For through-hole parts drills can be offset inside the pad and be round or a slot. Individual pads can also be rotated and have unique soldermask, net, or paste clearance. Pads can also have a solid connection or a thermal relief connection for easier manufacturing. Any combination of unique pads can be placed within a footprint.

Pcbnew easily generates all the documents necessary for production:

- Fabrication outputs:
  - Files for Photoplotters in GERBER RS274X format.
  - Files for drilling in EXCELLON format.
- Plot files in HPGL, SVG and DXF format.
- Plot and drilling maps in POSTSCRIPT format.
- Local Printout.

1.3 General remarks

Due to the degree of control necessary it is highly suggested to use a 3-button mouse with pcbnew. Many features such as panning and zooming require a 3-button mouse.

In the new release of KiCad, pcbnew has seen wide sweeping changes from developers at CERN. This includes features such as a new renderer (OpenGL and Cairo view modes), an interative push and shove router, differential and meander trace routing and tuning, a reworked Footprint Editor, and many other features. Please note that most of these new features **only** exist in the new OpenGL and Cairo view modes.

Chapter 2

Installation

2.1 Installation of the software

The installation procedure is described in the KiCad documentation.

2.2 Modifying the default configuration

A default configuration file `kicad.pro` is provided in `kicad/share/template`. This file is used as the initial configuration for all new projects.

This configuration file can be modified to change the libraries to be loaded.

To do this:

- Launch Pcbnew using kicad or directly. On Windows it is in `C:\kicad\bin\pcbnew.exe` and on Linux you can run `/usr/local/kicad/bin/kicad` or `/usr/local/kicad/bin/pcbnew` if the binaries are located in `/usr/local/kicad/bin`.
- Select Preferences - Libs and Dir.
- Edit as required.
- Save the modified configuration (Save Cfg) to `kicad/share/template/kicad.pro`.

2.3 Managing Footprint Libraries: legacy versions

You can have access to the library list initialization from the Preferences menu:

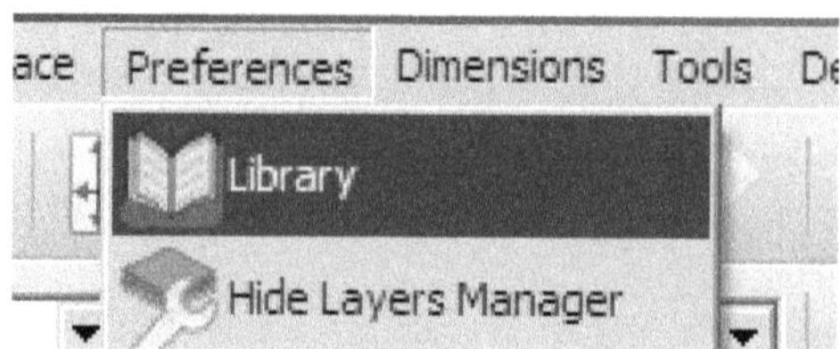

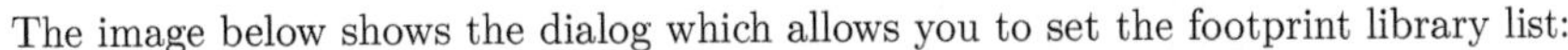

The image below shows the dialog which allows you to set the footprint library list:

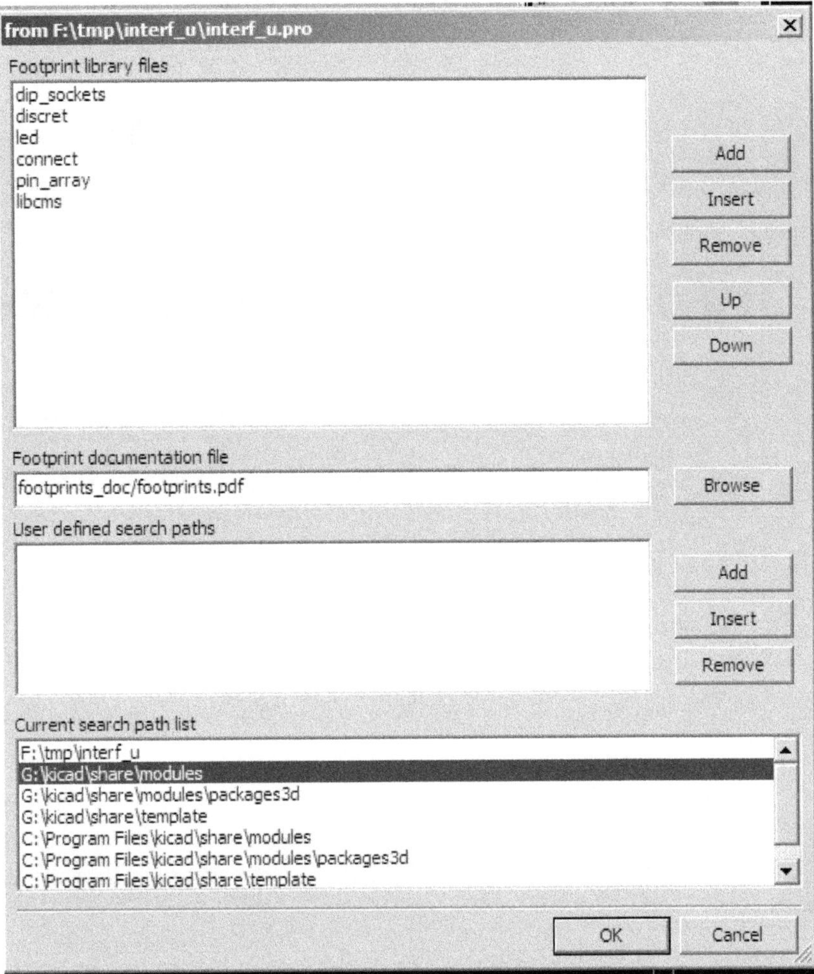

You can use this to add all the libraries that contain the footprints required for your project. You should also remove unused libraries from new projects to prevent footprint name clashes. Please note, there is an issue with the footprint library list when duplicate footprint names exist in more than one library. When this occurs, the footprint will be loaded from the first library found in the list. If this is an issue (you cannot load the footprint you want), either change the library list order using the "Up" and "Down" buttons in the dialog above or give the footprint a unique name using the footprint editor.

2.4 Managing Footprint Libraries: .pretty repositories

As of release 4.0, Pcbnew uses the new footprint library table implementation to manage footprint libraries. The information in the previous section is no longer valid. The library table manager is accessible by:

The image below shows the footprint library table editing dialog which can be opened by invoking the "Footprint Libraries Manager" entry from the "Preferences" menu.

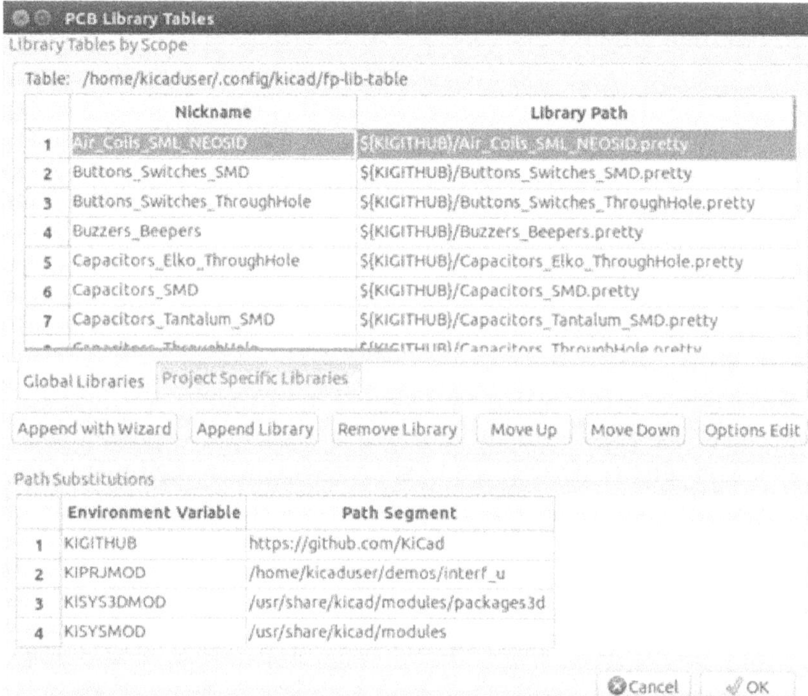

The footprint library table is used to map a footprint library of any supported library type to a library nickname. This nickname is used to look up footprints instead of the previous method which depended on library search path ordering. This allows Pcbnew to access footprints with the same name in different libraries by ensuring that the correct footprint is loaded from the appropriate library. It also allows Pcbnew to support loading libraries from different PCB editors such as Eagle and gEDA.

2.4.1 Global Footprint Library Table

The global footprint library table contains the list of libraries that are always available regardless of the currently loaded project file. The table is saved in the file `fp-lib-table` in the user' s home folder. The location of this folder is dependent on the operating system.

2.4.2 Project Specific Footprint Library Table

The project specific footprint library table contains the list of libraries that are available specifically for the currently loaded project file. The project specific footprint library table can only be edited when it is loaded along with the project board file. If no project file is loaded or there is no footprint library table file in the project path, an empty table is created which can be edited and later saved along with the board file.

2.4.3 Initial Configuration

The first time CvPcb or Pcbnew is run and the global footprint table file `fp-lib-table` is not found in the user′ s home folder, Pcbnew will attempt to copy the default footprint table file fp_global_table stored in the system′ s KiCad template folder to the file `fp-lib-table` in the user′ s home folder. If fp_global_table cannot be found, an empty footprint library table will be created in the user′ s home folder. If this happens, the user can either copy fp_global_table manually or configure the table by hand. The default footprint library table includes all of the standard footprint libraries that are installed as part of KiCad.

2.4.4 Adding Table Entries

In order to use a footprint library, it must first be added to either the global table or the project specific table. The project specific table is only applicable when a board file is open. Each library entry must have a unique nickname. This does not have to be related in any way to the actual library file name or path. The colon : character cannot be used anywhere in the nickname. Each library entry must have a valid path and/or file name depending on the type of library. Paths can be defined as absolute, relative, or by environment variable substitution. The appropriate plug in type must be selected in order for the library to be properly read. Pcbnew currently supports reading KiCad legacy, KiCad Pretty, Eagle, and gEDA footprint libraries. There is also a description field to add a description of the library entry. The option field is not used at this time so adding options will have no effect when loading libraries. Please note that you cannot have duplicate library nicknames in the same table. However, you can have duplicate library nicknames in both the global and project specific footprint library table. The project specific table entry will take precedence over the global table entry when duplicated names occur. When entries are defined in the project specific table, an fp-lib-table file containing the entries will be written into the folder of the currently open netlist.

2.4.5 Environment Variable Substitution

One of the most powerful features of the footprint library table is environment variable substitution. This allows you to define custom paths to where your libraries are stored in environment variables. Environment variable substitution is supported by using the syntax `${ENV_VAR_NAME}` in the footprint library path. By default, at run time Pcbnew defines the `$KISYSMOD` environment variable. This points to where the default footprint libraries that were installed with KiCad are located. You can override `$KISYSMOD` by defining it yourself which allows you to substitute your own libraries in place of the default KiCad footprint libraries. When a board file is loaded, Pcbnew also defines the `$KPRJMOD` using the board file path. This allows you to create libraries in the project path without having to define the absolute path to the library in the project specific footprint library table.

2.4.6 Using the GitHub Plugin

The GitHub plugin is a special plugin that provides an interface for read-only access to a remote GitHub repository consisting of pretty (Pretty is name of the KiCad footprint file format) footprints and optionally provides "Copy-On-Write" (COW) support for editing footprints read from the GitHub repo and saving them locally. Therefore the "GitHub" plugin is for **read-only for accessing remote pretty footprint libraries** at https://github.com. To add a GitHub entry to the footprint library table the "Library Path" in the footprint library table entry must be set to a valid GitHub URL.

For example:

```
https://github.com/liftoff-sr/pretty_footprints
```

Typically GitHub URLs take the form:

```
https://github.com/user_name/repo_name
```

The "Plugin Type" must be set to "Github". To enable the "Copy-On-Write" feature the option `allow_pretty_writing_to_this_dir` must be added to the "Options" setting of the footprint library table entry. This option is the "Library Path" for local storage of modified copies of footprints read from the GitHub repo. The footprints saved to this path are combined with the read-only part of the GitHub repository to create the footprint library. If this option is missing, then the GitHub library is read-only. If the option is present for a GitHub library, then any writes to this hybrid library will go to the local `*.pretty` directory. Note that the github.com resident portion of this hybrid COW library is always read-only, meaning you cannot delete anything or modify any footprint in the specified GitHub repository directly. The aggregate library type remains "Github" in all further discussions, but it consists of both the local read/write portion and the remote read-only portion.

The table below shows a footprint library table entry without the option `allow_pretty_writing_to_this_dir`:

Nickname	Library Path	Plugin Type	Options	Description
github	https://github.com/liftoff-sr/pretty_footprints	Github		Liftoff' s GH footprints

The table below shows a footprint library table entry with the COW option given. Note the use of the environment variable `${HOME}` as an example only. The github.pretty directory is located in `${HOME}/pretty/path`. Anytime you use the option `allow_pretty_writing_to_this_dir`, you will need to create that directory manually in advance and it must end with the extension `.pretty`.

Nickname	Library Path	Plugin Type	Options	Description
github	https://github.com/liftoff-sr/pretty_footprints	Github		Liftoff' s GH footprints

Footprint loads will always give precedence to the local footprints found in the path given by the option `allow_pretty_writing_to_this_dir`. Once you have saved a footprint to the COW library's local directory by doing a footprint save in the Footprint Editor, no GitHub updates will be seen when loading a footprint with the same name as one for which you've saved locally.

Always keep a separate local `*.pretty` directory for each GitHub library, never combine them by referring to the same directory more than once. Also, do not use the same COW (`*.pretty`) directory in a footprint library table entry. This would likely create a mess. The value of the option `allow_pretty_writing_to_this_dir` will expand any environment variable using the `${}` notation to create the path in the same way as the "Library Path" setting.

What's the point of COW? It is to turbo-charge the sharing of footprints. If you periodically email your COW pretty footprint modifications to the GitHub repository maintainer, you can help update the GitHub copy. Simply email the individual `*.kicad_mod` files you find in your COW directories to the maintainer of the GitHub repository. After you've received confirmation that your changes have been committed, you can safely delete your COW file(s) and the updated footprint from the read-only part of GitHub library will flow down. Your goal should be to keep the COW file set as small as possible by contributing frequently to the shared master copies at https://github.com.

Finally, Nginx can be used as a cache to the github server to speed up the loading of footprints. It can be installed locally or on a network server. There is an example configuration in KiCad sources at pcbnew/github/nginx.conf. The most straightforward way to get this working is to overwrite the default nginx.conf with this one and `export KIGITHUB=http://my_server:54321/KiCad`, where `my_server` is the IP or domain name of the machine running nginx.

2.4.7 Usage Patterns

Footprint libraries can be defined either globally or specifically to the currently loaded project. Footprint libraries defined in the user's global table are always available and are stored in the `fp-lib-table` file in the user's home folder. Global footprint libraries can always be accessed even when there is no project net list file opened. The project specific footprint table is active only for the currently open net list file. The project specific footprint library table is saved in the file fp-lib-table in the path of the currently open board file. You are free to define libraries in either table.

There are advantages and disadvantages to each method:

- You can define all of your libraries in the global table which means they will always be available when you need them.
  - The disadvantage of this is that you may have to search through a lot of libraries to find the footprint you are looking for.
- You can define all your libraries on a project specific basis.
  - The advantage of this is that you only need to define the libraries you actually need for the project which cuts down on searching.
  - The disadvantage is that you always have to remember to add each footprint library that you need for every project.
- You can also define footprint libraries both globally and project specifically.

One usage pattern would be to define your most commonly used libraries globally and the library only required for the project in the project specific library table. There is no restriction on how you define your libraries.

Chapter 3

General operations

3.1 Toolbars and commands

In Pcbnew it is possible to execute commands using various means:

- Text-based menu at the top of the main window.
- Top toolbar menu.
- Right toolbar menu.
- Left toolbar menu.
- Mouse buttons (menu options). Specifically:
  - The right mouse button reveals a pop-up menu the content of which depends on the element under the mouse arrow.
- Keyboard (Function keys `F1`, `F2`, `F3`, `F4`, `Shift`, `Delete`, `+`, `-`, `Page Up`, `Page Down` and `Space bar`). The `Escape` key generally cancels an operation in progress.

The screenshot below illustrates some of the possible accesses to these operations:

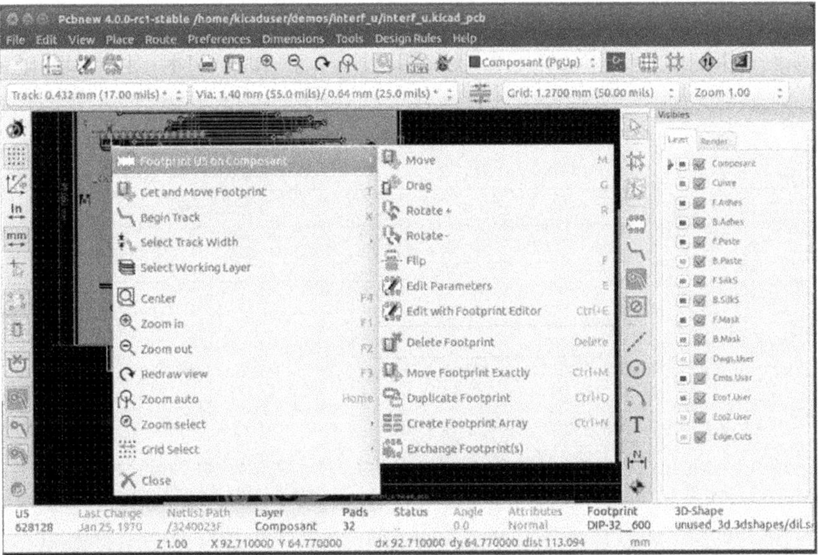

3.2 Mouse commands

3.2.1 Basic commands

- Left button
  - Single-click displays the characteristics of the footprint or text under the cursor in the lower status bar.
  - Double-click displays the editor (if the element is editable) of the element under the cursor.
- Centre button/wheel
  - Rapid zoom and some commands in layer manager.
  - Hold down the centre button and draw a rectangle to zoom to the described area. Rotation of the mouse wheel will allow you to zoom in and zoom out.
- Right button
  - Displays a pop-up menu

3.2.2 Operations on blocks

Operations to move, invert (mirror), copy, rotate and delete a block are all available via the pop-up menu. In addition, the view can zoom to the area described by the block.

The framework of the block is traced by moving the mouse while holding down the left mouse button. The operation is executed when the button is released.

By holding down one of the hotkeys `Shift` or `Ctrl`, or both keys `Shift` and `Ctrl` together, while the block is drawn the operation invert, rotate or delete is automatically selected as shown in the table below:

Action	Effect
Left mouse button held down	Trace framework to move block
`Shift` + Left mouse button held down	Trace framework for invert block
`Ctrl` + Left mouse button held down	Trace framework for rotating block 90°
`Shift` + `Ctrl` + Left mouse button held down	Trace framework to delete the block
Centre mouse button held down	Trace framework to zoom to block

When moving a block:

- Move block to new position and operate left mouse button to place the elements.
- To cancel the operation use the right mouse button and select Cancel Block from the menu (or press the `Esc` key).

Alternatively if no key is pressed when drawing the block use the right mouse button to display the pop-up menu and select the required operation.

For each block operation a selection window enables the action to be limited to only some elements.

3.3 Selection of grid size

During element layout the cursor moves on a grid. The grid can be turned on or off using the icon on the left toolbar.

Any of the pre-defined grid sizes, or a User Defined grid, can be chosen using the pop-up window, or the drop-down selector on the toolbar at the top of the screen. The size of the User Defined grid is set using the menu bar option Dimensions → User Grid Size.

3.4 Adjustment of the zoom level

The zoom level can be changed using any of the following methods:

- Open the pop-up window (using the right mouse button) and then select the desired zoom.
- Use the following function keys:
  - `F1`: Enlarge (zoom in)
  - `F2`: Reduce (zoom out)
  - `F3`: Redraw the display
  - `F4`: Centre view at the current cursor position
- Rotate the mouse wheel.
- Hold down the middle mouse button and draw a rectangle to zoom to the described area.

3.5 Displaying cursor coordinates

The cursor coordinates are displayed in inches or millimetres as selected using the *In* or *mm* icons on the left hand side toolbar.

Whichever unit is selected Pcbnew always works to a precision of 1/10,000 of inch.

The status bar at the bottom of the screen gives:

- The current zoom setting.
- The absolute position of the cursor.
- The relative position of the cursor. Note the relative coordinates (x,y) can be set to (0,0) at any position by pressing the space bar. The cursor position is then displayed relative to this new datum.

In addition the relative position of the cursor can be displayed using its polar co-ordinates (ray + angle). This can be turned on and off using the icon in the left hand side toolbar.

3.6 Keyboard commands - hotkeys

Many commands are accessible directly with the keyboard. Selection can be either upper or lower case. Most hot keys are shown in menus. Some hot keys that do not appear are:

- `Delete`: deletes a footprint or a track. (*Available only if the Footprint mode or the Track mode is active*)
- `V`: if the track tool is active switches working layer or place via, if a track is in progress.
- `+` and `-`: select next or previous layer.
- `?`: display the list of all hot keys.
- `Space`: reset relative coordinates.

3.7 Operation on blocks

Operations to move, invert (mirror), copy, rotate and delete a block are all available from the pop-up menu. In addition, the view can zoom to that described by the block.

The framework of the block is traced by moving the mouse while holding down the left mouse button. The operation is executed when the button is released.

By holding down one of the keys `Shift` or `Ctrl`, both `Shift` and `Ctrl` together, or `Alt`, while the block is drawn the operation invert, rotate, delete or copy is automatically selected as shown in the table below:

Action	Effect
Left mouse button held down	Move block
`Shift` + Left mouse button held down	Invert (mirror) block
`Ctrl` + Left mouse button held down	Rotate block 90°
`Shift` + `Ctrl` + Left mouse button held down	Delete the block
`Alt` + Left mouse button held down	Copy the block

When a block command is made, a dialog window is displayed, and items involved in this command can be chosen.

Any of the commands above can be cancelled via the same pop-up menu or by pressing the Escape key (`Esc`).

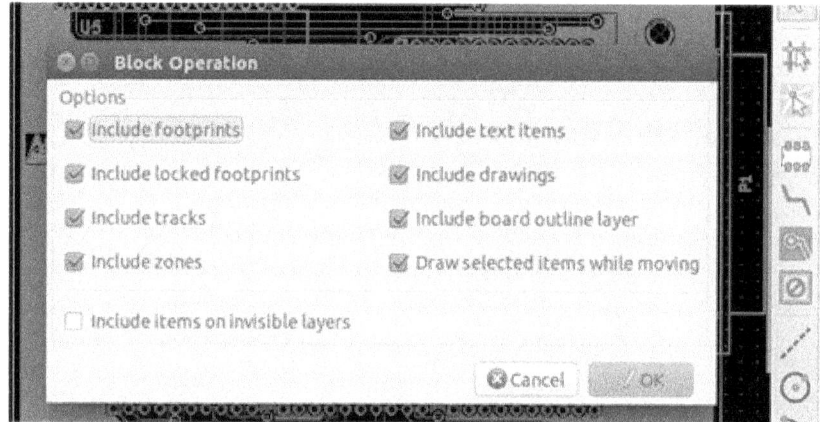

3.8 Units used in dialogs

Units used to display dimensions values are inch and mm. The desired unit can be selected by pressing the icon located in left toolbar: In mm However one can enter the unit used to define a value, when entering a new value.

Accepted units are:

1 **in**	1 inch
1 **"**	1 inch
25 **th**	25 thou
25 **mi**	25 mils, same as thou
6 **mm**	6 mm

The rules are:

- Spaces between the number and the unit are accepted.
- Only the first two letters are significant.
- In countries using an alternative decimal separator than the period, the period (`.`) can be used as well. Therefore `1,5` and `1.5` are the same in French.

3.9 Top menu bar

The top menu bar provides access to the files (loading and saving), configuration options, printing, plotting and the help files.

3.9.1 The File menu

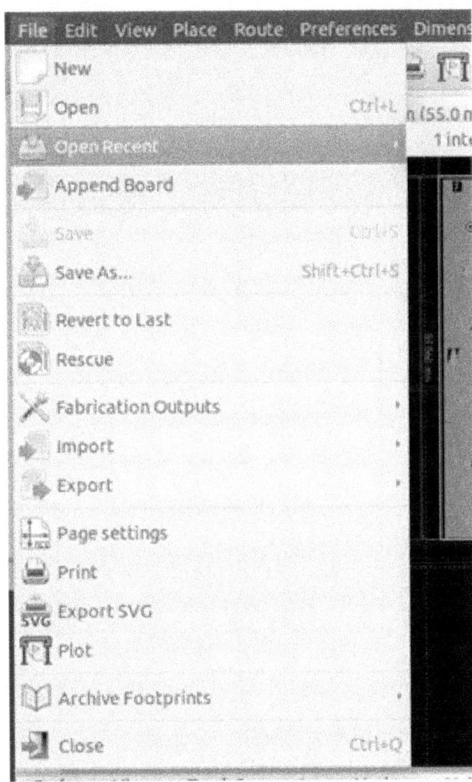

The File menu allows the loading and saving of printed circuits files, as well as printing and plotting the circuit board. It enables the export (with the format GenCAD 1.4) of the circuit for use with automatic testers.

3.9.2 Edit menu

Allows some global edit actions:

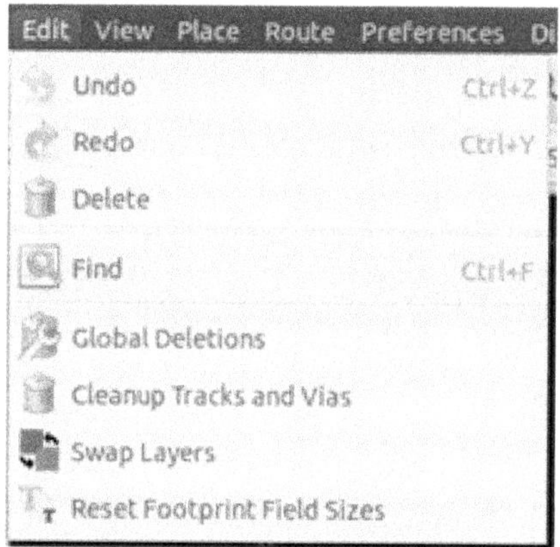

3.9.3 View menu

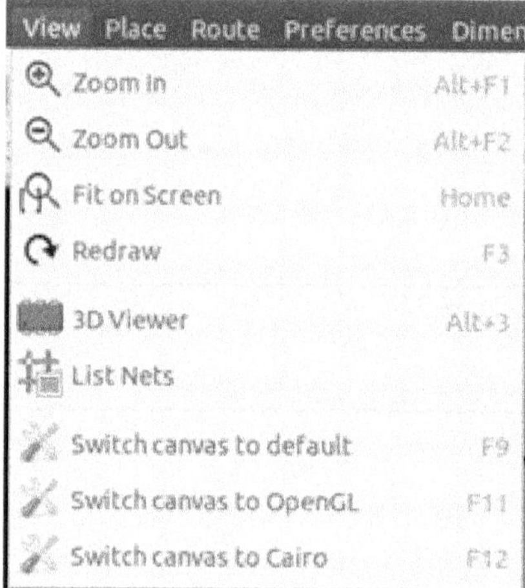

Zoom functions and 3D board display.

3.9.3.1 3D Viewer

Opens the 3D Viewer. Here is a sample:

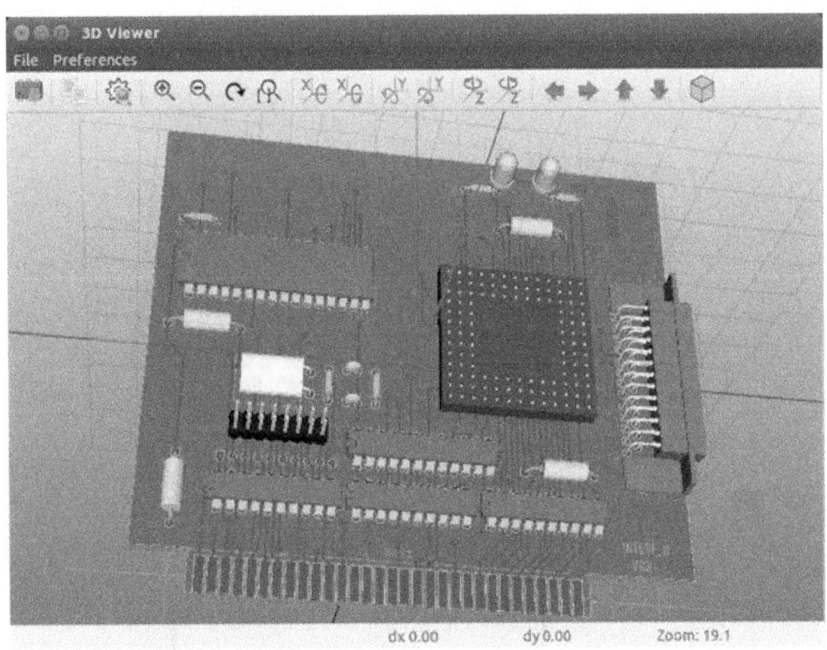

3.9.3.2 Switch canvas

Allows switching canvas.

- default
- OpenGL
- Cairo

3.9.4 Place menu

Same function as the right-hand toolbar.

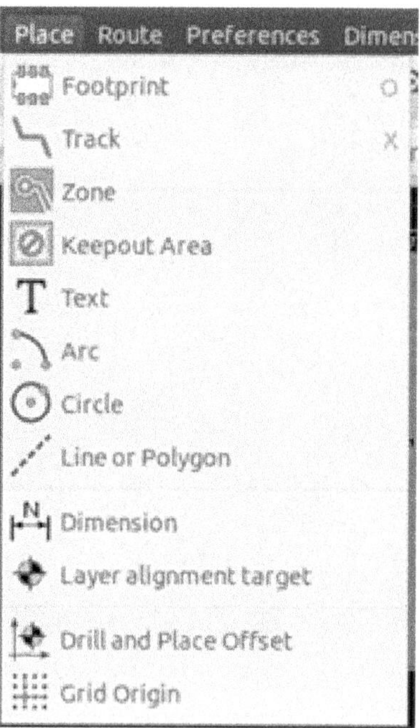

3.9.5 Route menu

Routing function.

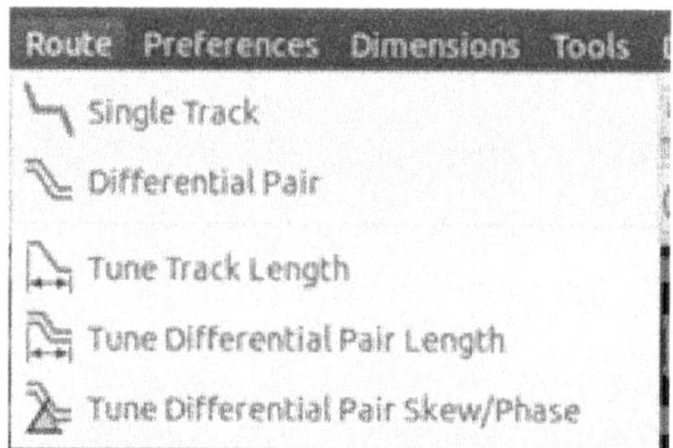

3.9.6 The Preferences menu

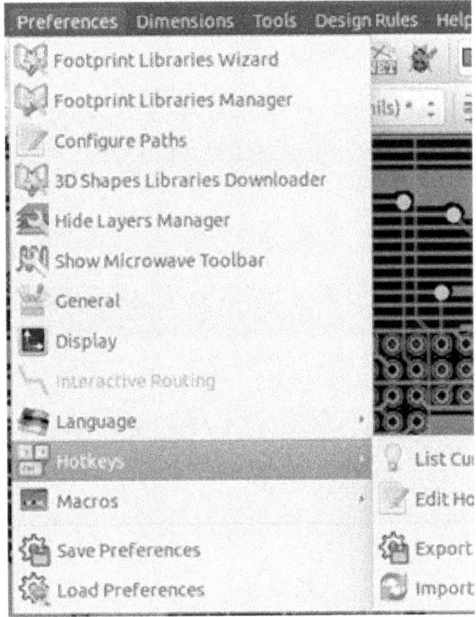

Allows:

- Selection of the footprint libraries.
- Hide/Show the Layers manager (colors selection for displaying layers and other elements. Also enables the display of elements to be turned on and off).
- Management of general options (units, etc.).
- The management of other display options.
- Creation, editing (and re-read) of the hot keys file.

3.9.7 Dimensions menu

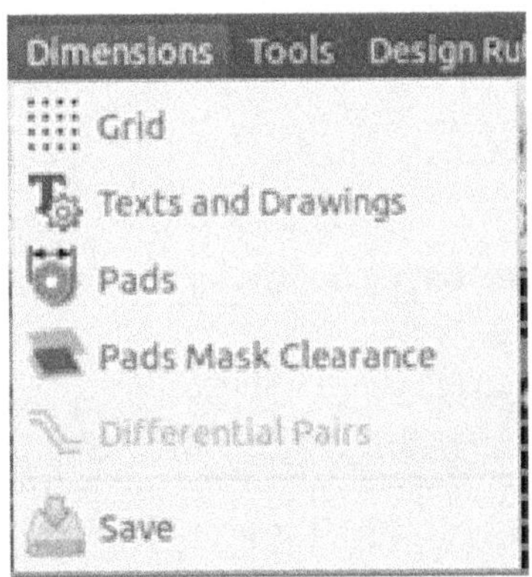

An important menu. Allows adjustment of:

- User grid size.
- Size of texts and the line width for drawings.
- Dimensions and characteristic of pads.
- Setting the global values for solder mask and solder paste layers

3.9.8 Tools menu

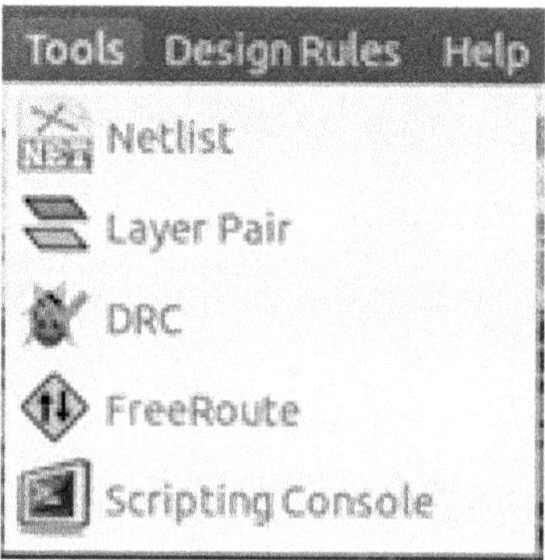

3.9.9 The Design Rules menu

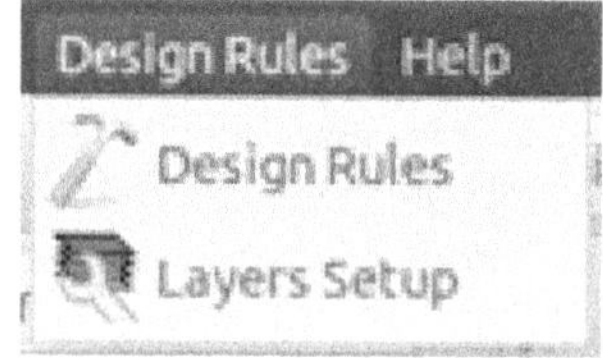

Provides access to 2 dialogs:

- Setting Design Rules (tracks and vias sizes, clearances).
- Setting Layers (number, enabled and layers names)

3.9.10 The Help menu

Provides access to the user manuals and to the version information menu (Pcbnew About).

3.10 Using icons on the top toolbar

This toolbar gives access to the principal functions of Pcbnew.

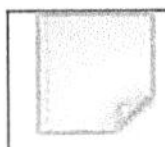	Creation of a new printed circuit.
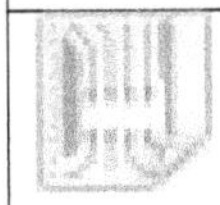	Opening of an old printed circuit.
	Save printed circuit.
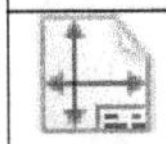	Selection of the page size and modification of the file properties.
	Opens Footprint Editor to edit library or pcb footprint.
	Opens Footprint Viewer to display library or pcb footprint.
	Undo/Redo last commands (10 levels)
	Display print menu.
	Display plot menu.
	Zoom in and Zoom out (relative to the centre of screen).
	Redraw the screen
	Fit to page
	Find footprint or text.
 NET	Netlist operations (selection, reading, testing and compiling).
	DRC (Design Rule Check): Automatic check of the tracks.
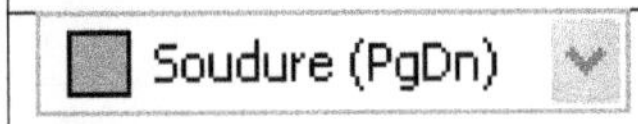 Soudure (PgDn)	Selection of the working layer.
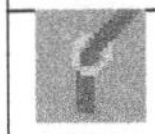	Selection of layer pair (for vias)
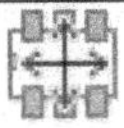	Footprint mode: when active this enables footprint options in the pop-up window.
	Routing mode: when active this enables routing options in the pop-up window
	Direct access to the router Freerouter
	Show / Hide the Python scripting console

3.10.1 Auxiliary toolbar

Track 17.0	Selection of thickness of track already in use.
Via 65.0	Selection of a dimension of via already in use.
	Automatic track width: if enabled when creating a new track, when starting on an existing track, the width of the new track is set to the width of the existing track.
Grid 50.0	Selection of the grid size.
Zoom 128	Selection of the zoom.

3.11 Right-hand side toolbar

This toolbar gives access to the editing tool to change the PCB shown in Pcbnew.

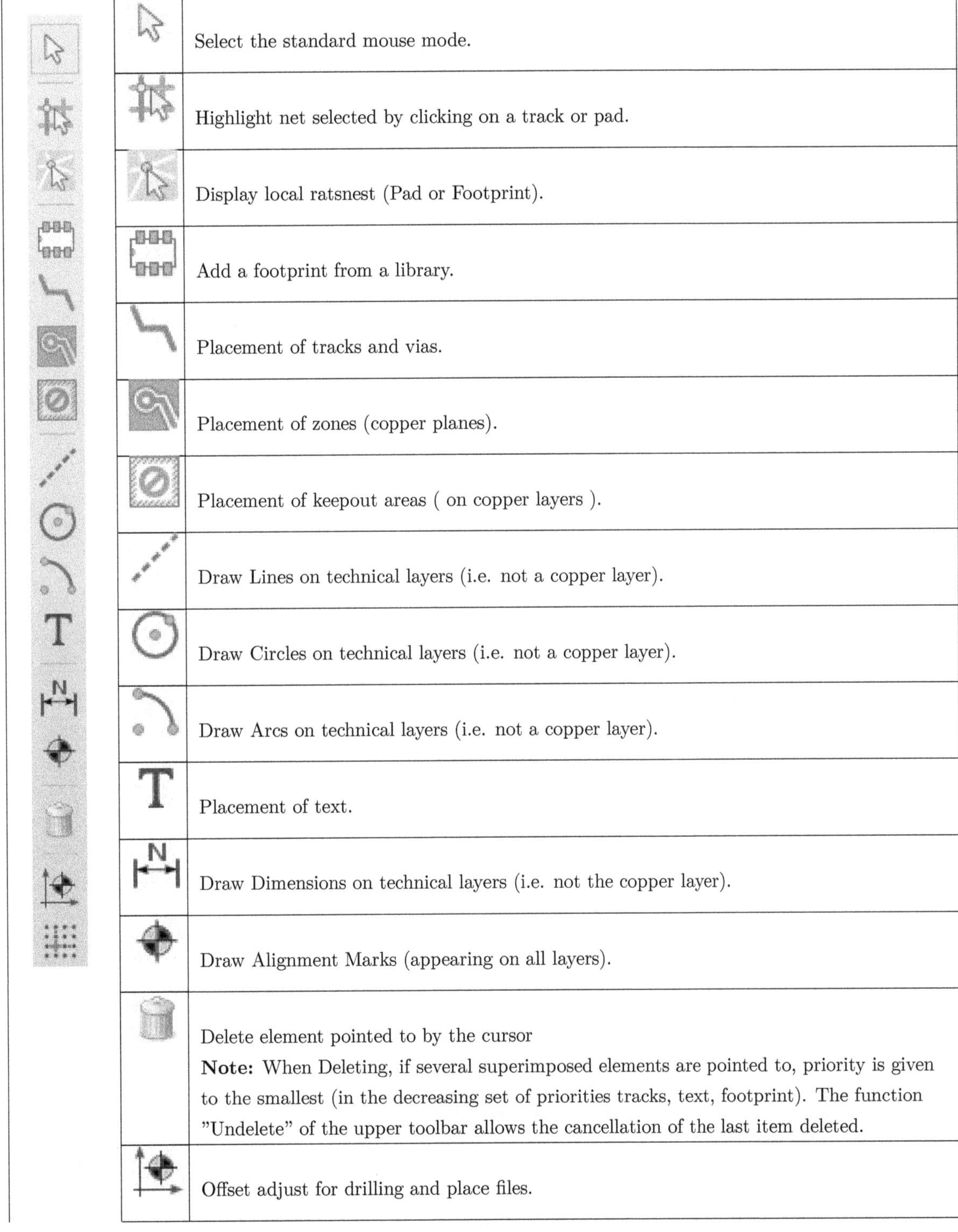

	Select the standard mouse mode.
	Highlight net selected by clicking on a track or pad.
	Display local ratsnest (Pad or Footprint).
	Add a footprint from a library.
	Placement of tracks and vias.
	Placement of zones (copper planes).
	Placement of keepout areas (on copper layers).
	Draw Lines on technical layers (i.e. not a copper layer).
	Draw Circles on technical layers (i.e. not a copper layer).
	Draw Arcs on technical layers (i.e. not a copper layer).
T	Placement of text.
	Draw Dimensions on technical layers (i.e. not the copper layer).
	Draw Alignment Marks (appearing on all layers).
	Delete element pointed to by the cursor **Note:** When Deleting, if several superimposed elements are pointed to, priority is given to the smallest (in the decreasing set of priorities tracks, text, footprint). The function "Undelete" of the upper toolbar allows the cancellation of the last item deleted.
	Offset adjust for drilling and place files.

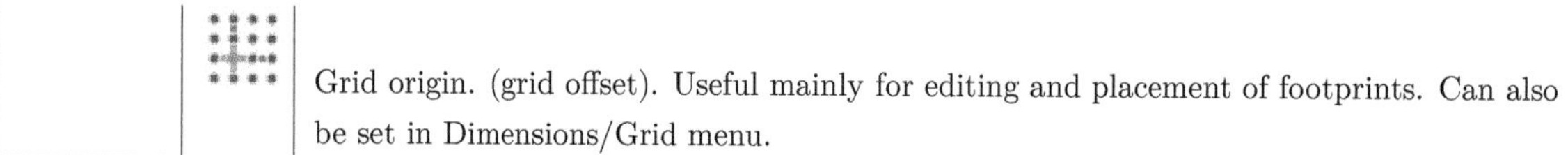

		Grid origin. (grid offset). Useful mainly for editing and placement of footprints. Can also be set in Dimensions/Grid menu.

- Placement of footprints, tracks, zones of copper, texts, etc.
- Net Highlighting.
- Creating notes, graphic elements, etc.
- Deleting elements.

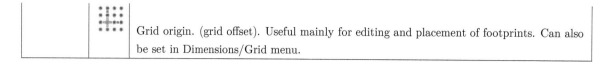

3.12 Left-hand side toolbar

The left hand-side toolbar provides display and control options that affect Pcbnew' s interface.

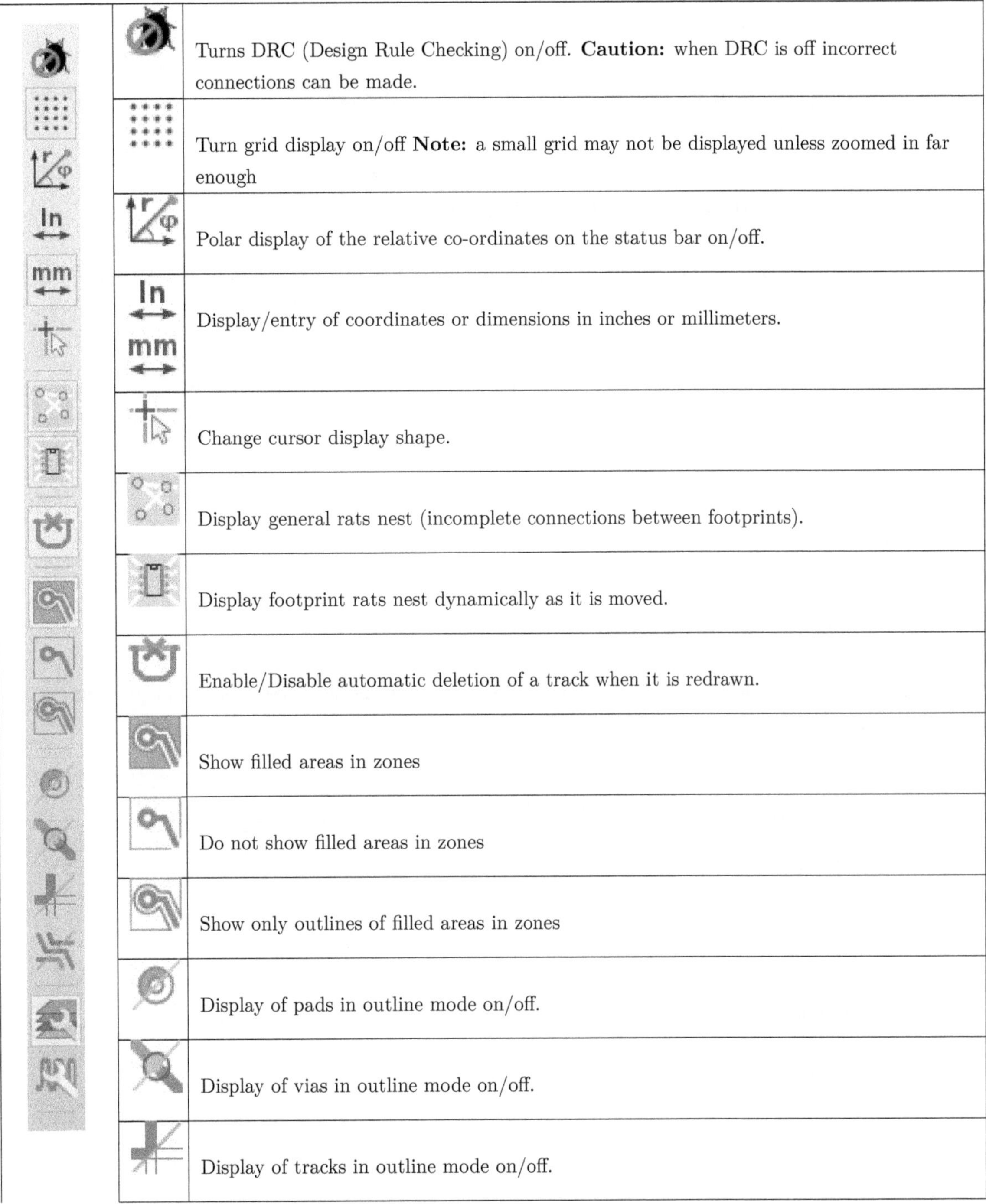

Icon	Description
	Turns DRC (Design Rule Checking) on/off. **Caution:** when DRC is off incorrect connections can be made.
	Turn grid display on/off **Note:** a small grid may not be displayed unless zoomed in far enough
	Polar display of the relative co-ordinates on the status bar on/off.
In / mm	Display/entry of coordinates or dimensions in inches or millimeters.
	Change cursor display shape.
	Display general rats nest (incomplete connections between footprints).
	Display footprint rats nest dynamically as it is moved.
	Enable/Disable automatic deletion of a track when it is redrawn.
	Show filled areas in zones
	Do not show filled areas in zones
	Show only outlines of filled areas in zones
	Display of pads in outline mode on/off.
	Display of vias in outline mode on/off.
	Display of tracks in outline mode on/off.

		High contrast display mode on/off. In this mode the active layer is displayed normally, all the other layers are displayed in gray. Useful for working on multi-layer circuits.
		Hide/Show the Layers manager
		Access to microwaves tools. Under development

3.13 Pop-up windows and fast editing

A right-click of the mouse opens a pop-up window. Its contents depends on the element pointed at by the cursor. This gives immediate access to:

- Changing the display (centre display on cursor, zoom in or out or selecting the zoom).
- Setting the grid size.
- Additionally a right-click on an element enables editing of the most commonly modified element parameters.

The screenshots below show what the pop-up windows looks like.

3.14 Available modes

There are 3 modes when using pop-up menus. In the pop-up menus, these modes add or remove some specific commands.

and disabled	Normal mode
enabled	Footprint mode
enabled	Tracks mode

3.14.1 Normal mode

- Pop-up menu with no selection:

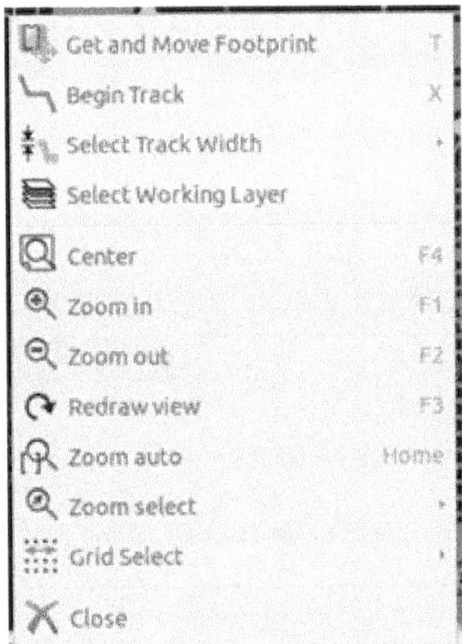

- Pop-up menu with track selected:

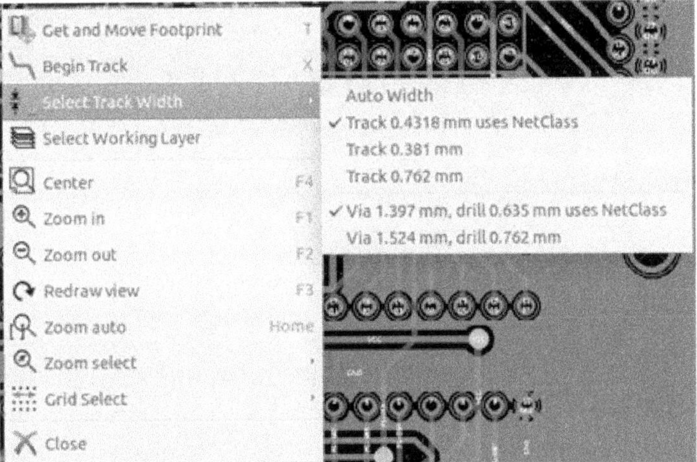

- Pop-up menu with footprint selected:

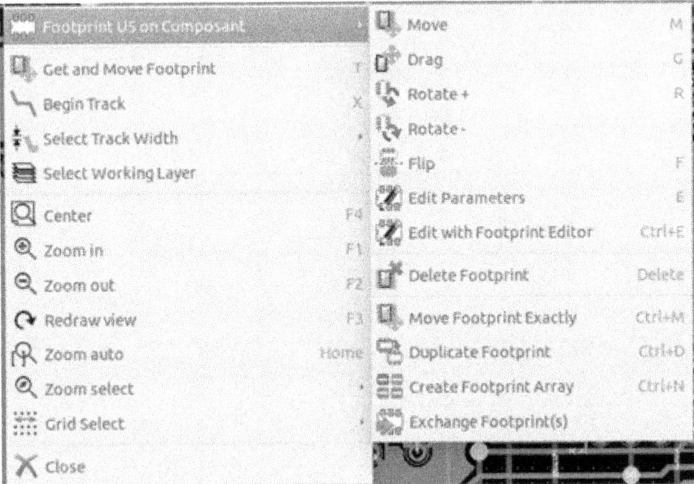

3.14.2 Footprint mode

Same cases in Footprint Mode (enabled)

- Pop-up menu with no selection:

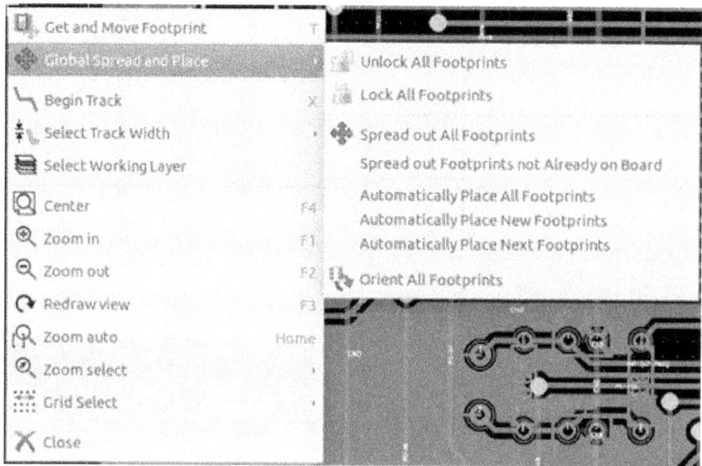

- Pop-up menu with track selected:

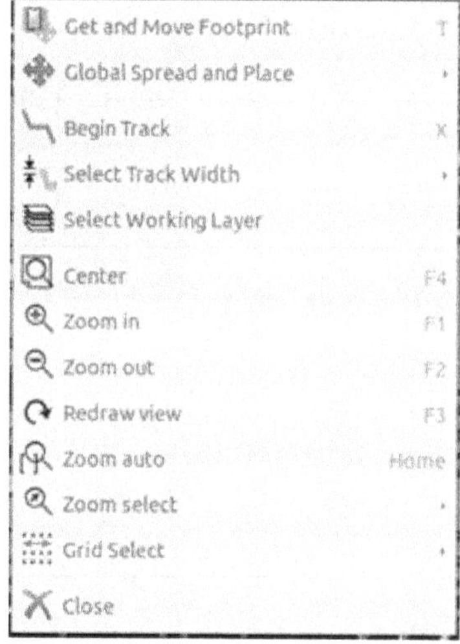

- Pop-up menu with footprint selected:

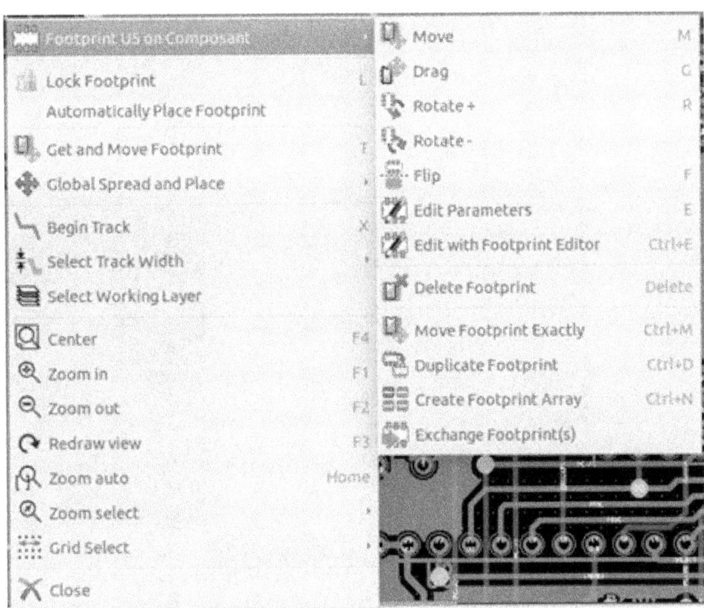

3.14.3 Tracks mode

Same cases in Track Mode (enabled)

- Pop-up menu with no selection:

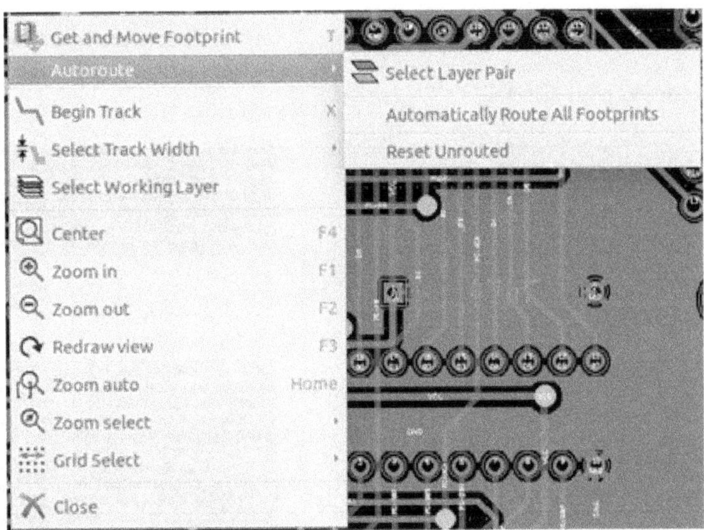

- Pop-up menu with track selected:

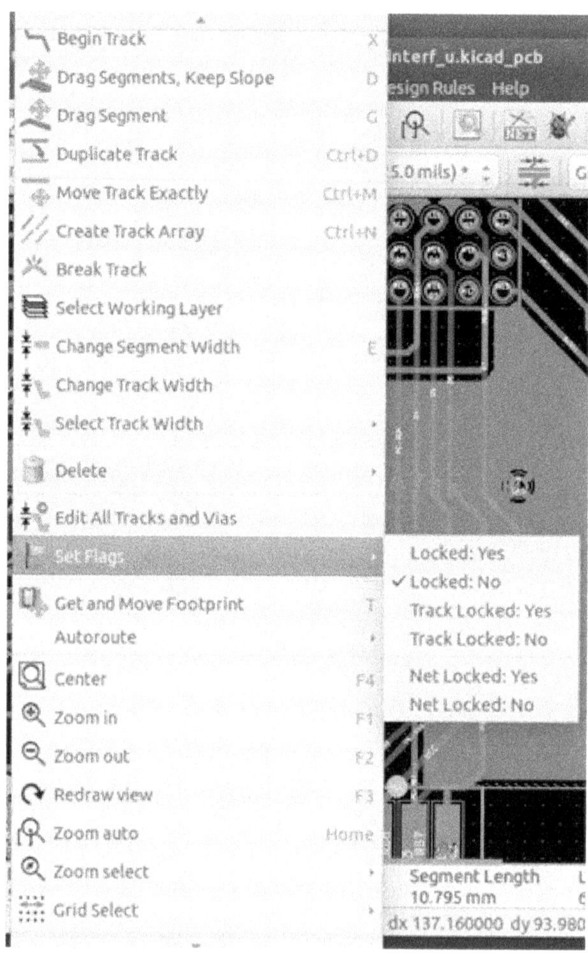

- Pop-up menu with footprint selected:

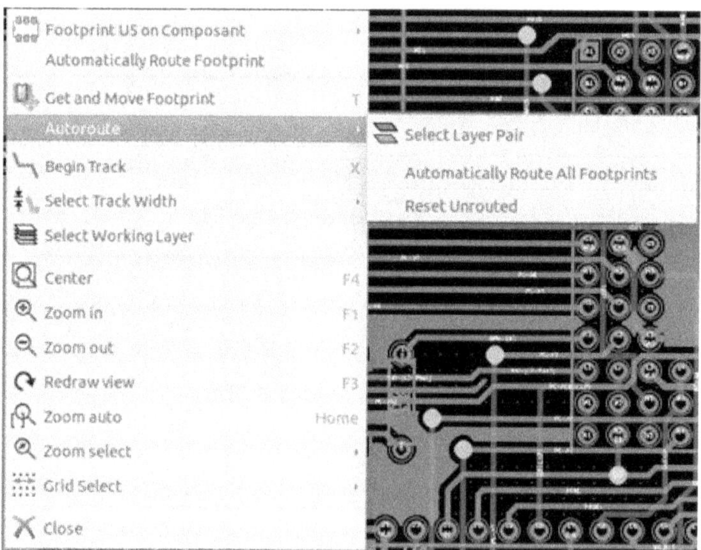

Chapter 4

Schematic Implementation

4.1 Linking a schematic to a printed circuit board

Generally speaking, a schematic sheet is linked to its printed circuit board by means of the netlist file, which is normally generated by the schematic editor used to make the schematic. Pcbnew accepts netlist files made with Eeschema or Orcad PCB 2. The netlist file, generated from the schematic is usually missing the footprints that correspond to the various components. Consequently an intermediate stage is necessary. During this intermediate process the association of components with footprints is performed. In KiCad, CvPcb is used to create this association and a file named `*.cmp` is produced. CvPcb also updates the netlist file using this information.

CvPcb can also output a "stuff file" `*.stf` which can be back annotated into the schematic file as the F2 field for each component, saving the task of re-assigning footprints in each schematic edit pass. In Eeschema copying a component will also copy the footprint assignment and set the reference designator as unassigned for later auto-incremental annotation.

Pcbnew reads the modified netlist file `.net` and, if it exists, the `.cmp` file. In the event of a footprint being changed directly in Pcbnew the `.cmp` file is automatically updated avoiding the requirement to run CvPcb again.

Refer to the figure of "Getting Started in KiCad" manual in the section *KiCad Workflow* that illustrates the work-flow of KiCad and how intermediate files are obtained and used by the different software tools that comprise KiCad.

4.2 Procedure for creating a printed circuit board

After having created your schematic in Eeschema:

- Generate the netlist using Eeschema.
- Assign each component in your netlist file to the corresponding land pattern (often called footprint) used on the printed circuit using Cvpcb.
- Launch Pcbnew and read the modified Netlist. This will also read the file with the footprint selections.

Pcbnew will then load automatically all the necessary footprints. Footprints can now be placed manually or automatically on the board and tracks can be routed.

4.3 Procedure for updating a printed circuit board

If the schematic is modified (after a printed circuit board has been generated), the following steps must be repeated:

- Generate a new netlist file using Eeschema.
- If the changes to the schematic involve new components, the corresponding footprints must be assigned using Cvpcb.
- Launch Pcbnew and re-read the modified netlist (this will also re-read the file with the footprint selections).

Pcbnew will then load automatically any new footprints, add the new connections and remove redundant connections. This process is called forward annotation and is a very common procedure when a PCB is made and updated.

4.4 Reading netlist file - loading footprints

4.4.1 Dialog box

Accessible from the icon

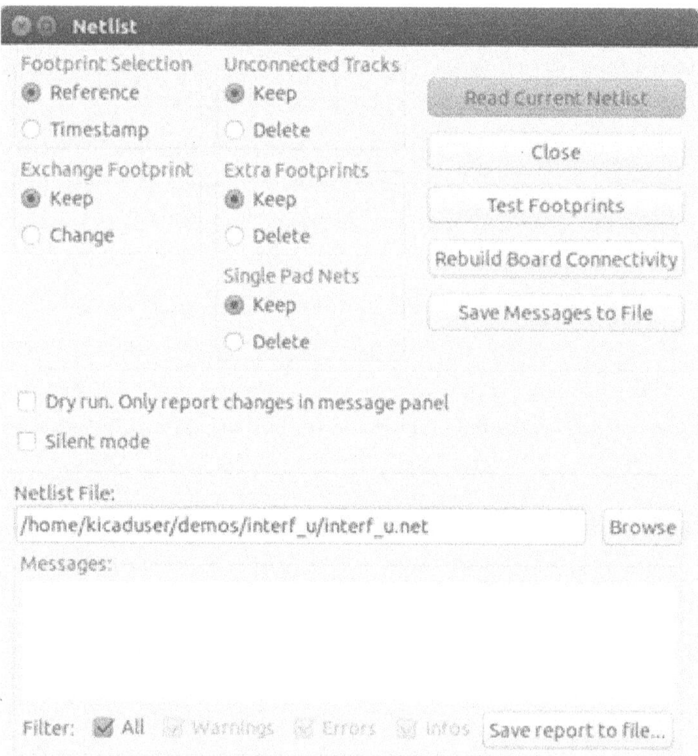

4.4.2 Available options

Footprint Selection	Components and corresponding footprints on board link: normal link is Reference (normal option Timestamp can be used after reannotation of schematic, if the previous annotation was destroyed (special option)
Exchange Footprint:	If a footprint has changed in the netlist: keep old footprint or change to the new one.
Unconnected Tracks	Keep all existing tracks, or delete erroneous tracks
Extra Footprints	Remove footprints which are on board but not in the netlist. Footprint with attribute "Locked" will not be removed.
Single Pad Nets	Remove single pad nets.

4.4.3 Loading new footprints

With the GAL backend when new footprints are found in the netlist file, they will be loaded, spread out, and be ready for you to place as a group where you would like.

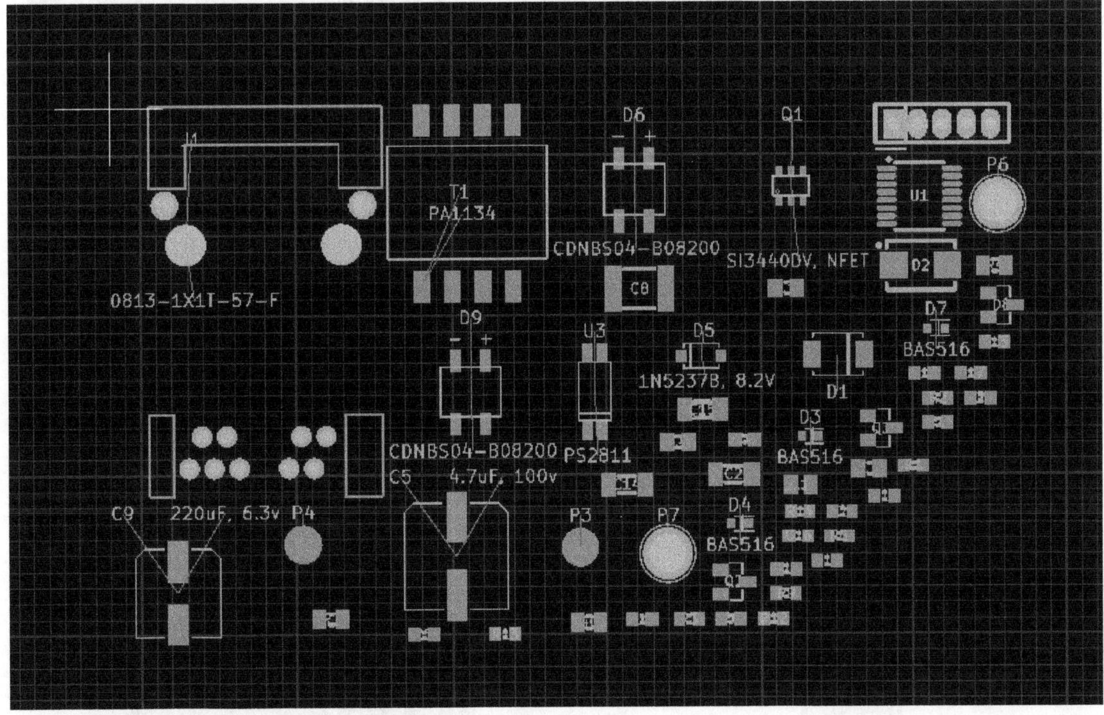

With the legacy backend when new footprints are found in the netlist file, they will be automatically loaded and placed at coordinate (0,0).

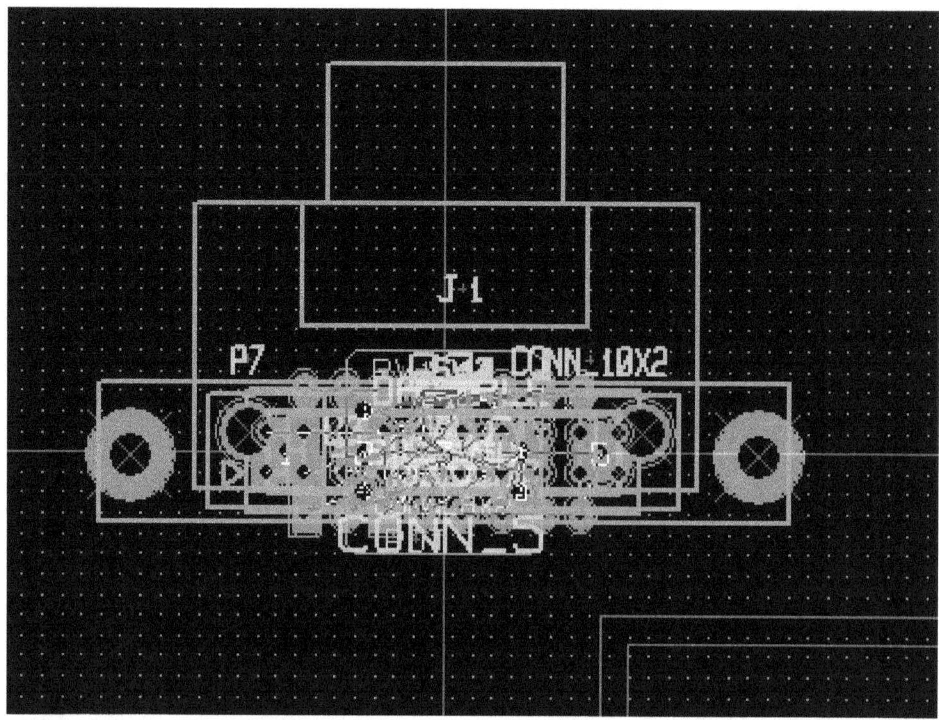

New footprints can be moved and arranged one by one. A better way is to automatically move (unstack) them:

Activate footprint mode ()

Move the mouse cursor to a suitable (free of component) area, and click on the right button:

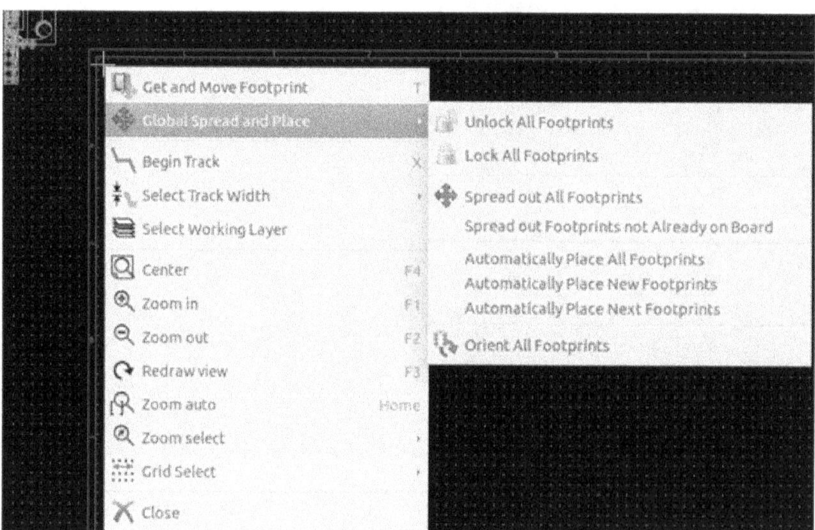

- Automatically Place New Footprints, if there is already a board with existing footprints.
- Automatically Place All Footprints, for the first time (when creating a board).

The following screenshot shows the results.

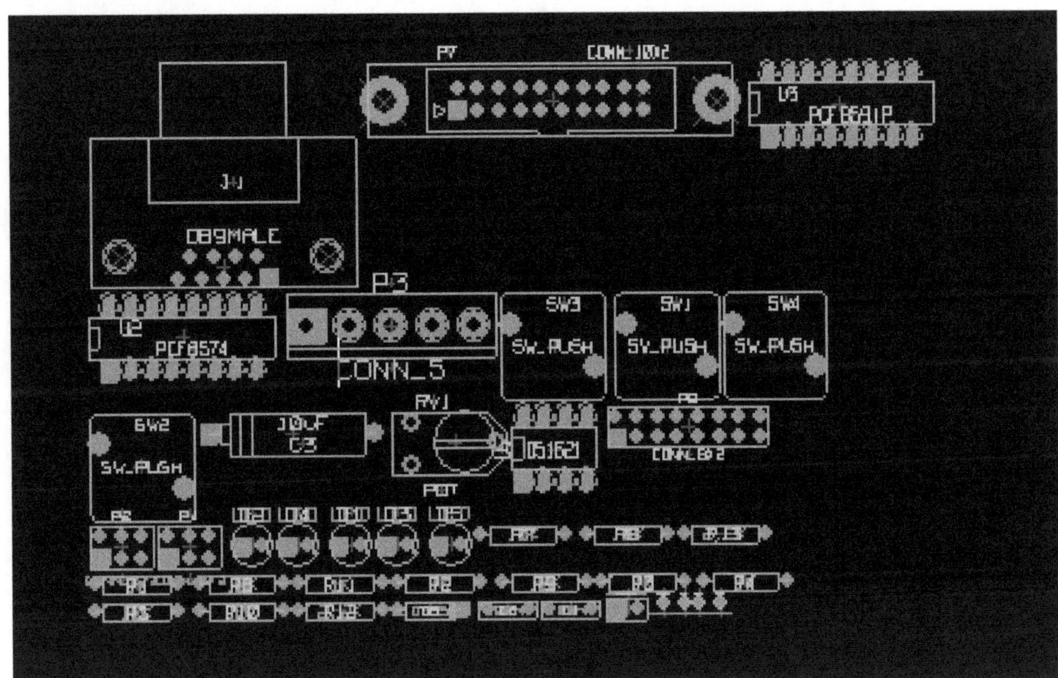

Chapter 5

Layers

5.1 Introduction

Pcbnew can work with 50 different layers:

- Between 1 and 32 copper layers for routing tracks.
- 14 fixed-purpose technical layers:
  - 12 paired layers (Front/Back): **Adhesive**, **Solder Paste**, **Silk Screen**, **Solder Mask**, **Courtyard**, **Fabrication**
  - 2 standalone layers: **Edge Cuts**, **Margin**
- 4 auxiliary layers that you can use any way you want: **Comments**, **E.C.O. 1**, **E.C.O. 2**, **Drawings**

5.2 Setting up layers

To open the **Layers Setup** from the menu bar, select **Design Rules → Layers Setup**.

The number of copper layers, their names, and their function are configured there. Unused technical layers can be disabled.

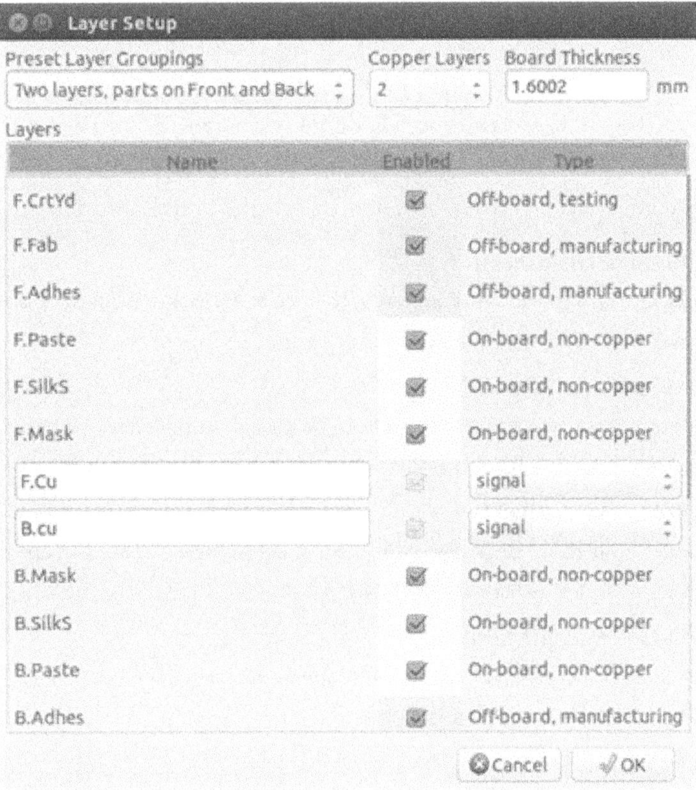

5.3 Layer Description

5.3.1 Copper Layers

Copper layers are the usual working layers used to place and re-arrange tracks. Layer numbers start from 0 (the first copper layer, on Front) and end at 31 (Back). Since components cannot be placed in **inner layers** (number 1 to 30), only layers number 0 and 31 are **component layer**.

The name of any copper layer is editable. Copper layers have a function attribute that is useful when using the external router *Freerouter*. Example of default layer names are **F.Cu** and **In0** for layer number 0.

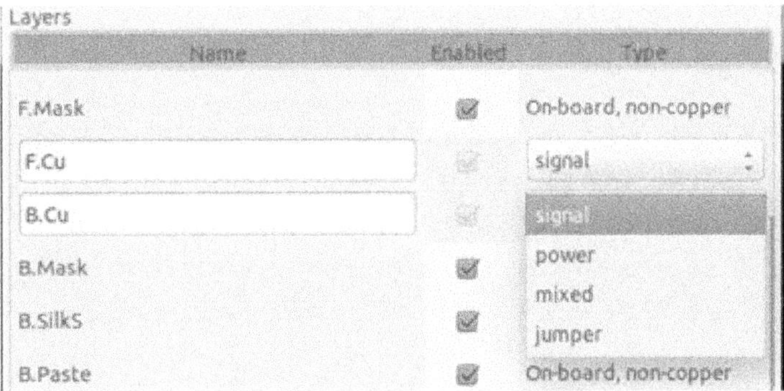

5.3.2 Paired Technical Layers

12 technical layers come in pairs: one for the front, one for the back. You can recognize them with the "F." or "B." prefix in their names. The elements making up a footprint (pad, drawing, text) of one of these layers are automatically mirrored and moved to the complementary layer when the footprint is flipped.

The paired technical layers are:

Adhesive (F.Adhes and B.Adhes)
These are used in the application of adhesive to stick SMD components to the circuit board, generally before wave soldering.

Solder Paste (F.Paste and B.Paste)
Used to produce a mask to allow solder paste to be placed on the pads of surface mount components, generally before reflow soldering. Usually only surface mount pads occupy these layers.

Silk Screen (F.SilkS and B.SilkS)
They are the layers where the drawings of the components appear. That's where you draw things like component polarity, first pin indicator, reference for mounting, …

Solder Mask (F.Mask and B.Mask)
These define the solder masks. All pads should appear on one of these layers (SMT) or both (for through hole) to prevent the varnish from covering the pads.

Courtyard (F.CrtYd and B.CrtYd)
Used to show how much space a component physically takes on the PCB.

Fabrication (F.Fab and B.Fab)
Footprint assembly (?).

5.3.3 Independant Technical Layers

Edge.Cuts
This layer is reserved for the drawing of circuit board outline. Any element (graphic, texts…) placed on this layer appears on all the other layers. Use this layer only to draw board outlines.

Margin
Board's edge setback outline (?).

5.3.4 Layers for general use

These layers are for any use. They can be used for text such as instructions for assembly or wiring, or construction drawings, to be used to create a file for assembly or machining. Their names are:

- Comments
- E.C.O. 1
- E.C.O. 2
- Drawings

5.4 Selection of the active layer

The selection of the active working layer can be done in several ways:

- Using the right toolbar (Layer manager).
- Using the upper toolbar.
- With the pop-up window (activated with the right mouse button).
- Using the + and - keys (works on copper layers only).
- By hot keys.

5.4.1 Selection using the layer manager

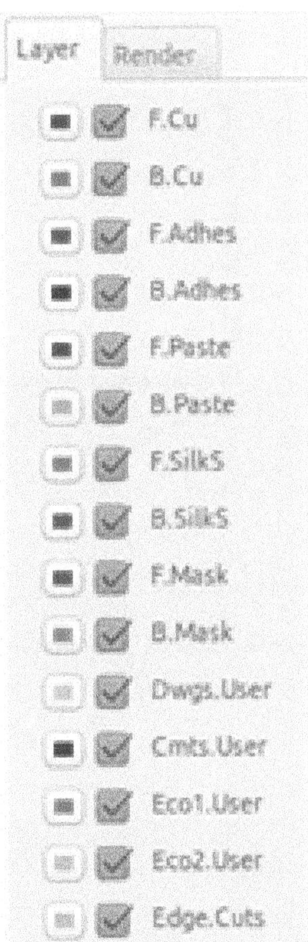

5.4.2 Selection using the upper toolbar

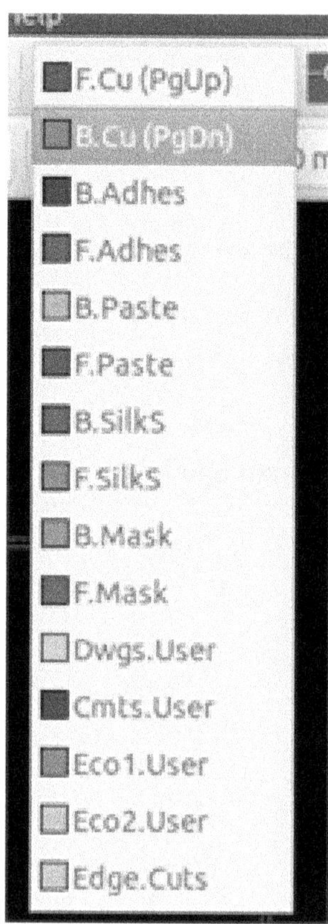

This directly selects the working layer.

Hot keys to select the working layer are displayed.

5.4.3 Selection using the pop-up window

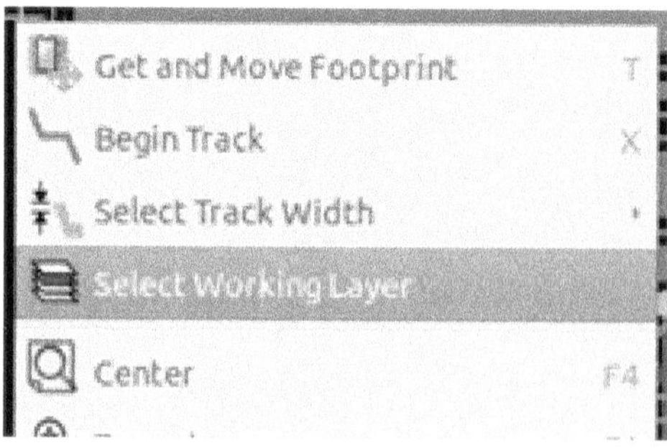

The Pop-up window opens a menu window which provides a choice for the working layer.

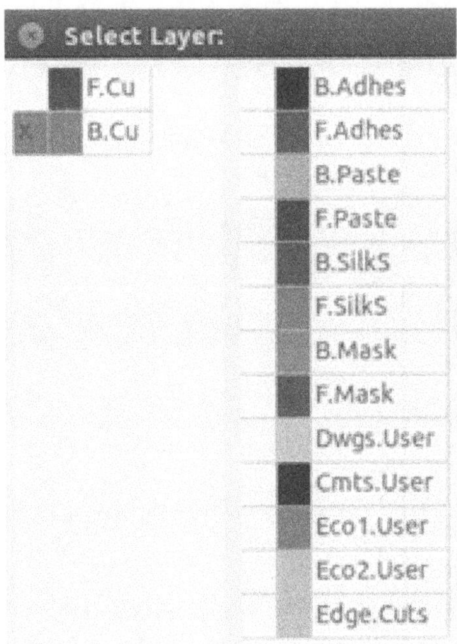

5.5 Selection of the Layers for Vias

If the **Add Tracks and Vias** icon is selected on the right hand toolbar, the Pop-Up window provides the option to change the layer pair used for vias:

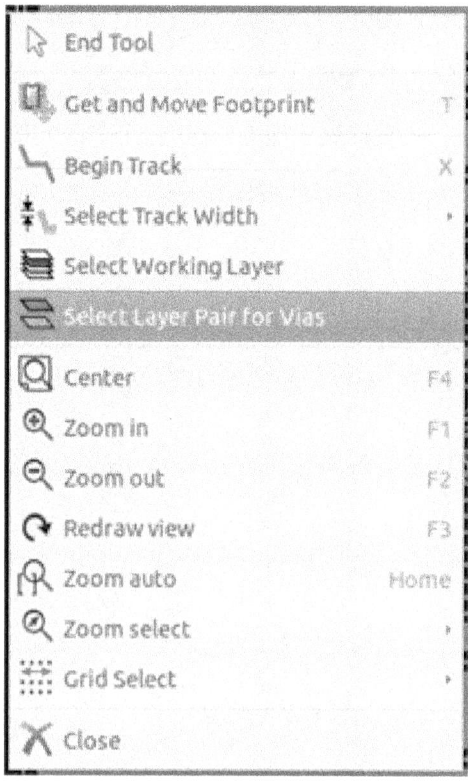

This selection opens a menu window which provides choice of the layers used for vias.

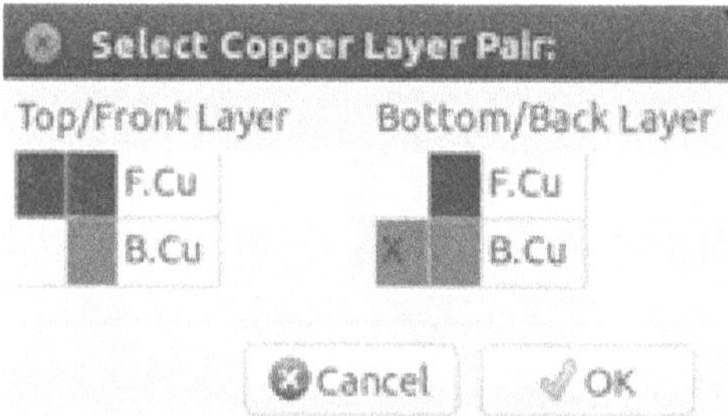

When a via is placed the working (active) layer is automatically switched to the alternate layer of the layer pair used for the vias.

One can also switch to another active layer by hot keys, and if a track is in progress, a via will be inserted.

5.6 Using the high-contrast mode

This mode is entered when the tool (in the left toolbar) is activated: 

When using this mode, the active layer is displayed like in the normal mode, but all others layers are displayed in gray color.

There are two useful cases:

5.6.1 Copper layers in high-contrast mode

When a board uses more than four layers, this option allows the active copper layer to be seen more easily:

Normal mode (back side copper layer active):

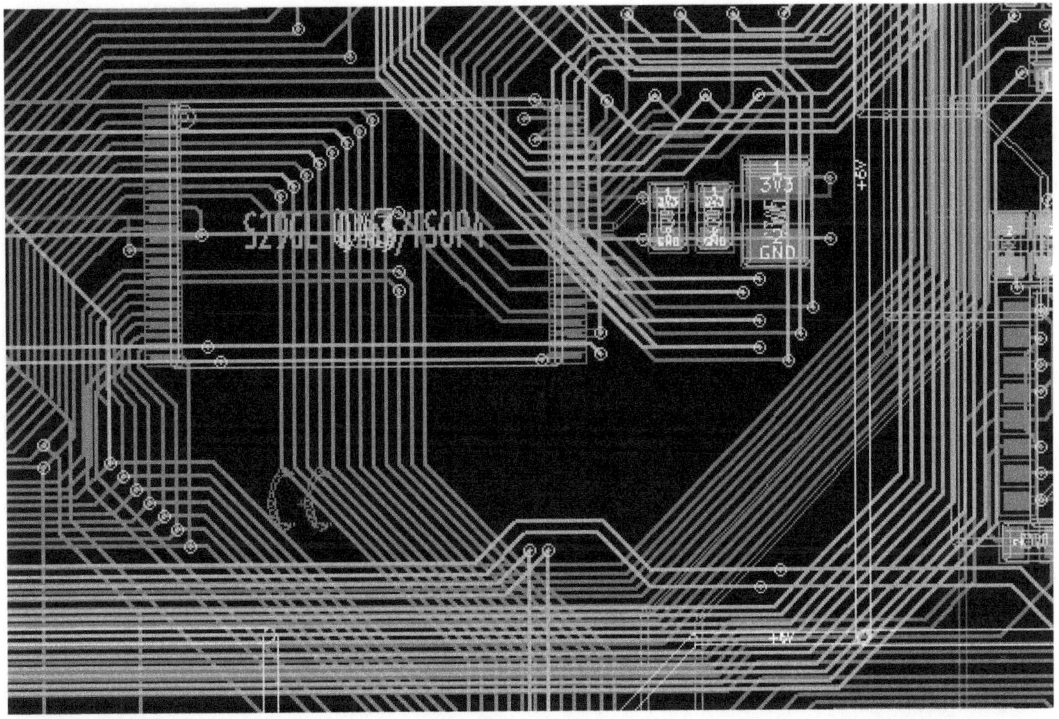

High-contrast mode (back side copper layer active):

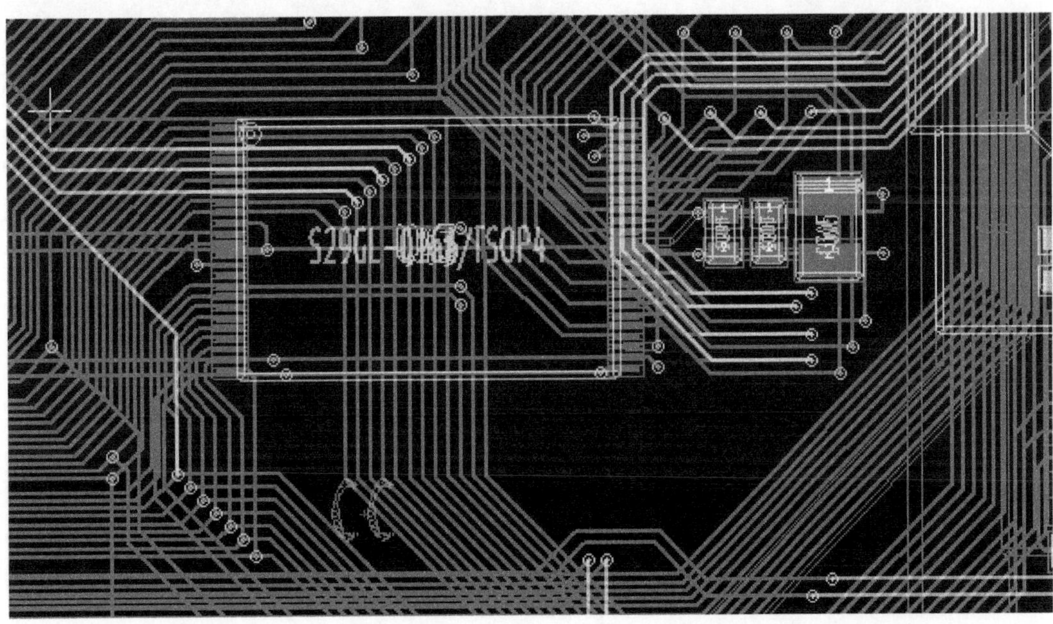

5.6.2 Technical layers

The other case is when it is necessary to examine solder paste layers and solder mask layers which are usually not displayed.

Masks on pads are displayed if this mode is active.

Normal mode (front side solder mask layer active):

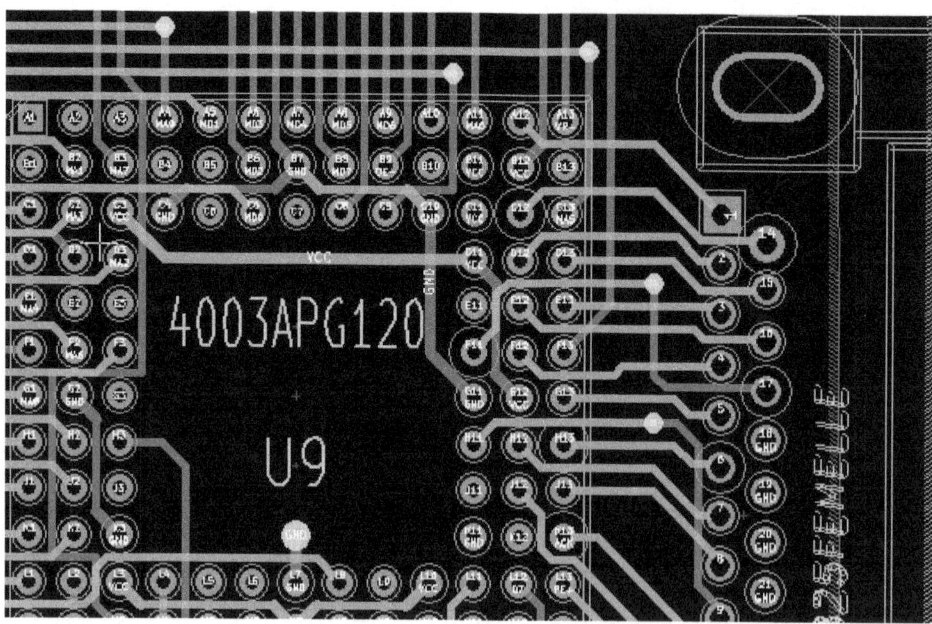

High-contrast mode (front side solder mask layer active):

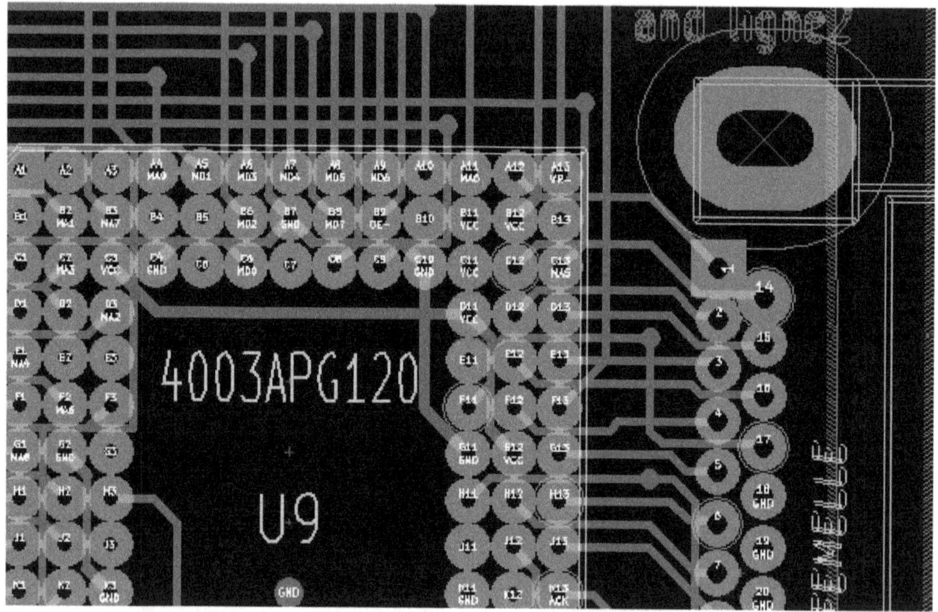

Chapter 6

Create and modify a board

6.1 Creating a board

6.1.1 Drawing the board outline

It is usually a good idea to define the outline of the board first. The outline is drawn as a sequence of line segments. Select *Edge.Cuts* as the active layer and use the *Add graphic line or polygon* tool to trace the edge, clicking at the position of each vertex and double-clicking to finish the outline. Boards usually have very precise dimensions, so it may be necessary to use the displayed cursor coordinates while tracing the outline. Remember that the relative coordinates can be zeroed at any time using the space bar, and that the display units can also be toggled using *Ctrl-U*. Relative coordinates enable very precise dimensions to be drawn. It is possible to draw a circular (or arc) outline:

1. Select the *Add graphic circle* or *Add graphic arc* tool
2. Click to fix the circle centre
3. Adjust the radius by moving the mouse
4. Finish by clicking again.

Note

The width of the outline can be adjusted in the Parameters menu (recommended width = 150 in 1/10 mils) or via the Options, but this will not be visible unless the graphics are displayed in other than outline mode.

The resulting outline might look something like this:

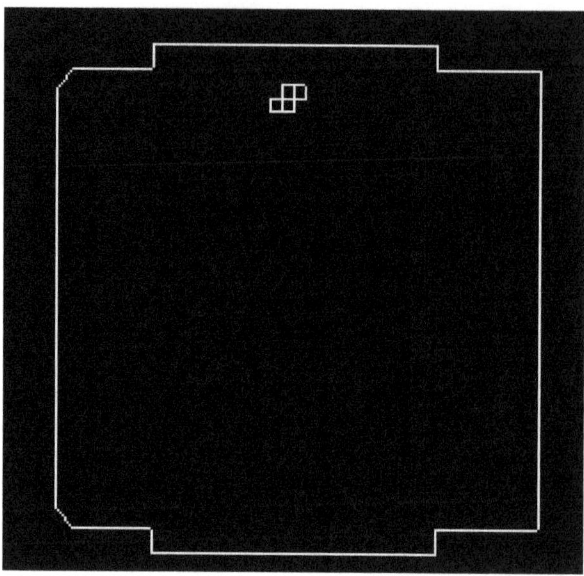

6.1.2 Using a DXF drawing for the board outline

As an alternative to drawing the board outline in Pcbnew directly, an outline can also be imported from a DXF drawing.

Using this feature allows for much more complex board shapes than is possible with the Pcbnew drawing capabilities.

For example a mechanical CAD package can be used to define a board shape that fits a particular enclosure.

6.1.2.1 Preparing the DXF drawing for import into KiCad

The **DXF** import capability in KiCad does not support DXF features like **POLYLINES** and **ELLIPSIS** and DXF files that use these features require a few conversion steps to prepare them for import.

A software package like LibreCAD can be used for this conversion.

As a first step, any **POLYLINES** need to be split (Exploded) into their original simpler shapes. In LibreCAD use the following steps:

1. Open a copy of the DXF file.
2. Select the board shape (selected shapes are shown with dashed lines).
3. In the **Modify** menu, select **Explode**.
4. Press ENTER.

As a next step, complex curves like **ELLIPSIS** need to be broken up in small line segments that *approximate* the required shape. This happens automatically when the DXF file is exported or saved in the older **DXF R12** file format (as the R12 format does not support complex curve shapes, CAD applications convert these shapes to line segements. Some CAD applications allow configuration of the number or the length of the line segments used). In LibreCAD the segment length it generally small enough for use in board shapes.

In LibreCAD, use the following steps to export to the **DXF R12** file format:

1. In the **File** menu, use **Save As**…
2. In the **Save Drawing As** dialog, there is a **Save as type:** selection near the bottom of the dialog. Select the option **Drawing Exchange DXF R12**.
3. Optionally enter a file name in the **File name:** field.
4. Click **Save**

Your DXF file is now ready for import into KiCad.

6.1.2.2 Importing the DXF file into KiCad

The following steps describe the import of the prepared DXF file as a board shape into KiCad. Note that the import bahaviour is slightly different depending on which *canvas* is used.

Using the "default" canvas mode:

1. In the **File** menu, select **Import** and then the **DXF File** option.
2. In the **Import DXF File** dialog use *Browse* to select the prepared DXF file to be imported.
3. In the *Place DXF origin (0,0) point:* option, select the placement of DXF origin relative to the board coordinates (the KiCad board has (0,0) in the top left corner). For the *User defined position* enter the coordinates in the *X Position* and *Y Position* fields.
4. In the *Layer* selection, select the board layer for the import. **Edge.Cuts** is needed for the board outline.
5. Click *OK*.

Using the "OpenGL" or "Cairo" canvas modes:

1. In the **File** menu, select **Import** and then the **DXF File** option.
2. In the **Import DXF File** dialog use *Browse* to select the prepared DXF file to be imported.
3. The *Place DXF origin (0,0) point:* option setting is ignored in this mode.
4. In the *Layer* selection, select the board layer for the import. **Edge.Cuts** is needed for the board outline.
5. Click *OK*.
6. The shape is now attached to your cursor and it can be moved around the board area.
7. Click to *drop* the shape on the board.

6.1.2.3 Example imported DXF shape

Here is an example of a DXF import with a board that had several elliptical segments approximated by a number of short line segments:

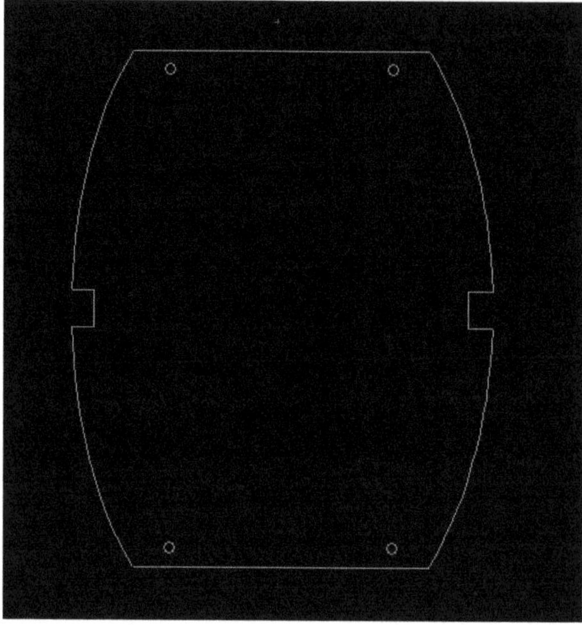

6.1.3 Reading the netlist generated from the schematic

Activate the NET icon to display the netlist dialog window:

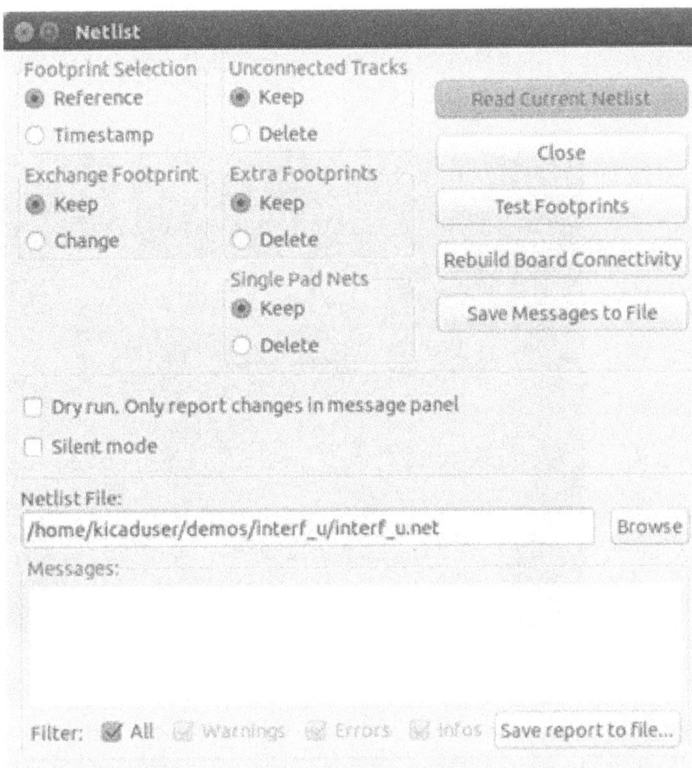

If the name (path) of the netlist in the window title is incorrect, use the *Select* button to browse to the desired netlist. Then *Read* the netlist. Any footprints not already loaded will appear, superimposed one upon another (we shall see below how to move them automatically).

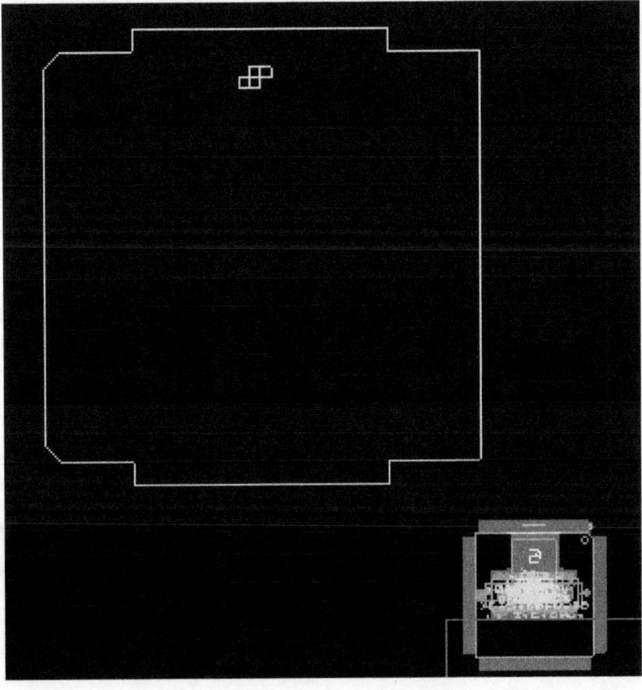

If none of the footprints have been placed, all of the footprints will appear on the board in the same place, making them difficult to recognize. It is possible to arrange them automatically (using the command *Global Spread and Place* accessed via the right mouse button). Here is the result of such automatic arrangement:

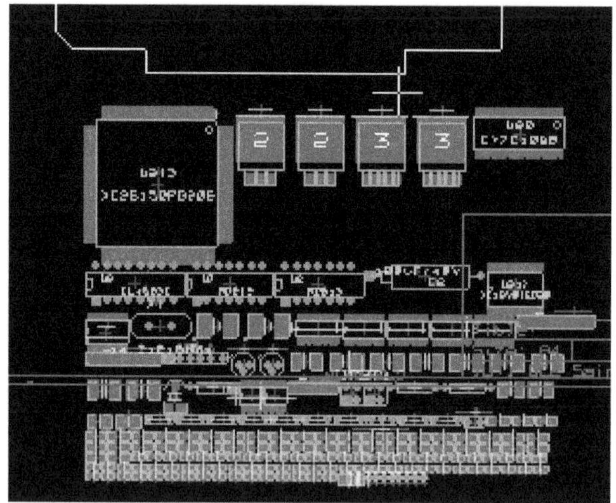

Note

If a board is modified by replacing an existing footprint with a new one (for example changing a 1/8W resistance to 1/2W) in CvPcb, it will be necessary to delete the existing component before Pcbnew will load the replacement footprint. However, if a footprint is to be replaced by an existing footprint, this is easier to do using the footprint dialog accessed by clicking the right mouse button over the footprint in question.

6.2 Correcting a board

It is very often necessary to correct a board following a corresponding change in the schematic.

6.2.1 Steps to follow

1. Create a new netlist from the modified schematic.
2. If new components have been added, link these to their corresponding footprint in CvPcb.
3. Read the new netlist in Pcbnew.

6.2.2 Deleting incorrect tracks

Pcbnew is able to automatically delete tracks that have become incorrect as a result of modifications. To do this, check the *Delete* option in the *Unconnected Tracks* box of the netlist dialog:

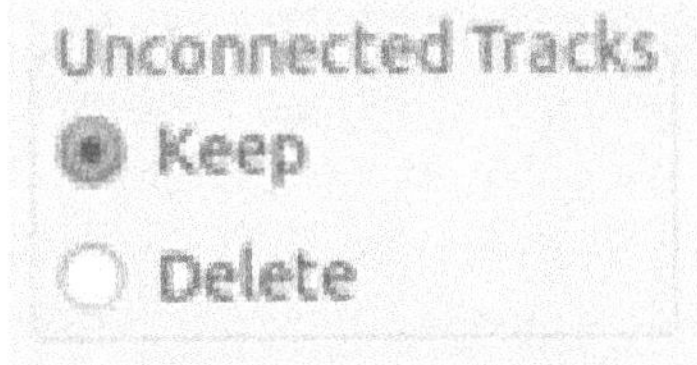

However, it is often quicker to modify such tracks by hand (the DRC function allows their identification).

6.2.3 Deleted components

Pcbnew can delete footprint corresponding to components that have been removed from the schematic. This is optional.

This is necessary because there are often footprints (holes for fixation screws, for instance) that are added to the PCB that never appear in the schematic.

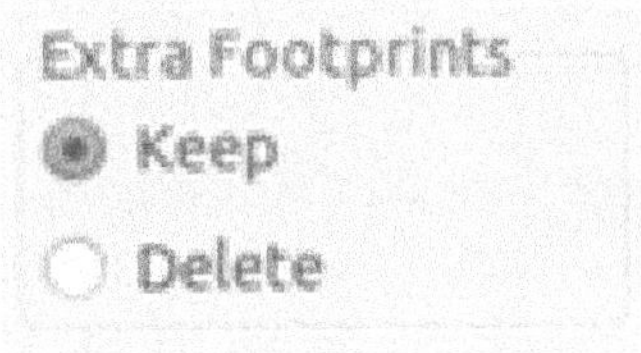

If the "Extra Footprints" option is checked, a footprint corresponding to a component not found in the netlist will be deleted, unless they have the option "Locked" active. It is a good idea to activate this option for "mechanical" footprints:

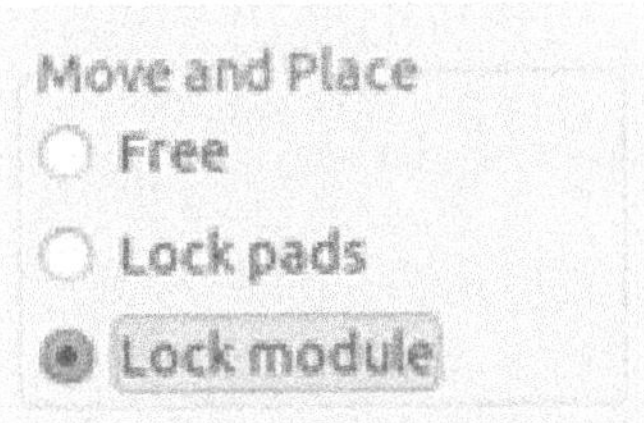

6.2.4 Modified footprints

If a footprint is modified in the netlist (using CvPcb), but the footprint has already been placed, it will not be modified by Pcbnew, unless the corresponding option of the *Exchange Footprint* box of the netlist dialog is checked:

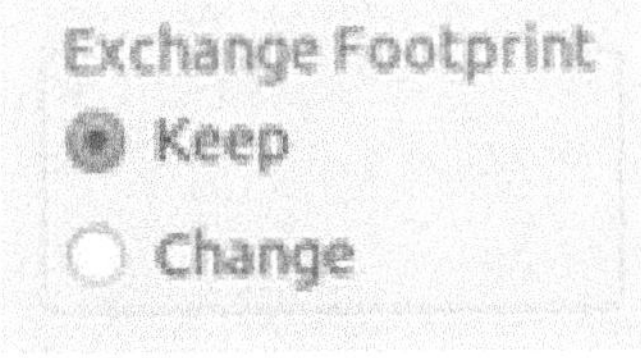

Changing a footprint (replacing a resistor with one of a different size, for instance) can be effected directly by editing the footprint.

6.2.5 Advanced options - selection using time stamps

Sometimes the notation of the schematic is changed, without any material changes in the circuit (this would concern the references - like R5, U4···).The PCB is therefore unchanged (except possibly for the silkscreen markings). Nevertheless, internally, components and footprints are represented by their reference. In this situation, the *Timestamp* option of the netlist dialog may be selected before re-reading the netlist:

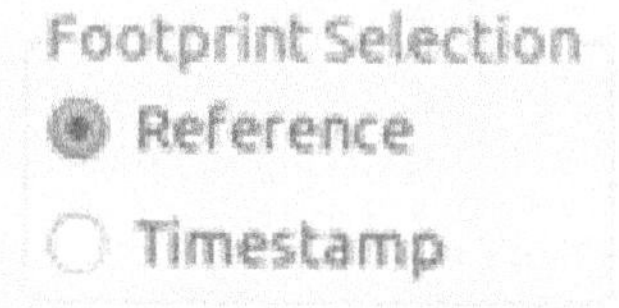

With this option, Pcbnew no longer identifies footprints by their reference, but by their time stamp instead. The time stamp is automatically generated by Eeschema (it is the time and date when the component was placed in the schematic).

Warning

Great care should be exercised when using this option (save the file first!). This is because the technique is complicated in the case of components containing multiple parts (e.g. a 7400 has 4 parts and one case). In this situation, the time stamp is not uniquely defined (for the 7400 there would be up to four - one for each part). Nevertheless, the time stamp option usually resolves re-annotation problems.

6.3 Direct exchange for footprints already placed on board

Changing a footprint (or some identical footprints) to another footprint is very useful, and is very easy:

1. Click on a footprint to open the Edit dialog box.
2. Activate Change Footprints.

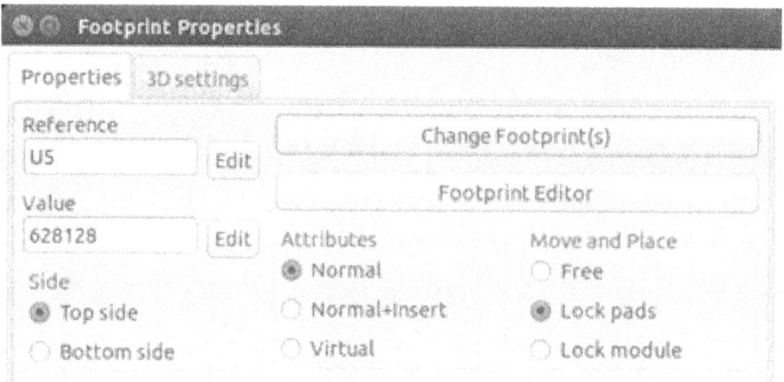

Options for Change Footprint(s):

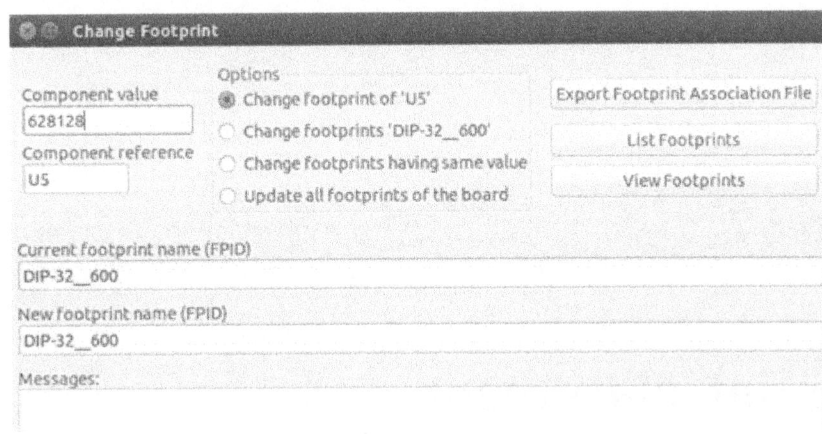

One must choose a new footprint name and use:

- **Change footprint of *xx*** for the current footprint
- **Change footprints *yy*** for all footprints like the current footprint.
- **Change footprints having same value** for all footprints like the current footprint, restricted to components which have the same value.
- **Update all footprints of the board** for reloading of all footprints on board.

Chapter 7

Footprint placement

7.1 Assisted placement

Whilst moving footprints the footprint ratsnest (the net connections) can be displayed to assist the placement. To enable this the icon of the left toolbar must be activated.

7.2 Manual placement

Select the footprint with the right mouse button then choose the Move command from the menu. Move the footprint to the required position and place it with the left mouse button. If required the selected footprint can also be rotated, inverted or edited. Select Cancel from the menu (or press the Esc key) to abort.

Here you can see the display of the footprint ratsnest during a move:

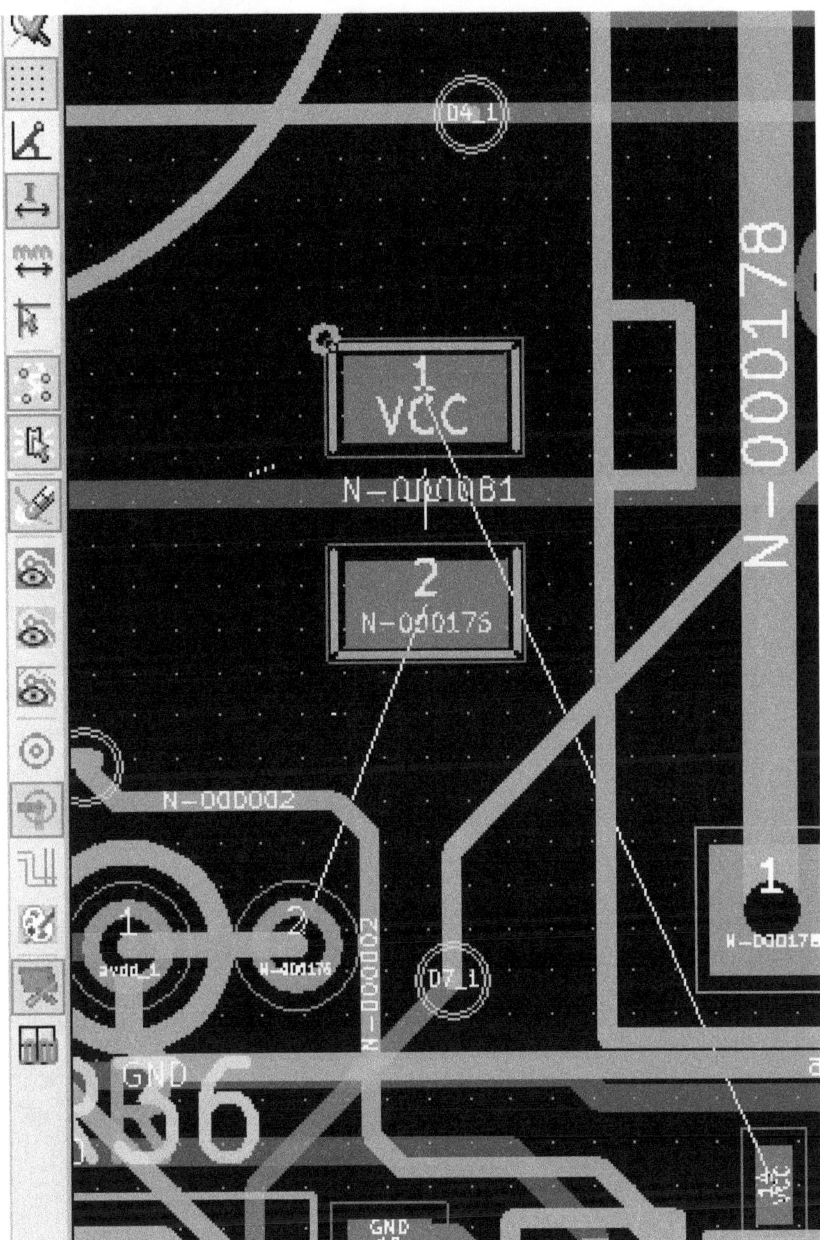

The circuit once all the footprints are placed may be as shown:

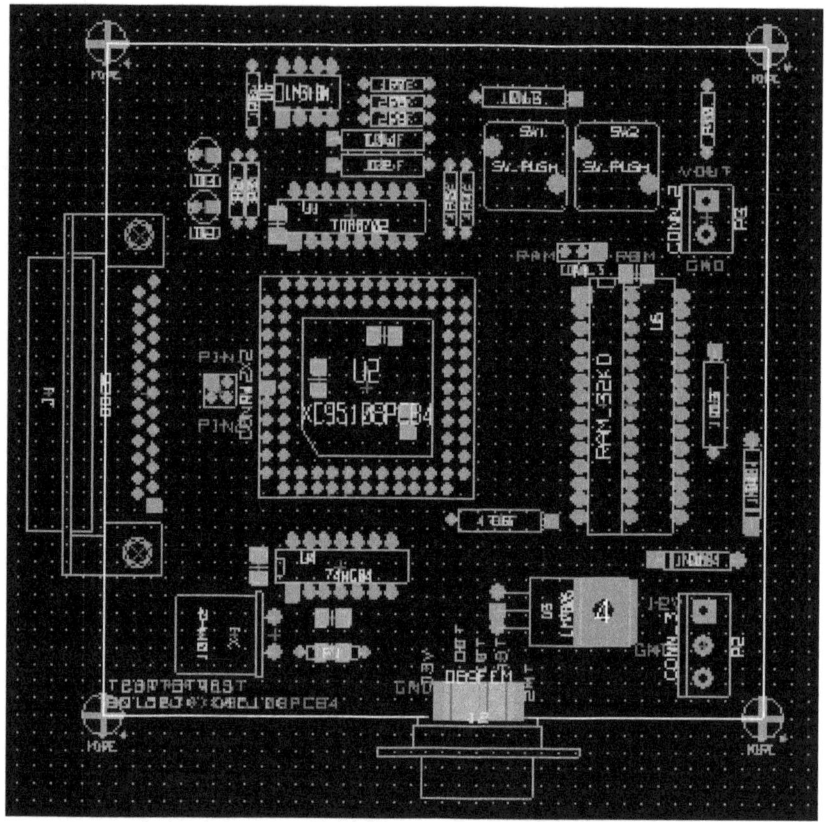

7.3 Automatic Footprint Distribution

Generally speaking, footprints can only be moved if they have not been "Fixed". This attribute can be turned on and off from the pop-up window (click right mouse button over footprint) whilst in Footprint Mode, or through the Edit Footprint Menu.

As stated in the last chapter, new footprints loaded during the reading of the netlist appear piled up at a single location on the board. Pcbnew allows an automatic distribution of the footprints to make manual selection and placement easier.

- Select the option "Footprint Mode" (Icon on the upper toolbar).
- The pop-up window activated by the right mouse button becomes:

If there is a footprint under the cursor:

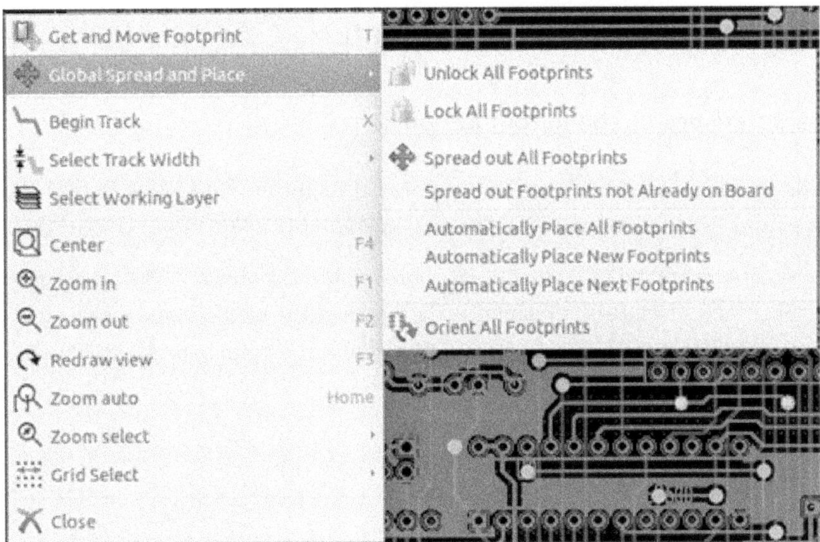

If there is nothing under the cursor:

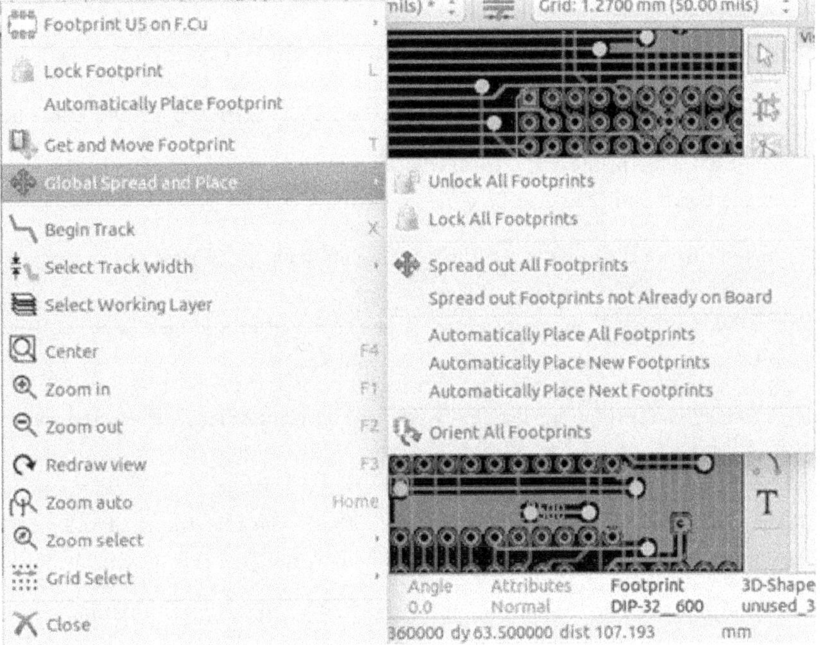

In both cases the following commands are available:

- **Spread out All Footprints** allows the automatic distribution of all the footprints not Fixed. This is generally used after the first reading of a netlist.
- **Spread out Footprints not Already on Board** allows the automatic distribution of the footprints which have not been placed already within the PCB outline. This command requires that an outline of the board has been drawn to determine which footprints can be automatically distributed.

7.4 Automatic placement of footprints

7.4.1 Characteristics of the automatic placer

The automatic placement feature allows the placement of footprints onto the 2 faces of the circuit board (however switching a footprint onto the copper layer is not automatic).

It also seeks the best orientation (0, 90, -90, 180 degrees) of the footprint. The placement is made according to an optimization algorithm, which seeks to minimize the length of the ratsnest, and which seeks to create space between the larger footprints with many pads. The order of placement is optimized to initially place these larger footprints with many pads.

7.4.2 Preparation

Pcbnew can thus place the footprints automatically, however it is necessary to guide this placement, because no software can guess what the user wants to achieve.

Before an automatic placement is carried out one must:

- Create the outline of the board (It can be complex, but it must be closed if the form is not rectangular).
- Manually place the components whose positions are imposed (Connectors, clamp holes, etc).
- Similarly, certain SMD footprints and critical components (large footprints for example) must be on a specific side or position on the board and this must be done manually.
- Having completed any manual placement these footprints must be "Fixed" to prevent them being moved. With the Footprint Mode icon selected right click on the footprint and pick "Fix Footprint" on the Pop-up menu. This can also be done through the Edit/Footprint Pop-up menu.
- Automatic placement can then be carried out. With the Footprint Mode icon selected, right click and select Glob(al) Move and Place - then Autoplace All Footprints.

During automatic placement, if required, Pcbnew can optimize the orientation of the footprints. However rotation will only be attempted if this has been authorized for the footprint (see Edit Footprint Options).

Usually resistors and non-polarized capacitors are authorized for 180 degrees rotation. Some footprints (small transistors for example) can be authorized for +/- 90 and 180 degrees rotation.

For each footprint one slider authorizes 90 degree Rot(ation) and a second slider authorizes 180 degree Rot(ation). A setting of 0 prevents rotation, a setting of 10 authorizes it, and an intermediate value indicates a preference for/against rotation.

The rotation authorization can be done by editing the footprint once it is placed on the board. However it is preferable to set the required options to the footprint in the library as these settings will then be inherited each time the footprint is used.

7.4.3 Interactive auto-placement

It may be necessary during automatic placement to stop (press Esc key) and manually re-position a footprint. Using the command Autoplace Next Footprint will restart the autoplacement from the point at which it was stopped.

The command Autoplace new footprints allows the automatic placement of the footprints which have not been placed already within the PCB outline. It will not move those within the PCB outline even if they are not "fixed".

The command Autoplace Footprint makes it possible to execute an autoplacement on the footprint pointed to by the mouse, even if its *fixed* attribute is active.

7.4.4 Additional note

Pcbnew automatically determines the possible zone of placement of the footprints by respecting the shape of the board outline, which is not necessarily rectangular (It can be round, or have cutouts, etc).

If the board is not rectangular, the outline must be closed, so that Pcbnew can determine what is inside and what is outside the outline. In the same way, if there are internal cutouts, their outline will have to be closed.

Pcbnew calculates the possible zone of placement of the footprints using the outline of the board, then passes each footprint in turn over this area in order to determine the optimum position at which to place it.

Chapter 8

Setting routing parameters

8.1 Current settings

8.1.1 Accessing the main dialog

The most important parameters are accessed from the following drop-down menu:

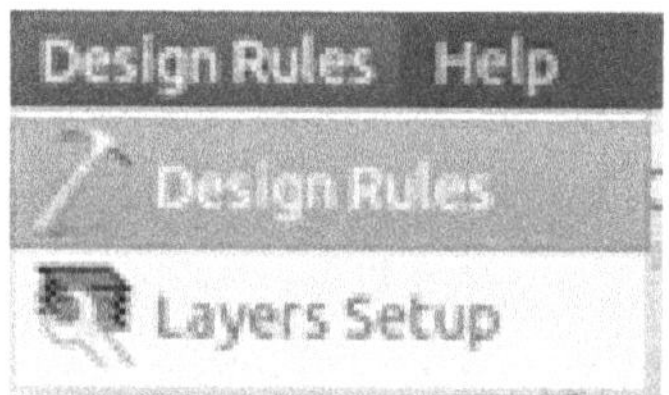

and are set in the Design Rules dialog.

8.1.2 Current settings

Current settings are displayed in the top toolbar.

8.2 General options

The General options menu is available via the top toolbar link Preferences → General dialog.

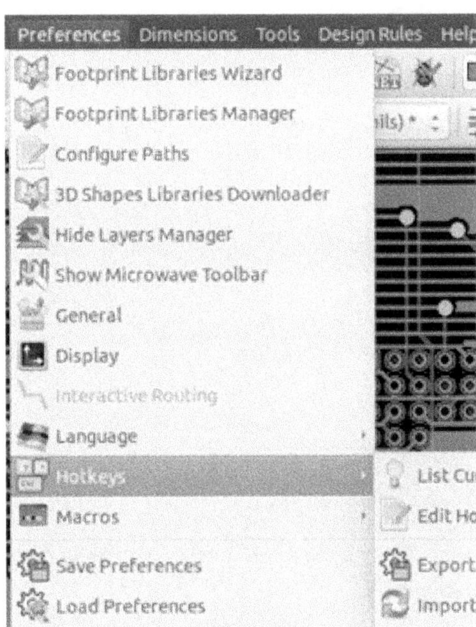

The dialog looks like the following:

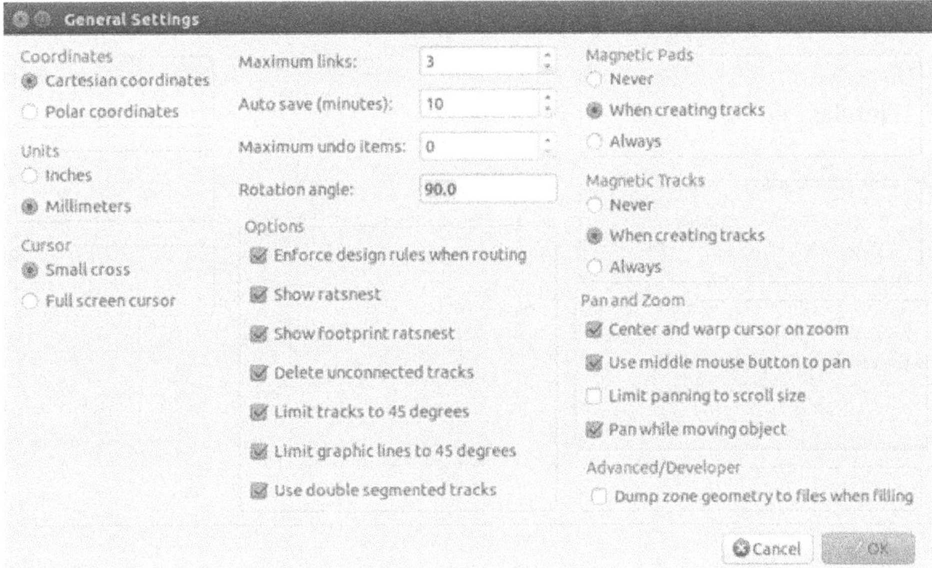

For the creation of tracks the necessary parameters are:

- **Tracks 45 Only**: Directions allowed for track segments are 0, 45 or 90 degrees.
- **Double Segm Track**: When creating tracks, 2 segments will be displayed.
- **Tracks Auto Del**: When recreating tracks, the old one will be automatically deleted if considered redundant.
- **Magnetic Pads**: The graphic cursor becomes a pad, centered in the pad area.
- **Magnetic Tracks**: The graphic cursor becomes the track axis.

8.3 Netclasses

Pcbnew allows you to define different routing parameters for each net. Parameters are defined by a group of nets.

- A group of nets is called a Netclass.
- There is always a netclass called "default".
- Users can add other Netclasses.

A netclass specifies:

- The width of tracks, via diameters and drills.
- The clearance between pads and tracks (or vias).
- When routing, Pcbnew automatically selects the netclass corresponding to the net of the track to create or edit, and therefore the routing parameters.

8.3.1 Setting routing parameters

The choice is made in the menu: Design Rules → Design Rules.

8.3.2 Netclass editor

The Netclass editor allows you to:

- Add or delete Netclasses.
- Set routing parameters values: clearance, track width, via sizes.
- Group nets in netclasses.

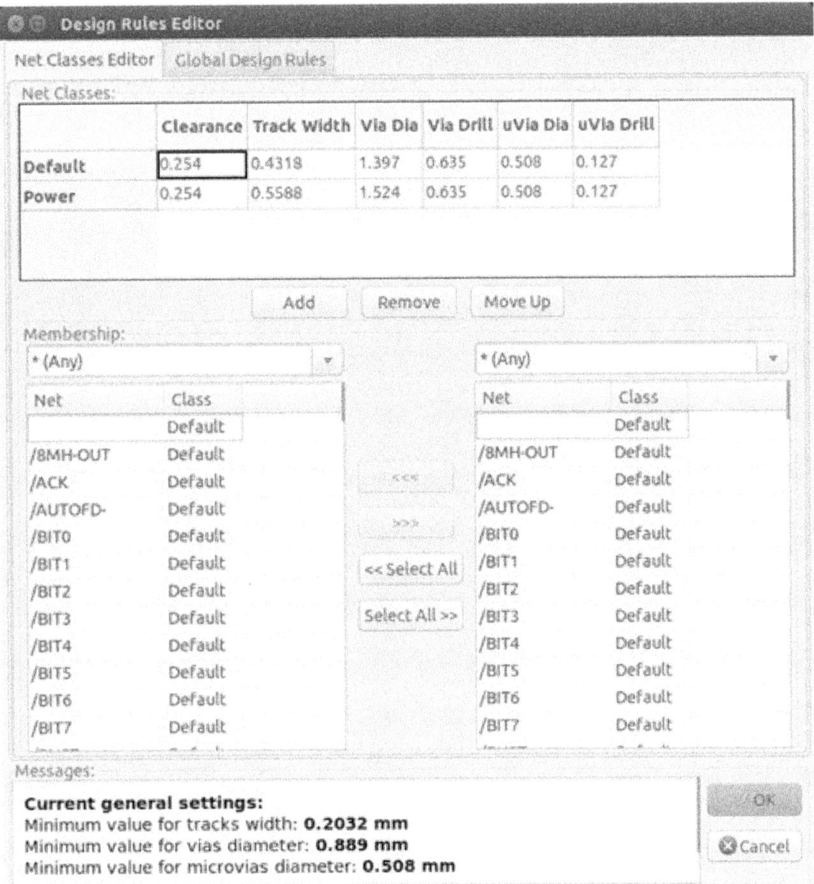

8.3.3 Global Design Rules

The global design rules are:

- Enabling/disabling Blind/buried Vias use.
- Enabling/disabling Micro Vias use.
- Minimum Allowed Values for tracks and vias.

A DRC error is raised when a value smaller than the minimum value specified is encountered. The second dialog panel is:

This dialog also allows to enter a "stock" of tracks and via sizes.

When routing, one can select one of these values to create a track or via, instead of using the netclass' s default value.

Useful in critical cases when a small track segment must have a specific size.

8.3.4 Via parameters

Pcbnew handles 3 types of vias:

- Through vias (usual vias).
- Blind or buried vias.
- Micro Vias, like buried vias but restricted to an external layer to its nearest neighbor. They are intended to connect BGA pins to the nearest inner layer. Their diameter is usually very small and they are drilled by laser.

By default, all vias have the same drill value.

This dialog specifies the smallest acceptable values for via parameters. On a board, a via smaller than specified here generates a DRC error.

8.3.5 Track parameters

Specify the minimum acceptable track width. On a board, a track width smaller than specified here generates a DRC error.

8.3.6 Specific sizes

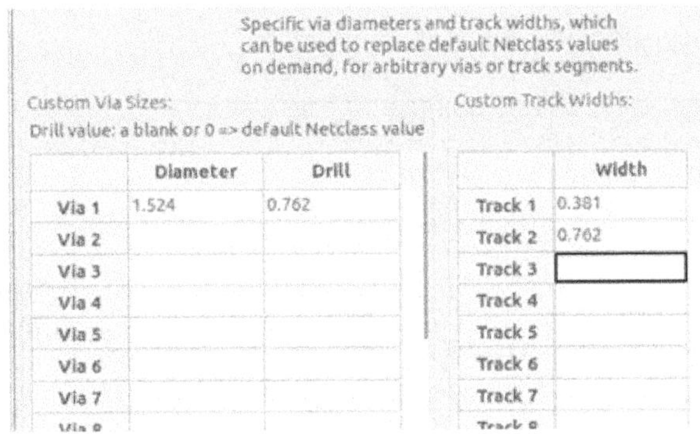

One can enter a set of extra tracks and/or via sizes. While routing a track, these values can be used on demand instead of the values from the current netclass values.

8.4 Examples and typical dimensions

8.4.1 Track width

Use the largest possible value and conform to the minimum sizes given here.

Units	CLASS 1	CLASS 2	CLASS 3	CLASS 4	CLASS 5
mm	0.8	0.5	0.4	0.25	0.15
mils	31	20	16	10	6

8.4.2 Insulation (clearance)

Units	CLASS 1	CLASS 2	CLASS 3	CLASS 4	CLASS 5
mm	0.7	0.5	0.35	0.23	0.15
mils	27	20	14	9	6

Usually, the minimum clearance is very similar to the minimum track width.

8.5 Examples

8.5.1 Rustic

- Clearance: 0.35 mm (0.0138 inches).
- Track width: 0.8 mm (0.0315 inches).
- Pad diameter for ICs and vias: 1.91 mm (0.0750 inches).
- Pad diameter for discrete components: 2.54 mm (0.1 inches).
- Ground track width: 2.54 mm (0.1 inches).

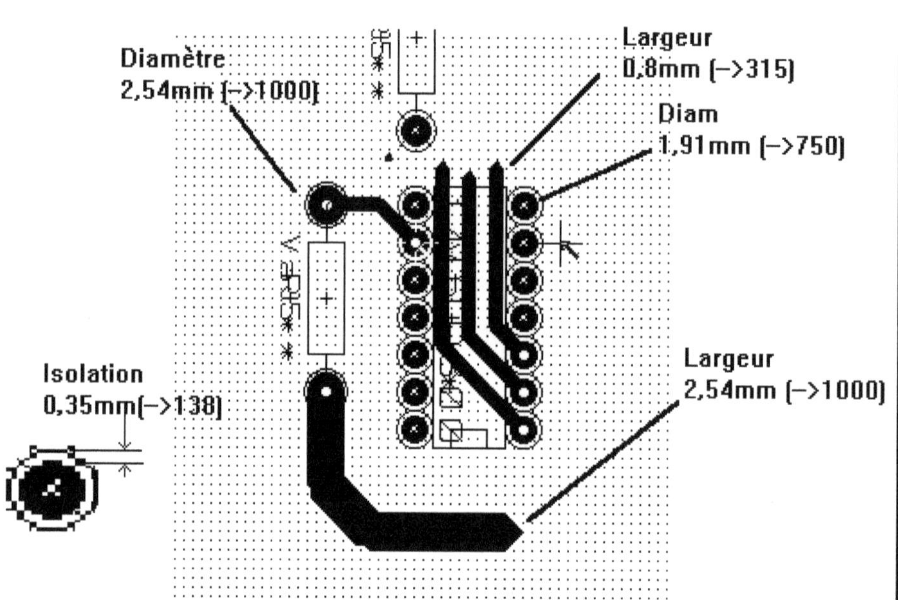

8.5.2 Standard

- Clearance: 0.35mm (0.0138 inches).
- Track width: 0.5mm (0.0127 inches).
- Pad diameter for ICs: make them elongated in order to allow tracks to pass between IC pads and yet have the pads offer a sufficient adhesive surface (1.27 x 2.54 mm -→ 0.05 x 0.1 inches).
- Vias: 1.27 mm (0.0500 inches).

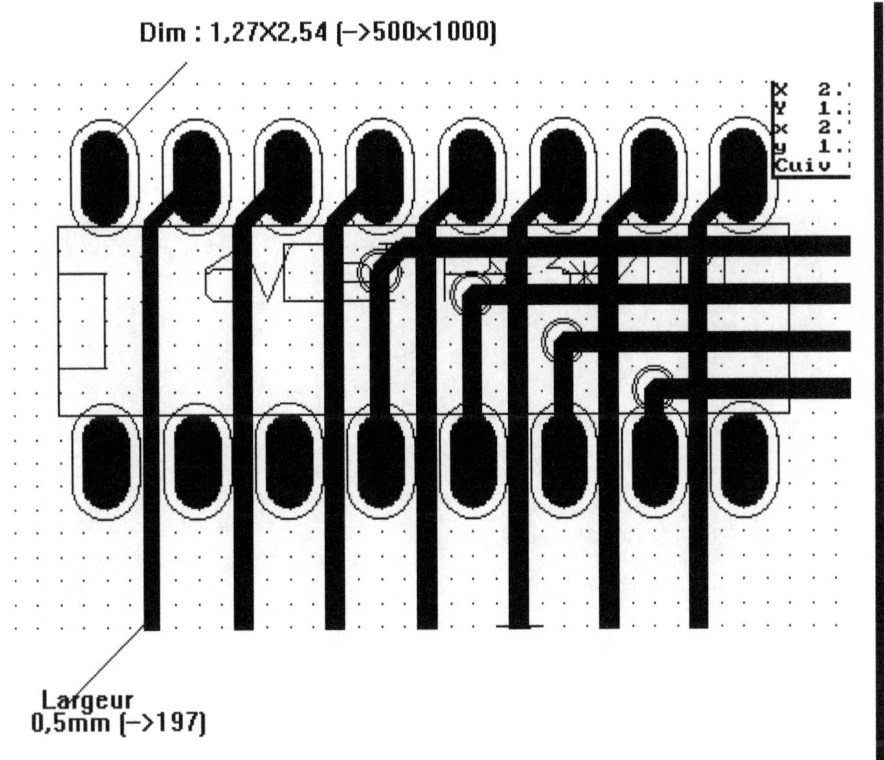

8.6 Manual routing

Manual routing is often recommended, because it is the only method offering control over routing priorities. For example, it is preferable to start by routing power tracks, making them wide and short and keeping analog and digital supplies well separated. Later, sensitive signal tracks should be routed. Amongst other problems, automatic routing often requires many vias. However, automatic routing can offer a useful insight into the positioning of footprints. With experience, you will probably find that the automatic router is useful for quickly routing the *obvious* tracks, but the remaining tracks will best be routed by hand.

8.7 Help when creating tracks

Pcbnew can display the full ratsnest, if the button 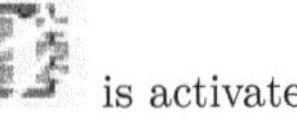 is activated.

The button allows one to highlight a net (click to a pad or an existing track to highlight the corresponding net).

The DRC checks tracks in real time while creating them. One cannot create a track which does not match the DRC rules. It is possible to disable the DRC by clicking on the button. This is, however, not recommended, use it only in specific cases.

8.7.1 Creating tracks

A track can be created by clicking on the button . A new track must start on a pad or on another track, because Pcbnew must know the net used for the new track (in order to match the DRC rules).

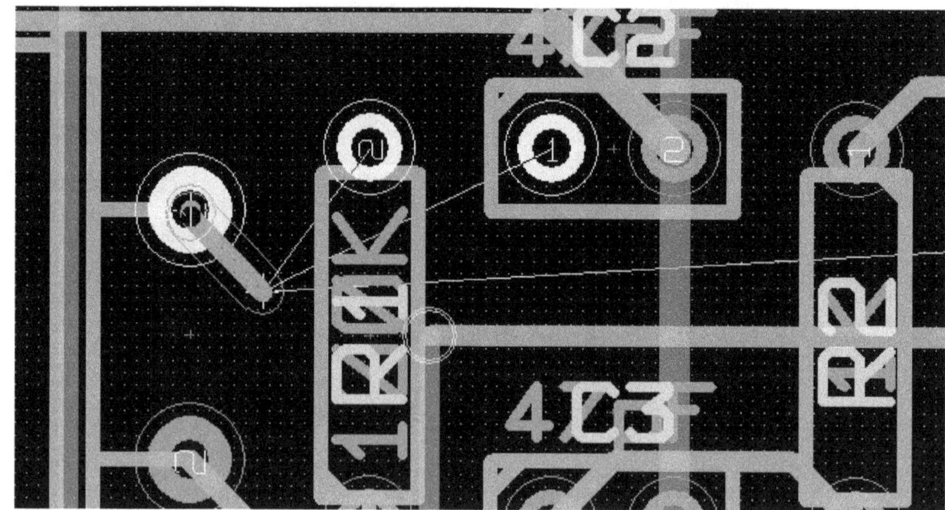

When creating a new track, Pcbnew shows links to nearest unconnected pads, link number set in option "Max. Links" in General Options.

End the track by double-clicking, by the pop-up menu or by its hot key.

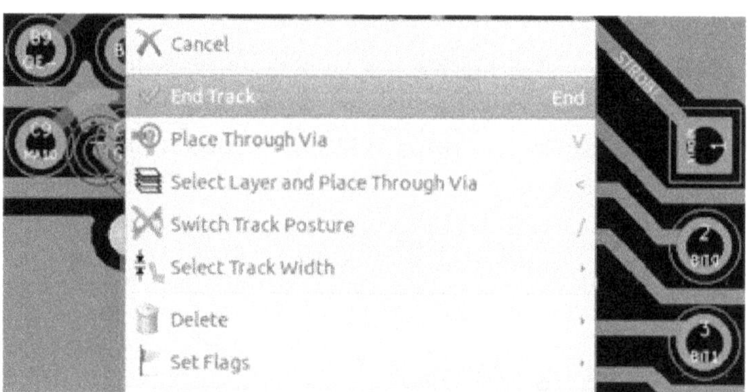

8.7.2 Moving and dragging tracks

When the button is active, the track where the cursor is positioned can be moved with the hotkey *M*. If you want to drag the track you can use the hotkey *G*.

8.7.3 Via Insertion

A via can be inserted only when a track is in progress:

- By the pop-up menu.
- By the hotkey *V*.
- By switching to a new copper layer using the appropriate hotkey.

8.8 Select/edit the track width and via size

When clicking on a track or a pad, Pcbnew automatically selects the corresponding Netclass, and the track size and via dimensions are derived from this netclass.

As previously seen, the Global Design Rules editor has a tool to insert extra tracks and via sizes.

- The horizontal toolbar can be used to select a size.
- When the button is active, the current track width can be selected from the pop-up menu (accessible as well when creating a track).
- The user can utilize the default Netclasses values or a specified value.

8.8.1 Using the horizontal toolbar

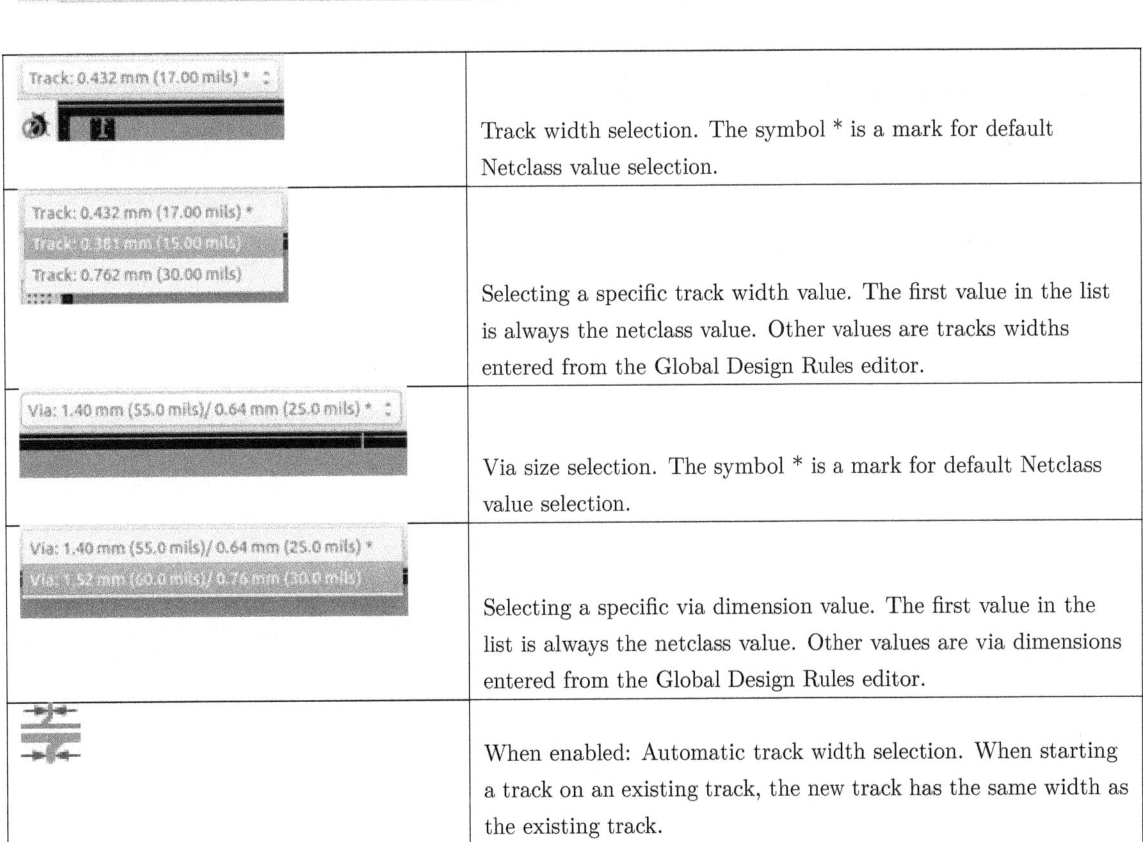

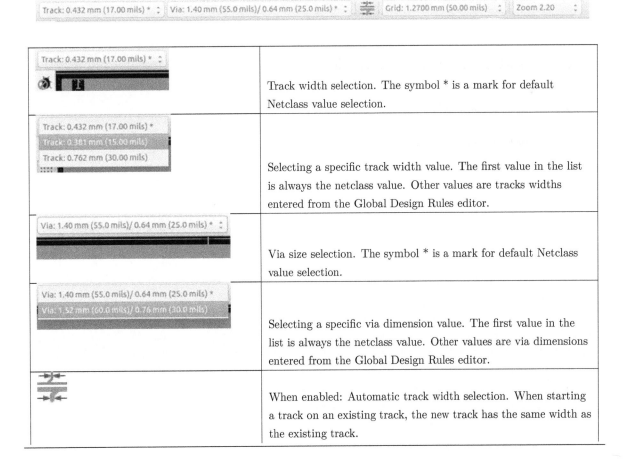

Track: 0.432 mm (17.00 mils) *	Track width selection. The symbol * is a mark for default Netclass value selection.
Track: 0.432 mm (17.00 mils) * Track: 0.381 mm (15.00 mils) Track: 0.762 mm (30.00 mils)	Selecting a specific track width value. The first value in the list is always the netclass value. Other values are tracks widths entered from the Global Design Rules editor.
Via: 1.40 mm (55.0 mils)/ 0.64 mm (25.0 mils) *	Via size selection. The symbol * is a mark for default Netclass value selection.
Via: 1.40 mm (55.0 mils)/ 0.64 mm (25.0 mils) * Via: 1.52 mm (60.0 mils)/ 0.76 mm (30.0 mils)	Selecting a specific via dimension value. The first value in the list is always the netclass value. Other values are via dimensions entered from the Global Design Rules editor.
	When enabled: Automatic track width selection. When starting a track on an existing track, the new track has the same width as the existing track.

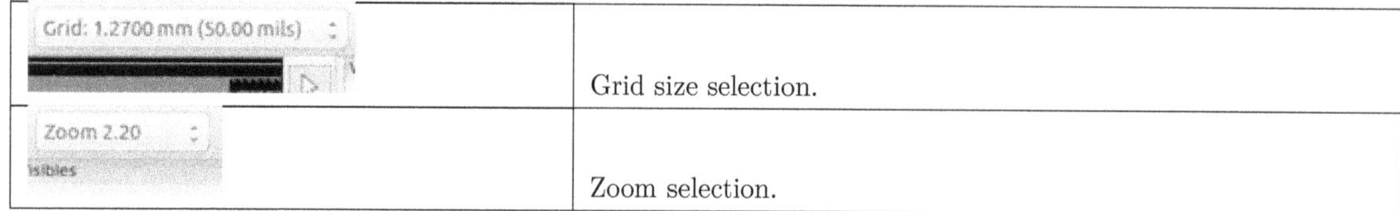

Grid: 1.2700 mm (50.00 mils)	Grid size selection.
Zoom 2.20	Zoom selection.

8.8.2 Using the pop-up menu

One can select a new size for routing, or change to a previously created via or track segment:

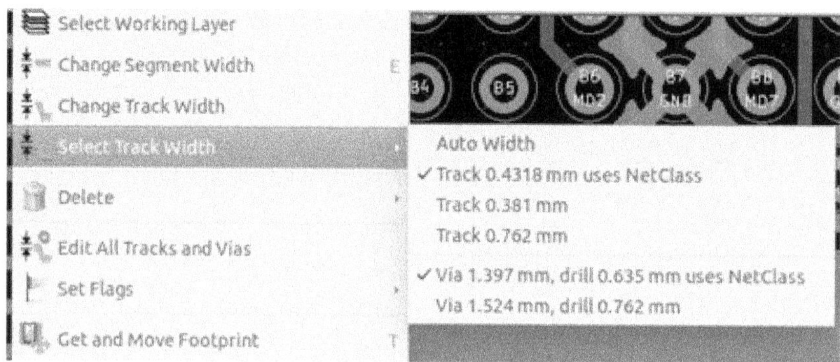

If you want to change many via (or track) sizes, the best way is to use a specific Netclass for the net(s) that must be edited (see global changes).

8.9 Editing and changing tracks

8.9.1 Change a track

In many cases redrawing a track is required.

New track (in progress):

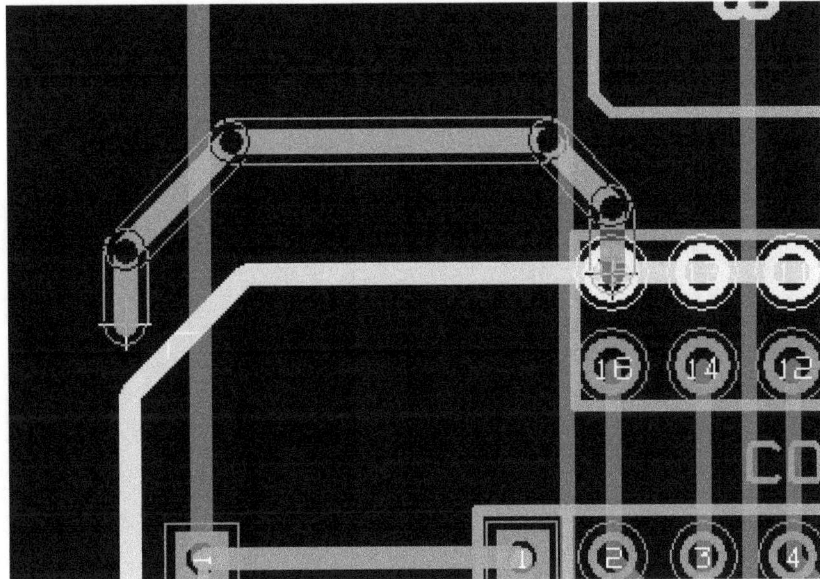

When finished:

Pcbnew will automatically remove the old track if it is redundant.

8.9.2 Global changes

Global tracks and via sizes dialog editor is accessible via the pop-up window by right clicking on a track:

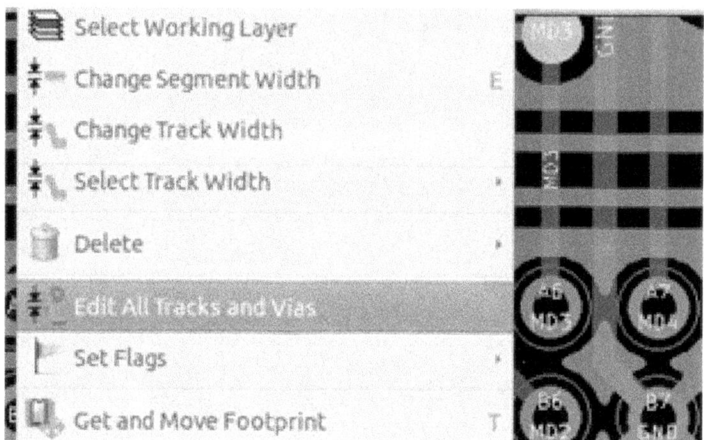

The dialog editor allows global changes of tracks and/or vias for:

- The current net.
- The whole board.

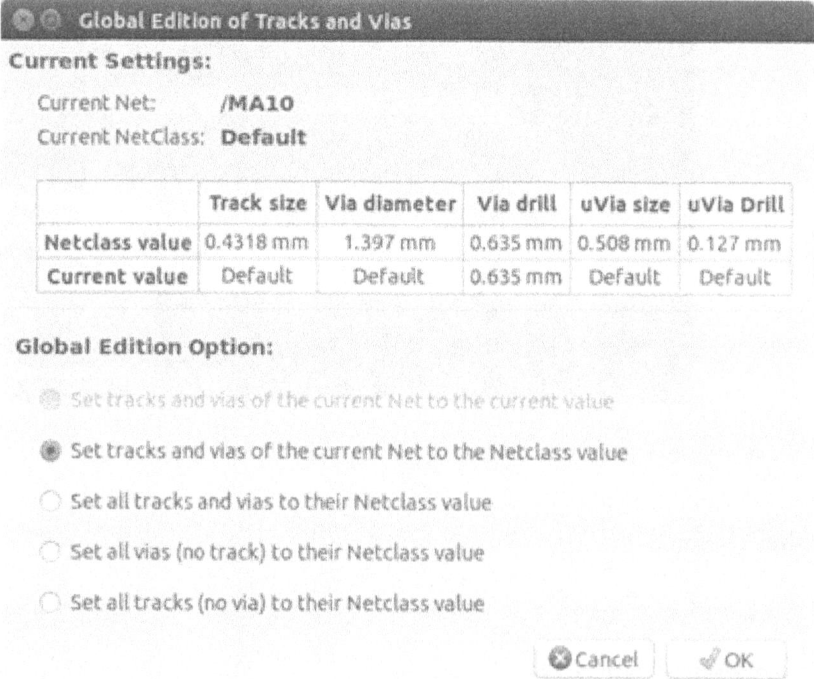

Chapter 9

Interactive Router

The Interactive Router lets you quickly and efficiently route your PCBs by shoving off or walking around items on the PCB that collide with the trace you are currently drawing.

Following modes are supported:

- **Highlight collisions**, which highlights all violating objects with a nice, shiny green color and shows violating clearance regions.
- **Shove**, attempting to push and shove all items colliding with the currently routed track.
- **Walk around**, trying to avoid obstacles by hugging/walking around them.

9.1 Setting up

Before using the Interactive Router, please set up these two things:

- **Clearance settings** To set the clearances, open the *Design Rules* dialog and make sure at least the default clearance value looks sensible.

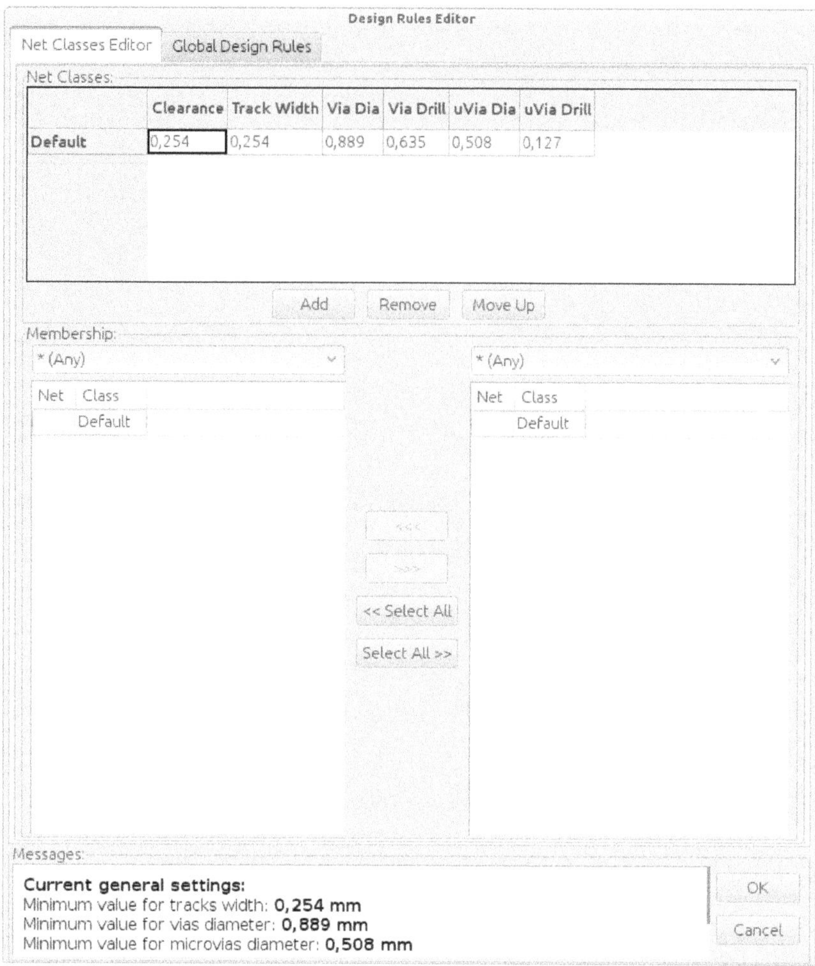

- **Enable OpenGL mode** By selecting *View→Switch canvas to OpenGL* menu option or pressing **F11**.

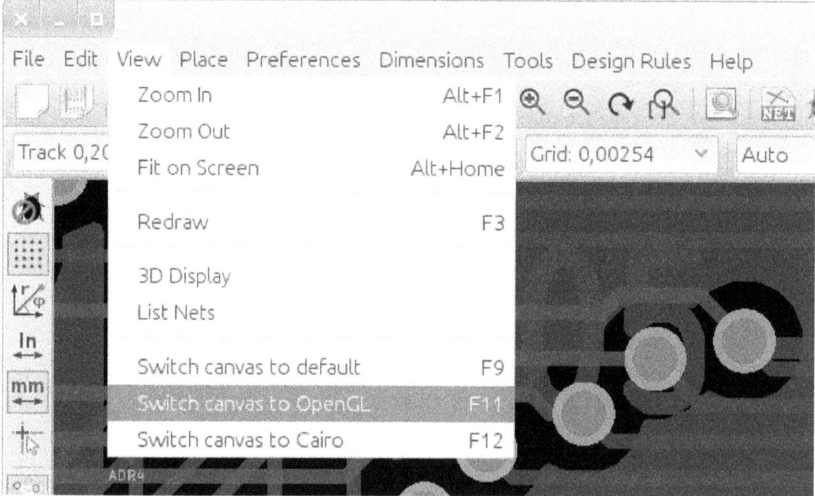

9.2 Laying out tracks

To activate the router tool press the *Interactive Router* button or the **X** key. The cursor will turn into a cross and the tool name, will appear in the status bar.

To start a track, click on any item (a pad, track or a via) or press the **X** key again hovering the mouse over that item. The new track will use the net of the starting item. Clicking or pressing **X** on empty PCB space starts a track with no net assigned.

Move the mouse to define shape of the track. The router will try to follow the mouse trail, hugging unmovable obstacles (such as pads) and shoving colliding traces/vias, depending on the mode. Retreating the mouse cursor will cause the shoved items to spring back to their former locations.

Clicking on a pad/track/via in the same net finishes routing. Clicking in empty space fixes the segments routed so far and continues routing the trace.

In order to stop routing and undo all changes (shoved items, etc.), simply press **Esc**.

Pressing **V** or selecting *Place Through Via* from the context menu while routing a track attaches a via at the end of the trace being routed. Pressing **V** again disables via placement. Clicking in any spot establishes the via and continues routing.

Pressing / or selecting *Switch Track Posture* from the context menu toggles the direction of the initial track segment between straight or diagonal.

Note

By default, the router snaps to centers/axes of the items. Snapping can be disabled by holding **Shift** while routing or selecting items.

9.3 Setting track widths and via sizes

There are several ways to pre-select a track width/via size or to change it during routing:

- Use standard KiCad shortcuts.
- Press **W** or select *Custom Track Width* from the context menu to type in a custom track width/via size.
- Pick a predefined width from the *Select Track Width* sub-menu of the context menu.
- Select *Use the starting track width* in the *Select Track Width* menu to pick the width from the start item (or the traces already connected to it).

9.4 Dragging

The router can drag track segments, corners and vias. To drag an item, click on it with **Ctrl** key pressed, hover the mouse and press **G** or select *Drag Track/Via* from the context menu. Finish dragging by clicking again or abort by pressing *Esc*.

9.5 Options

The router behavior can be configured by pressing *E* or selecting *Routing Options* from the context menu while in the Track mode. It opens a window like the one below:

The options are:

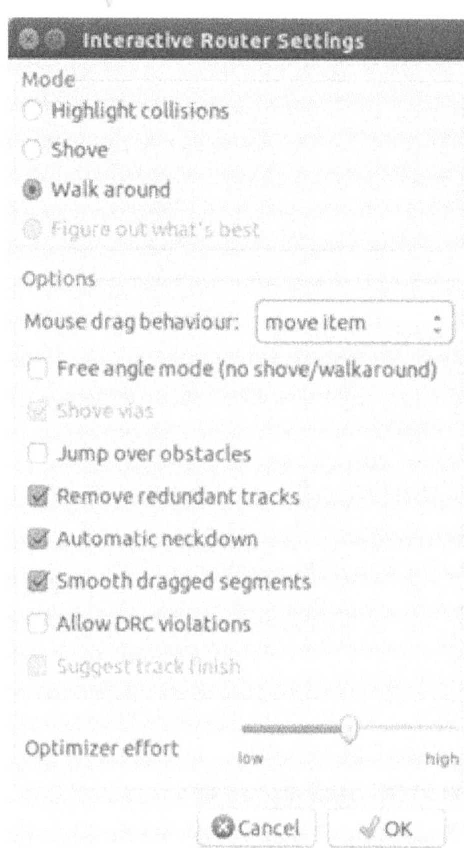

- **Mode** - select how the router handles DRC violation (shoving, walking around, etc.)
- **Shove vias** - when disabled, vias are treated as un-movable objects and hugged instead of shoved.
- **Jump over obstacles** - when enabled, the router tries to move colliding traces behind solid obstacles (e.g. pads) instead of "reflecting" back the collision
- **Remove redundant tracks** - removes loops while routing (e.g. if the new track ensures same connectivity as an already existing one, the old track is removed). Loop removal works locally (only between the start and end of the currently routed trace).
- **Automatic neckdown** - when enabled, the router tries to break out pads/vias in a clean way, avoiding acute angles and jagged breakout traces.
- **Smooth dragged segments** - when enabled, the router attempts to merge several jagged segments into a single straight one (dragging mode).

- **Allow DRC violations** (*Highlight collisions* mode only) - allows to establish a track even if is violating the DRC rules.
- **Optimizer effort** - defines how much time the router shall spend optimizing the routed/shoved traces. More effort means cleaner routing (but slower), less effort means faster routing but somewhat jagged traces.

Chapter 10

Creating copper zones

Copper zones are defined by an outline (closed polygon), and can include holes (closed polygons inside the outline). A zone can be drawn on a copper layer or alternatively on a technical layer.

10.1 Creating zones on copper layers

Pad (and track) connections to filled copper areas are checked by the DRC engine. A zone must be filled (not just created) to connect pads. Pcbnew currently uses track segments or polygons to fill copper areas.

Each option has its advantages and its disadvantages, the main disadvantage being increased screen redraw time on slower machines. The final result is however the same.

For calculation time reasons, the zone filling is not recreated after each change, but only:

- If a filling zone command is executed.
- When a DRC test is performed.

Copper zones must be filled or refilled after changes in tracks or pads are made. Copper zones (usually ground and power planes) are usually attached to a net.

In order to create a copper zone you should:

- Select parameters (net name, layer…). Turning on the layer and highlighting this net is not mandatory but it is good practice.
- Create the zone limit (If not, the entire board will be filled.).
- Fill the zone.

Pcbnew tries to fill all zones in one piece, and usually, there will be no unconnected copper blocks. It can happen that some areas remain unfilled. Zones having no net are not cleaned and can have insulated areas.

10.2 Creating a zone

10.2.1 Creating the limits of a zone

Use the tool . The active layer must be a copper layer. When clicking to start the zone outline, the following dialog box will be opened.

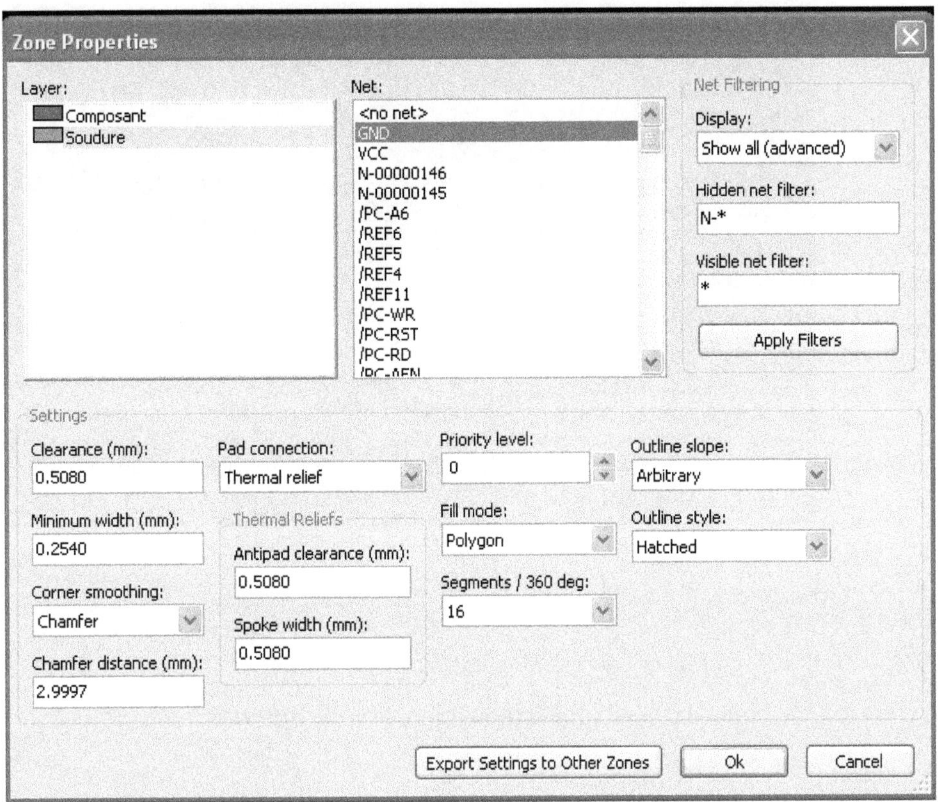

You can specify all parameters for this zone:

- Net
- Layer
- Filling options
- Pad options
- Priority level

Draw the zone limit on this layer. This zone limit is a polygon, created by left-clicking at each corner. A double-click will end and close the polygon. If the starting point and ending point are not at the same coordinate, Pcbnew will add a segment from the end point to the start point.

Note

- The DRC control is active when creating zone outlines.
- A corner which creates a DRC error will not be accepted by Pcbnew.

In the following image you can see an example of a zone limit (polygon in thin hatched line):

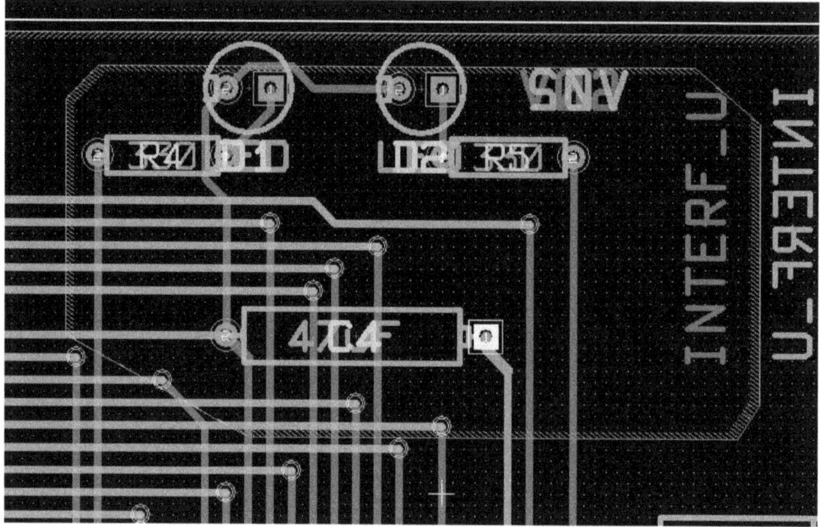

10.2.2 Priority level

Sometimes a small zone must be created inside a large zone.

This is possible if the small zone has a higher priority level than the large zone.

Level setting:

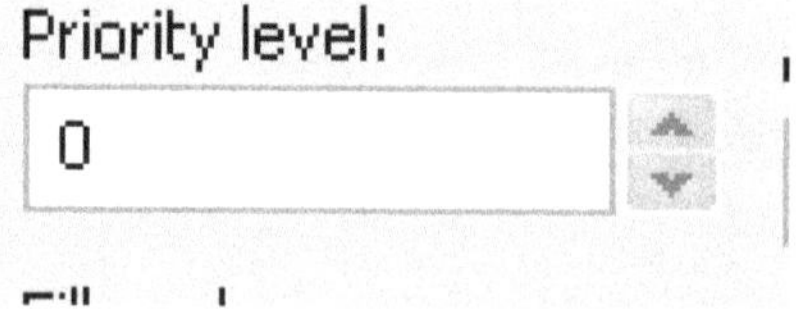

Here is an example:

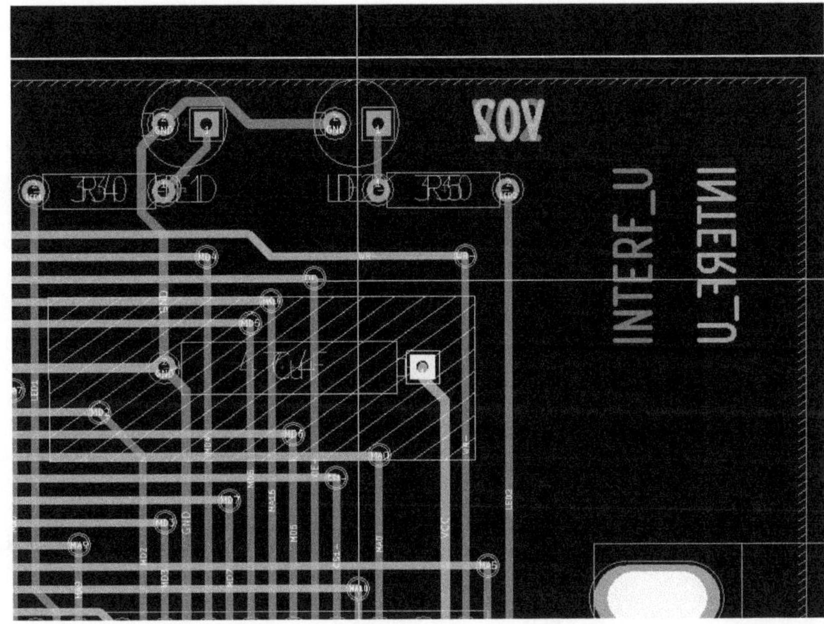

After filling:

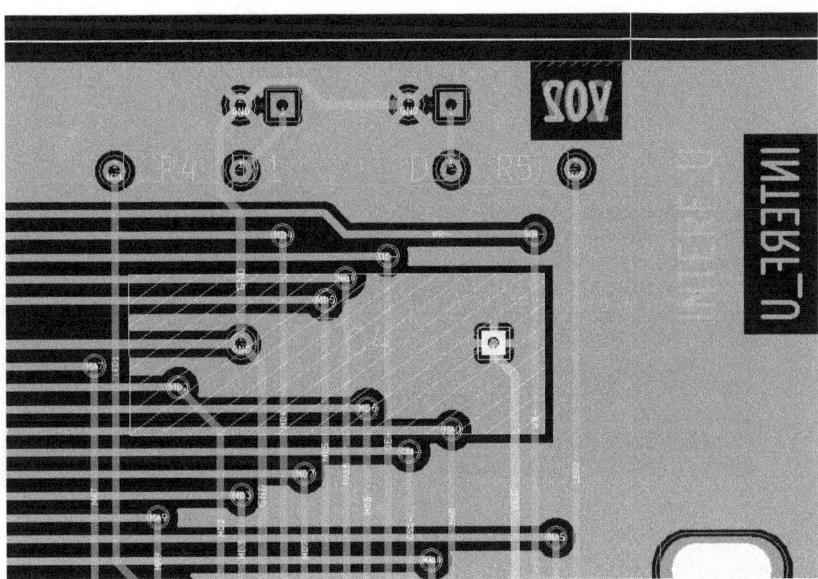

10.2.3 Filling the zone

When filling a zone, Pcbnew removes all unconnected copper islands. To access the zone filling command, right-click on the edge zone.

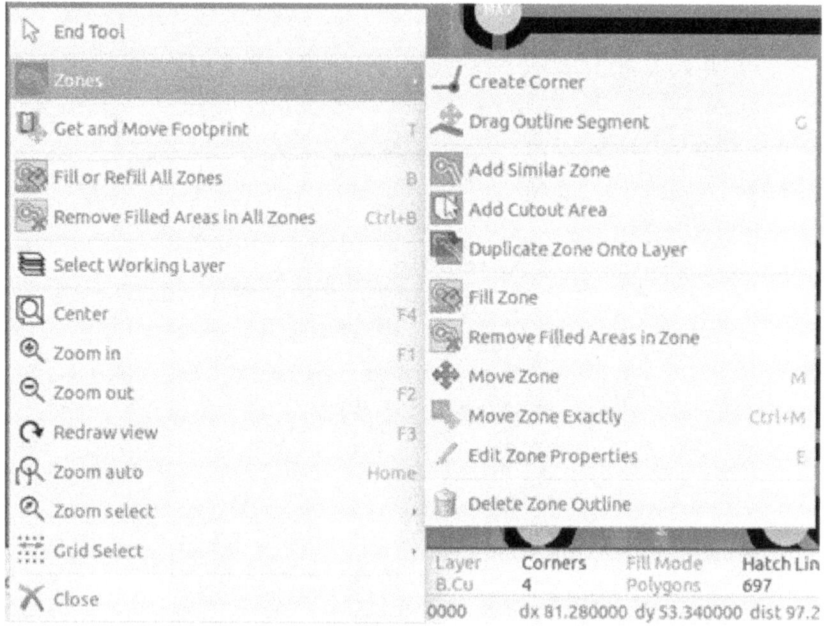

Activate the "Fill Zone" command. Below is the filling result for a starting point inside the polygon:

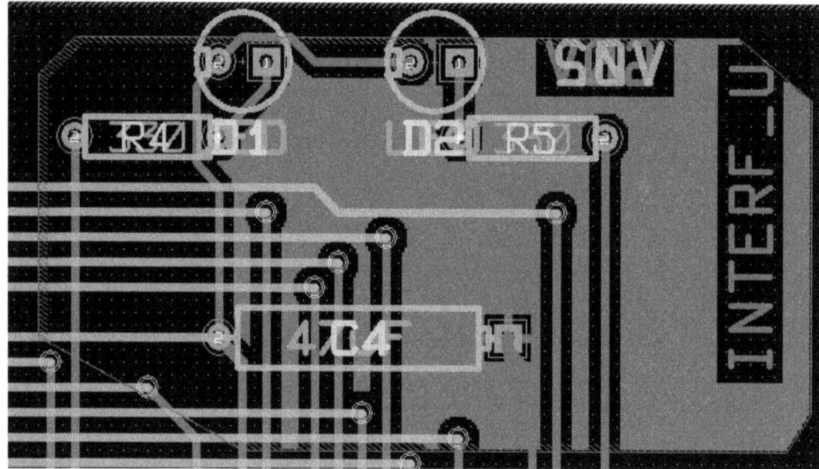

The polygon is the border of the filling area. You can see a non-filled area inside the zone, because this area is not accessible:

- A track creates a border, and
- There is no starting point for filling in this area.

Note

You can use many polygons to create cutout areas. Here you can see an example:

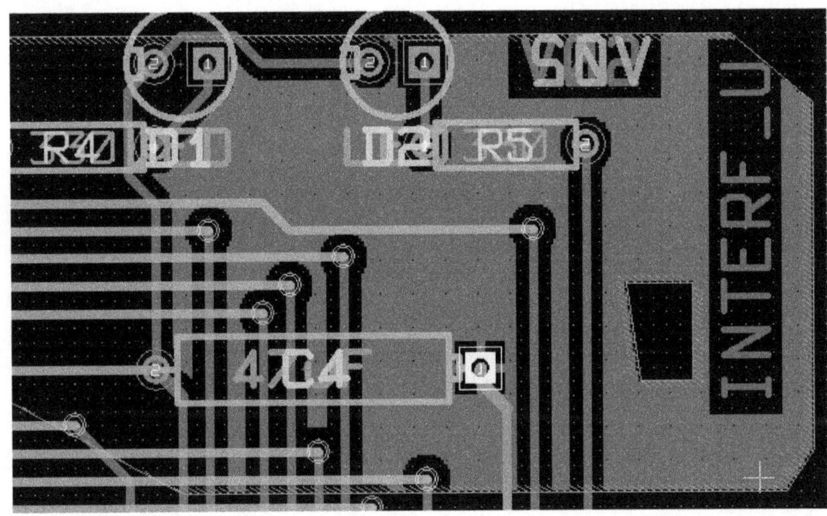

10.3 Filling options

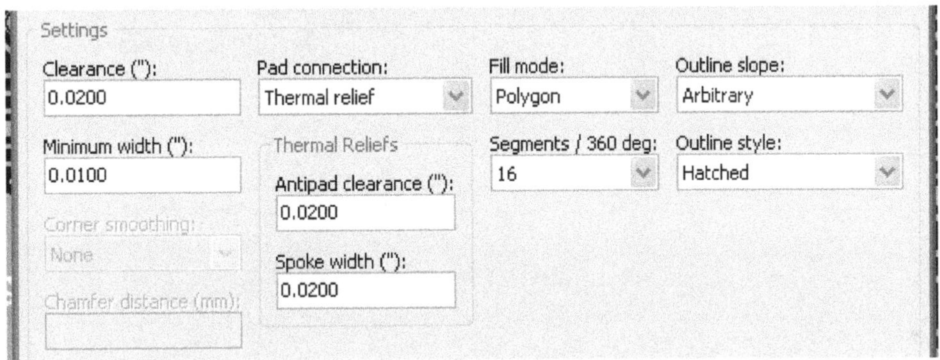

When you fill an area, you must choose:

- The mode for filling.
- The clearance and minimum copper thickness.
- How pads are drawn inside the zone (or connected to this zone).
- Thermal relief parameters.

10.3.1 Filling mode

Zones can be filled using polygons or segments. The result is the same. If you have problems with polygon mode (slow screen refresh) you should use segments.

10.3.2 Clearance and minimum copper thickness

A good choice for clearance is a grid that is a bit bigger than the routing grid. Minimum copper thickness value ensures that there are no too small copper ares.

Warning

if this value is too large, small shapes like thermal stubs in thermal reliefs cannot be drawn.

10.3.3 Pad options

Pads of the net can either be included or excluded from the zone, or connected by thermal reliefs.

- If included, soldering and un-soldering can be very difficult due to the high thermal mass of the large copper area.

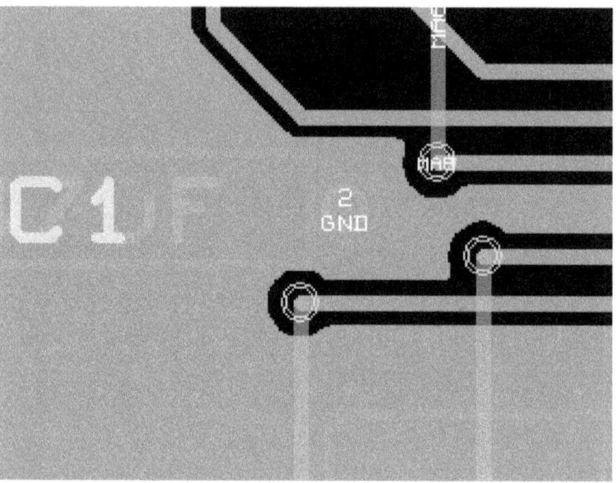

- If excluded, the connection to the zone will not be very good.
  - The zone can be filled only if tracks exists to connect zone areas.
  - Pads must be connected by tracks.

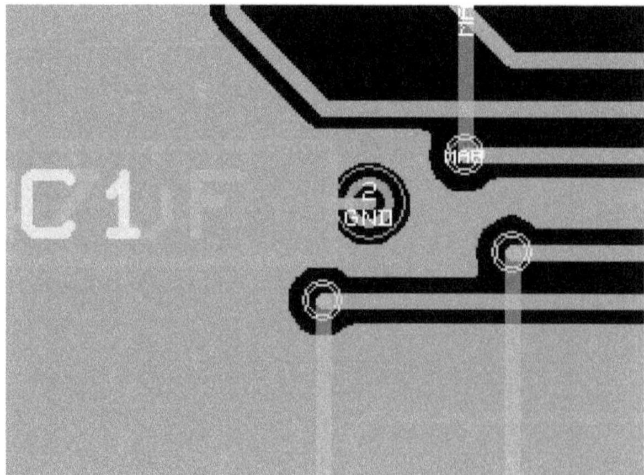

- A thermal relief is a good compromise.
  - Pad is connected by 4 track segments.
  - The segment width is the current value used for the track width.

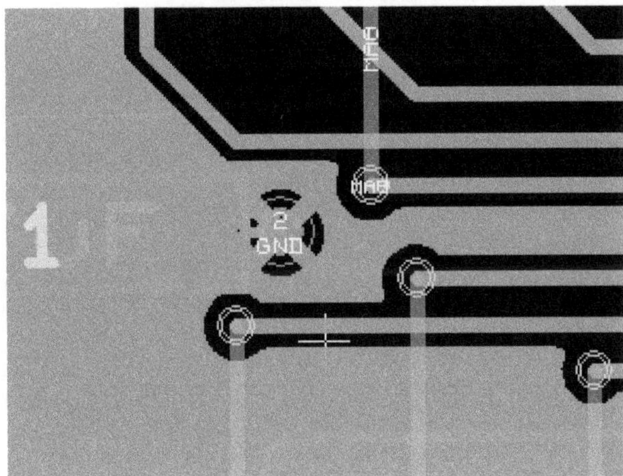

10.3.4 Thermal relief parameters

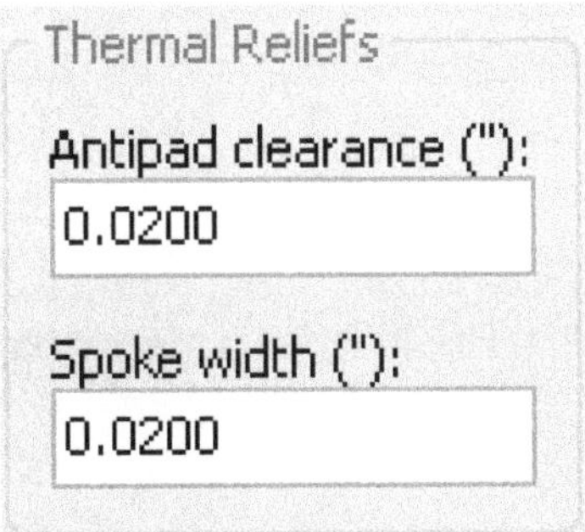

You can set two parameters for thermal reliefs:

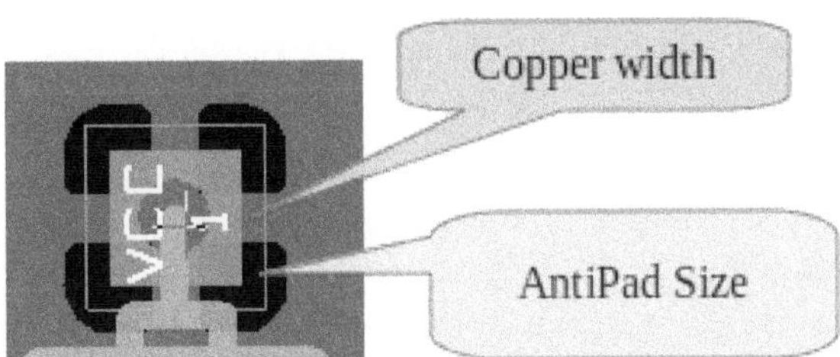

10.3.5 Choice of parameters

The copper width value for thermal reliefs must be bigger than the minimum thickness value for the copper zone. If not, they cannot be drawn.

Additionally, a too large value for this parameter or for antipad size does not allow one to create a thermal relief for small pads (like pad sizes used for SMD components).

10.4 Adding a cutout area inside a zone

A zone must already exist. To add a cutout area (a non-filled area inside the zone):

- Right-click on an existing edge outline.
- Select Add Cutout Area.

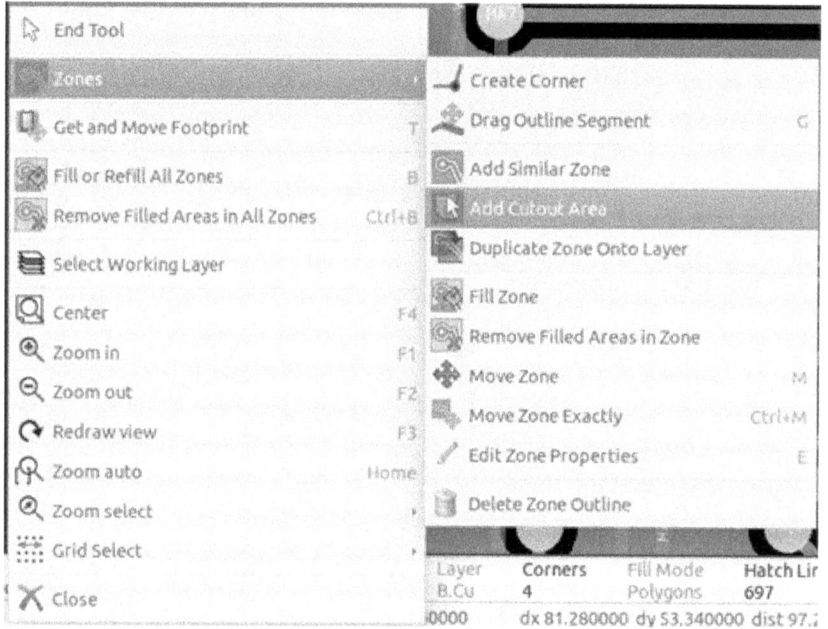

- Create the new outline.

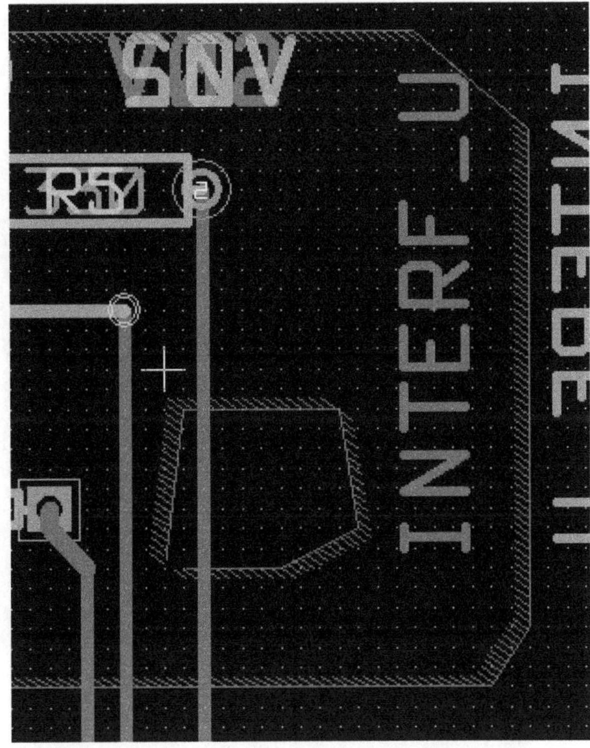

10.5 Outlines editing

An outline can be modified by:

- Moving a corner or an edge.
- Deleting or adding a corner.
- Adding a similar zone, or a cutout area.

If polygons are overlapping they will be combined.

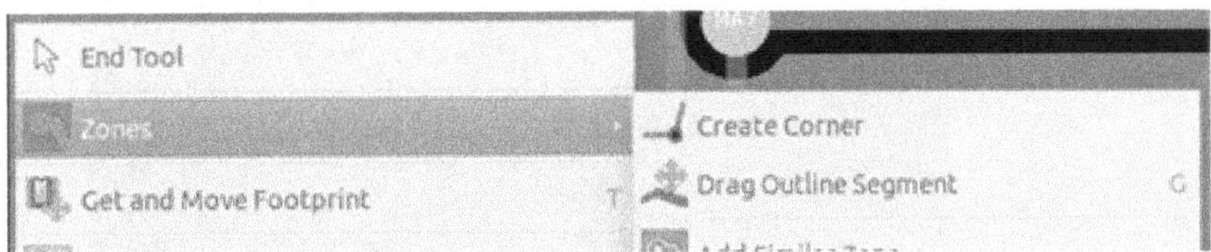

To do that, right-click on a corner or on an edge, then select the proper command.

Here is a corner (from a cutout) that has been moved:

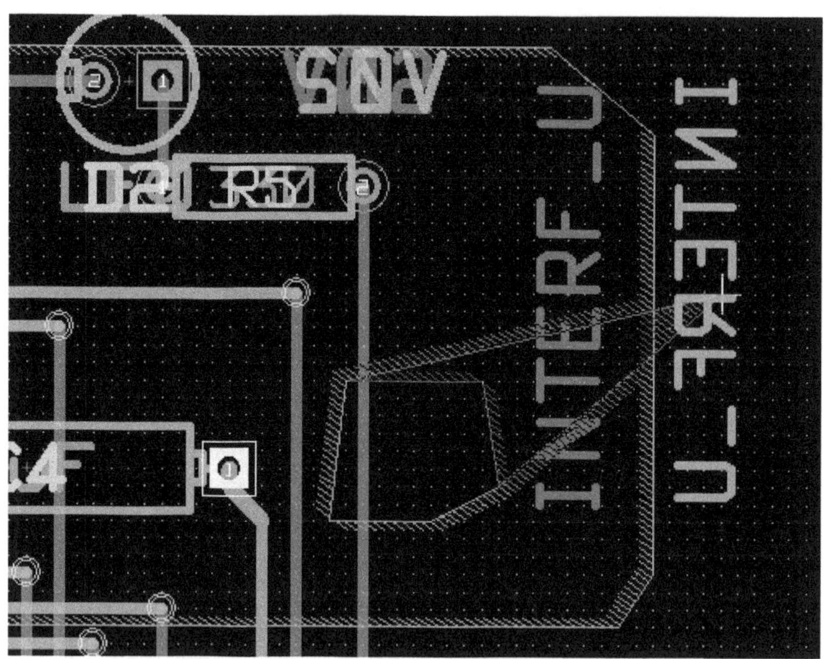

Here is the final result:

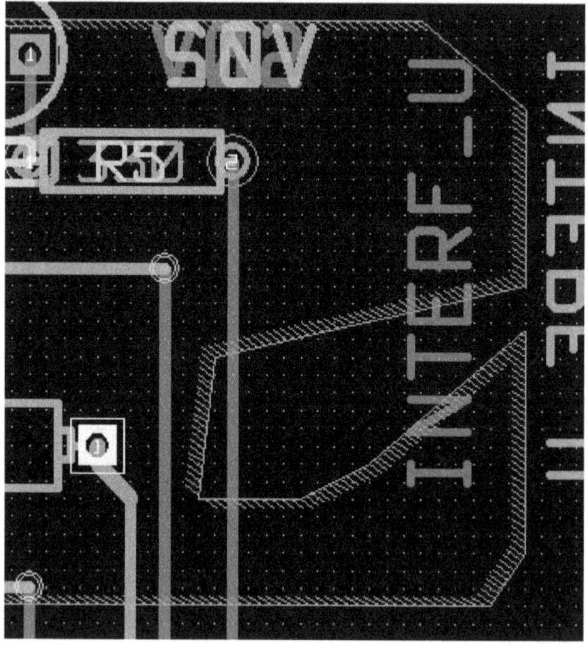

Polygons are combined.

10.5.1 Adding a similar zone

Adding the similar zone:

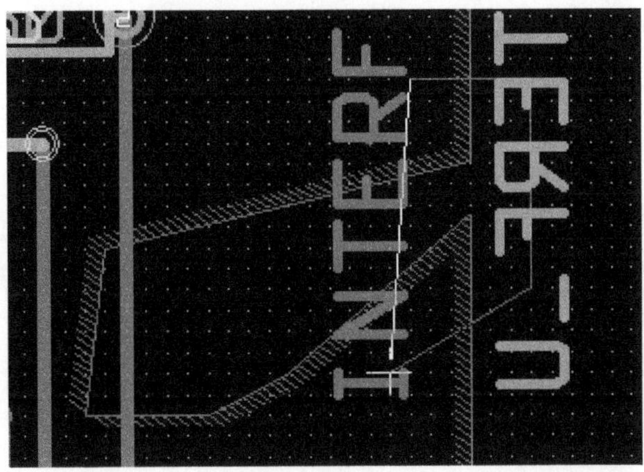

Final result:

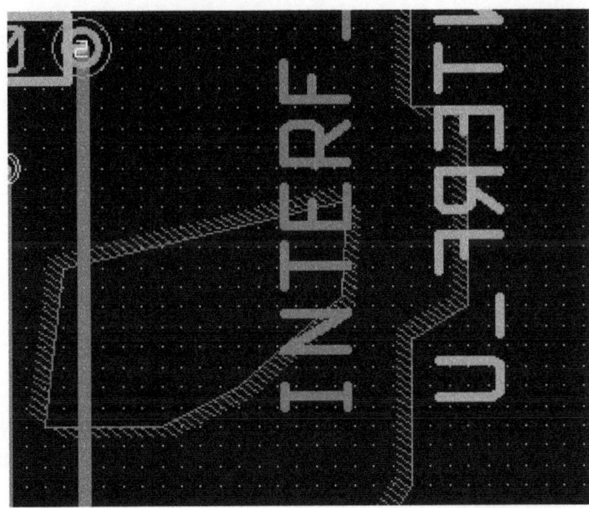

10.6 Editing zone parameters

When right-clicking on an outline, and using *Edit Zone Params* the Zone params Dialog box will open. Initial parameters can be inputted . If the zone is already filled, refilling it will be necessary.

10.7 Final zone filling

When the board is finished, one must fill or refill all zones. To do this:

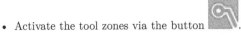

- Activate the tool zones via the button .
- Right-click to display the pop-up menu.

- Use Fill or Refill All Zones: 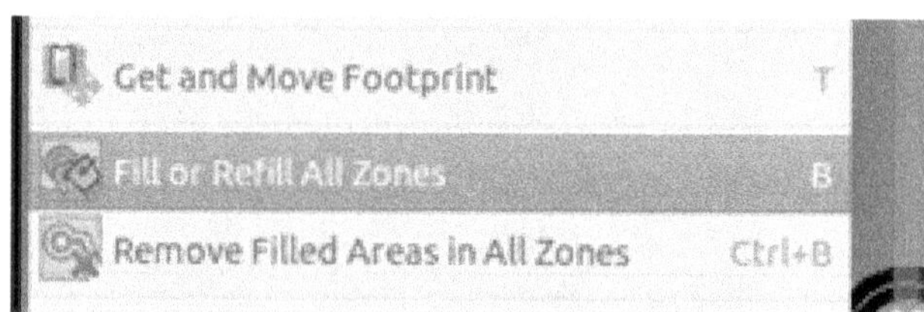

Warning
Calculation can take some time if the filling grid is small.

10.8 Change zones net names

After editing a schematic, you can change the name of any net. For instance VCC can be changed to +5V.

When a global DRC control is made Pcbnew checks if the zone net name exists, and displays an error if not.

Manually editing the zone parameters will be necessary to change the old name to the new one.

10.9 Creating zones on technical layers

10.9.1 Creating zone limits

This is done using the button . The active layer must be a technical layer.

When clicking to start the zone outline, this dialog box is opened:

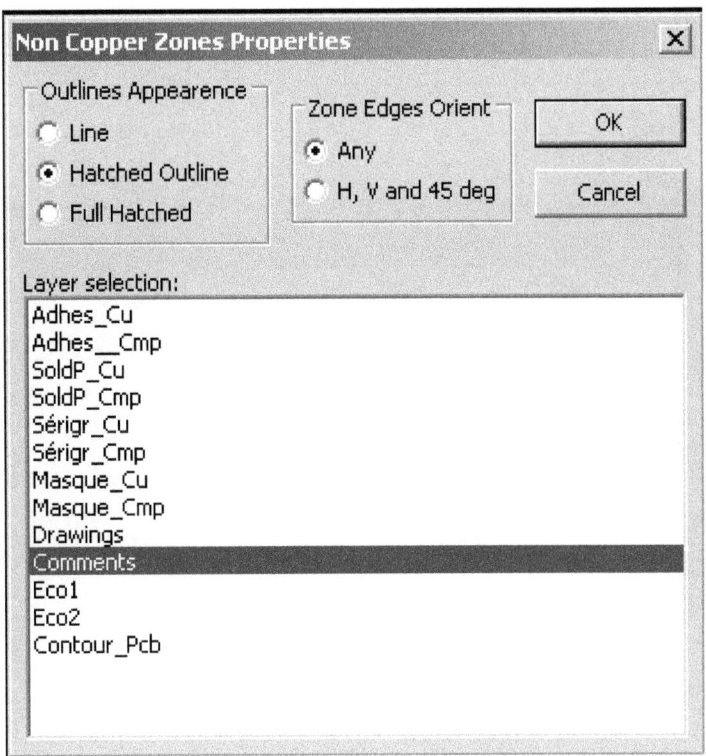

Select the technical layer to place the zone and draw the zone outline like explained previously for copper layers.

Note

- For editing outlines use the same method as for copper zones.
- If necessary, cutout areas can be added.

10.10 Creating a Keepout area

Select the tool 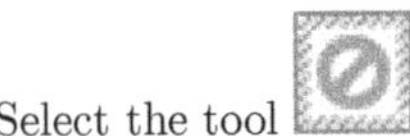

The active layer should be a copper layer.

After clicking on the starting point of a new keepout area, the dialog box is opened:

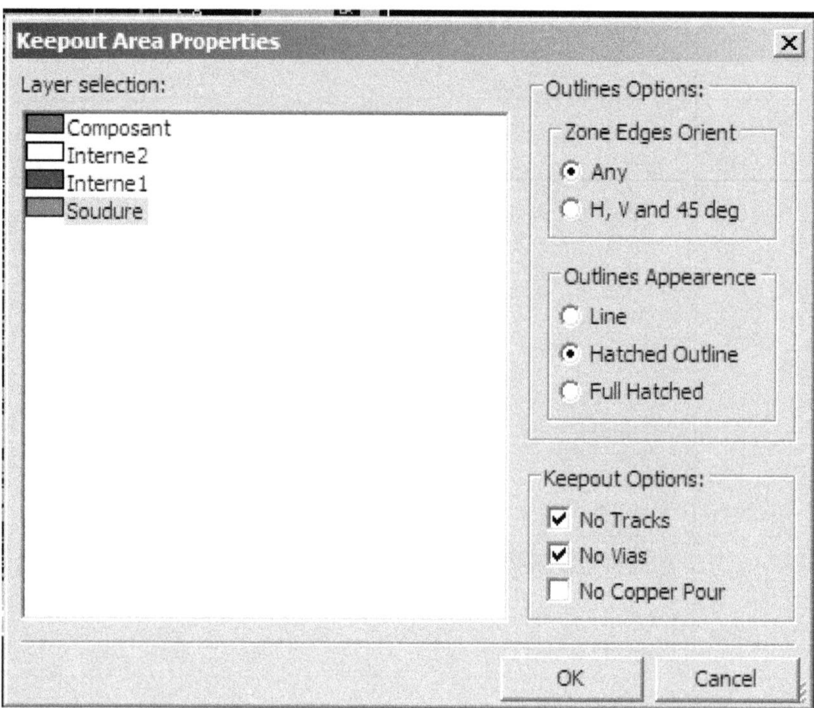

One can select disallowed items:

- Tracks.
- Vias.
- Copper pours.

When a track or a via is inside a keepout which does not allow it, a DRC error will be raised.

For copper zones, the area inside a keepout with no copper pour will be not filled. A keep-out area is a like a zone, so editing its outline is analogous to copper zone editing.

Chapter 11

Files for circuit fabrication

Let us see now what the steps are for the creation of the necessary files for the production of your printed circuit board.

All files generated by KiCad are placed in the working directory which is the same directory that contains the xxxx.brd file for the printed circuit board.

11.1 Final preparations

The generation of the necessary files for the production of your printed circuit board includes the following preparatory steps.

- Mark any layer (e.g., *top or front* and *bottom or back*) with the project name by placing appropriate text upon each of the layers.
- All text on copper layers (sometimes called *solder* or *bottom*) must be mirrored.
- Create any ground planes, modifying traces as required to ensure they are contiguous.
- Place alignment crosshairs and possibly the dimensions of the board outline (these are usually placed on one of the general purpose layers).

Here is an example showing all of these elements, except ground planes, which have been omitted for better visibility:

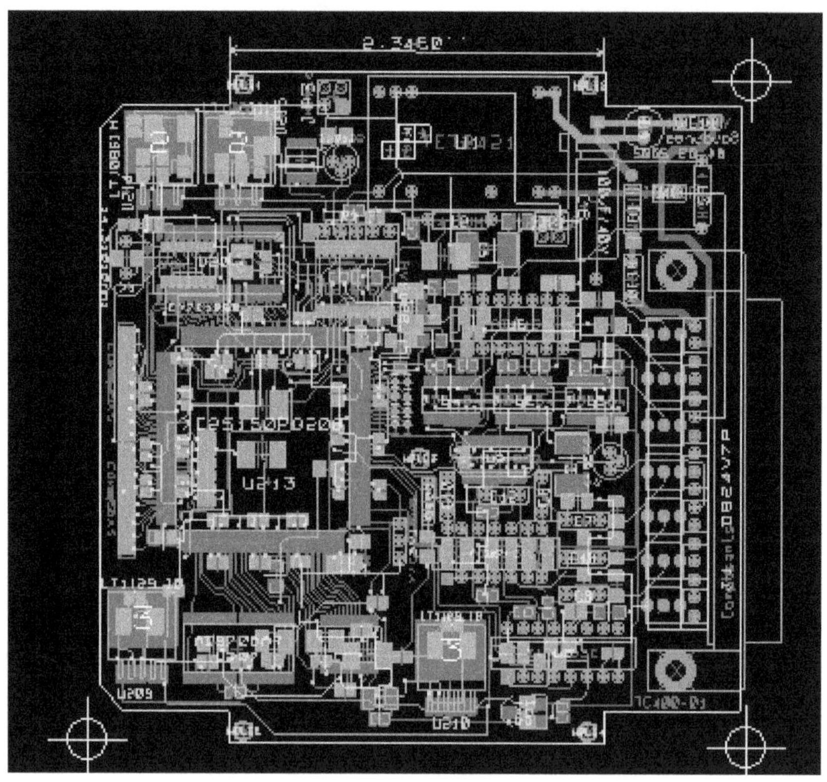

A color key for the 4 copper layers has also been included: 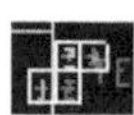

11.2 Final DRC test

Before generating the output files, a global DRC test is very strongly recommended.

Zones are filled or refilled when starting a DRC. Press the button  to launch the following DRC dialog:

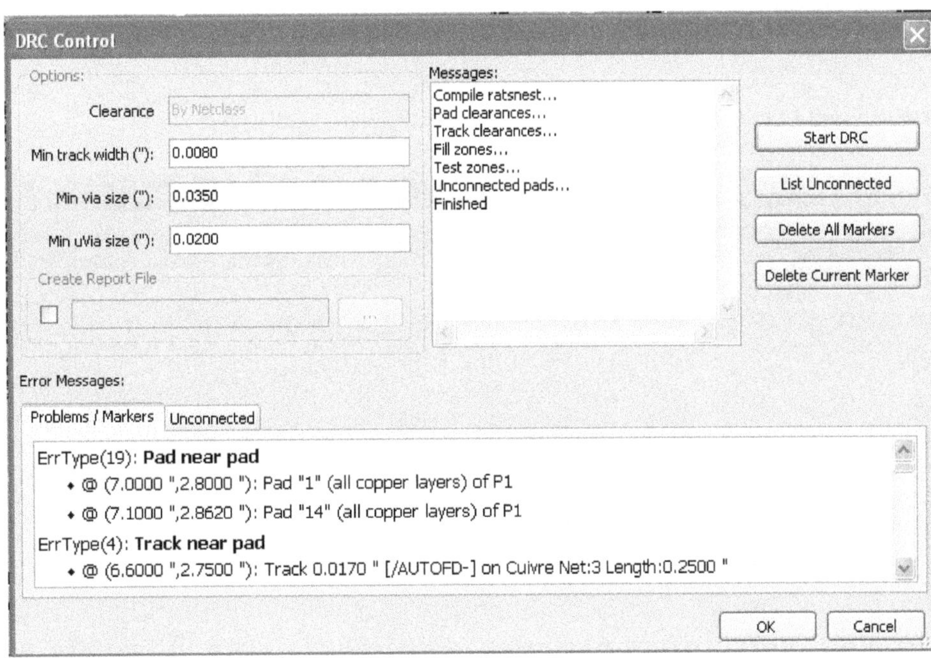

Adjust the parameters accordingly and then press the "Start DRC" button.

This final check will prevent any unpleasant surprises.

11.3 Setting coordinates origin

Set the coordinates origin for the photo plot and drill files, one must place the auxiliary axis on this origin. Activate the icon . Move the auxiliary axis by left-clicking on the chosen location.

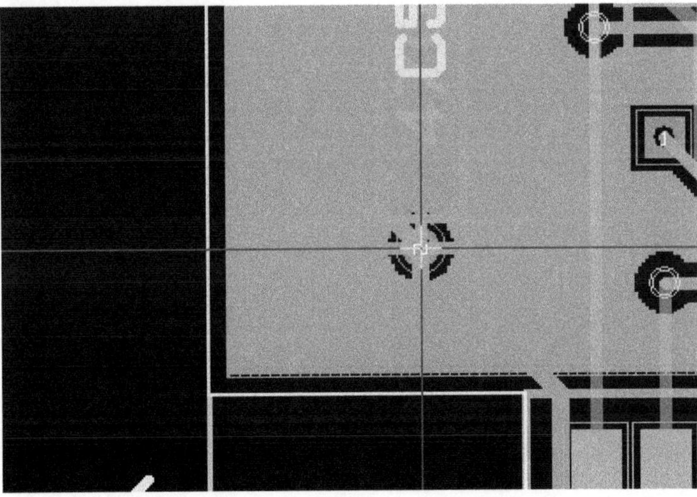

11.4 Generating files for photo-tracing

This is done via the Files/Plot menu option and invokes the following dialog:

Usually, the files are in the GERBER format. Nevertheless, it is possible to produce output in both HPGL and POSTSCRIPT formats. When Postscript format is selected, this dialog will appear.

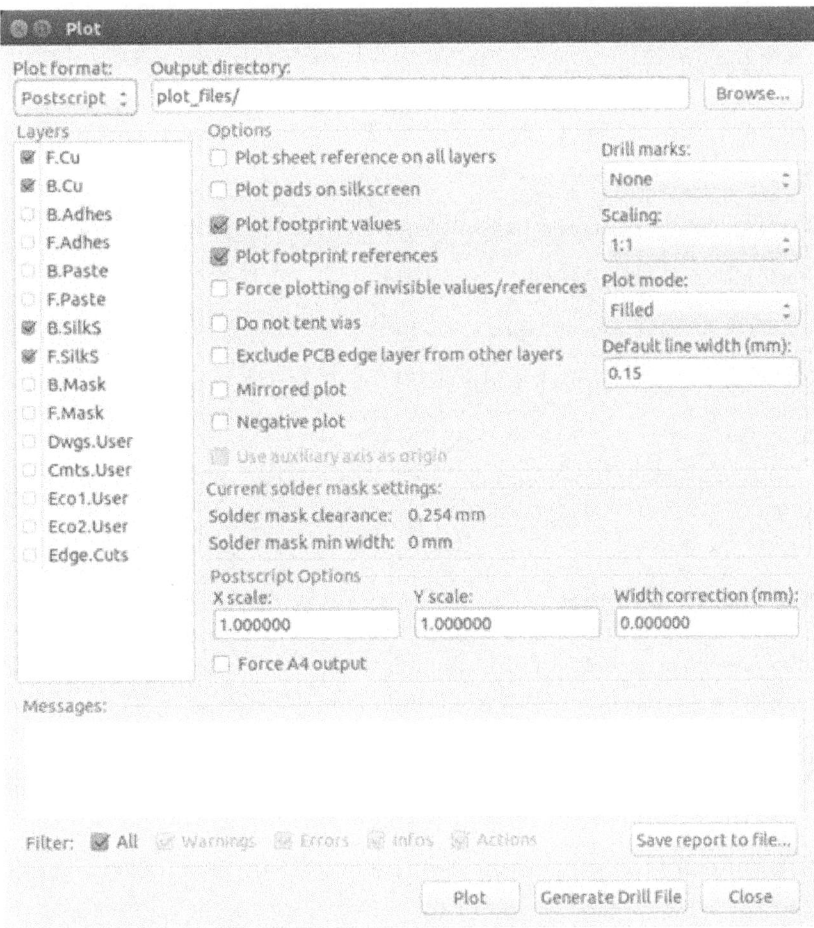

In these formats, a fine scale adjust can be used to compensate for the plotter accuracy and to have a true scale of 1 for the output:

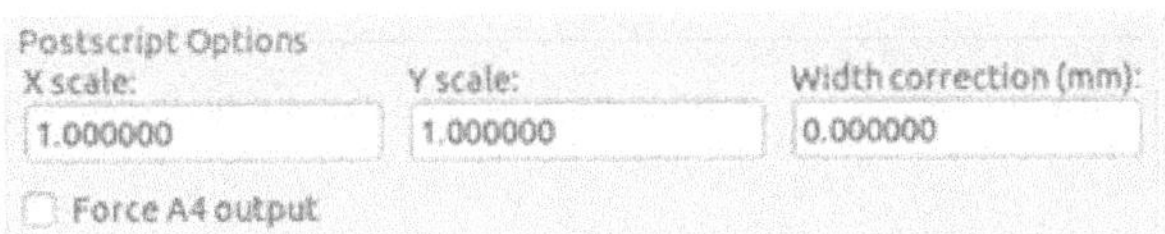

11.4.1 GERBER format

For each layer, Pcbnew generates a separate file following the GERBER 274X standard, by default in 4.6 format (each coordinate in the file is represented by 10 digits, of which 4 are before the decimal point and 6 follow it), units in inches, and a scale of 1.

It is normally necessary to create files for all of the copper layers and, depending on the circuit, for the silkscreen, solder mask, and solder paste layers. All of these files can be produced in one step, by selecting the appropriate check boxes.

For example, for a double-sided circuit with silkscreen, solder mask and solder paste (for SMD components), 8 files should be generated (*xxxx* represents the name of the .brd file).

- xxxx-F_Cu.gbr for the component side.
- xxxx-B_Cu.gbr for the copper side.
- xxxx-F_SilkS.gbr for the component-side silkscreen markings.
- xxxx-B_SilkS.gbr for the copper-side silkscreen markings.
- xxxx-F_Paste.gbr for the component-side solder paste.
- xxxx-B_Paste.gbr for the copper-side solder paste.
- xxxx-F_Mask.gbr for the component-side solder mask.
- xxxx-B_Mask.gbr for the copper-side solder mask.

GERBER file format:

The format used by Pcbnew is RS274X format 4.6, Imperial, Leading zero omitted, Abs format. These are very usual settings.

11.4.2 POSTSCRIPT format

The standard extension for the output files is .ps in the case of postscript output. As for HPGL output, the tracing can be at user-selected scales and can be mirrored. If the Org = Centre option is active, the origin for the coordinates of the tracing table is assumed to be in the centre of the drawing.

If the Print Sheet Ref option is active, the sheet cartridge is traced.

11.4.3 Plot options

Gerber format:

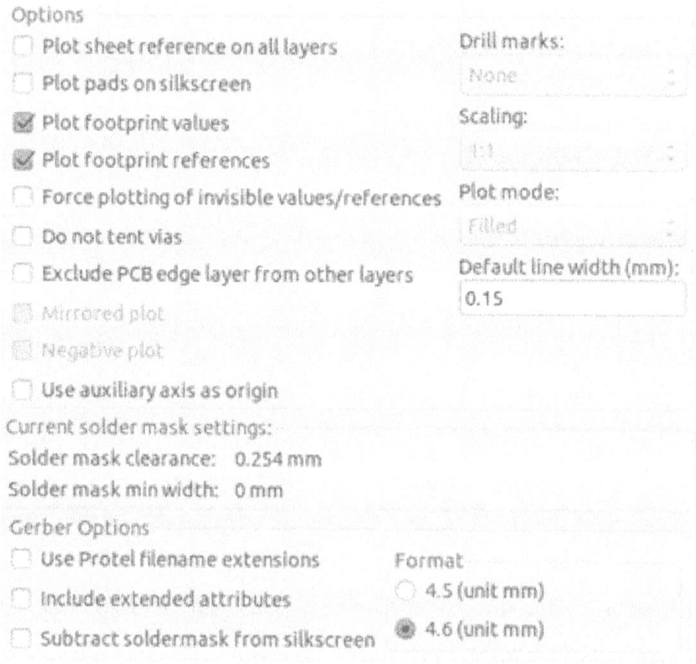

Options
Plot sheet reference on all layers
Plot pads on silkscreen
Plot footprint values
Plot footprint references
Force plotting of invisible values/references
Do not tent vias
Exclude PCB edge layer from other layers
Mirrored plot
Negative plot
Use auxiliary axis as origin
Drill marks:
None
Scaling:
1:1
Plot mode:
Filled
Default line width (mm):
0.15
Current solder mask settings:
Solder mask clearance: 0.254 mm
Solder mask min width: 0 mm
Gerber Options
Use Protel filename extensions
Include extended attributes
Subtract soldermask from silkscreen
Format
4.5 (unit mm)
4.6 (unit mm)

Other formats:

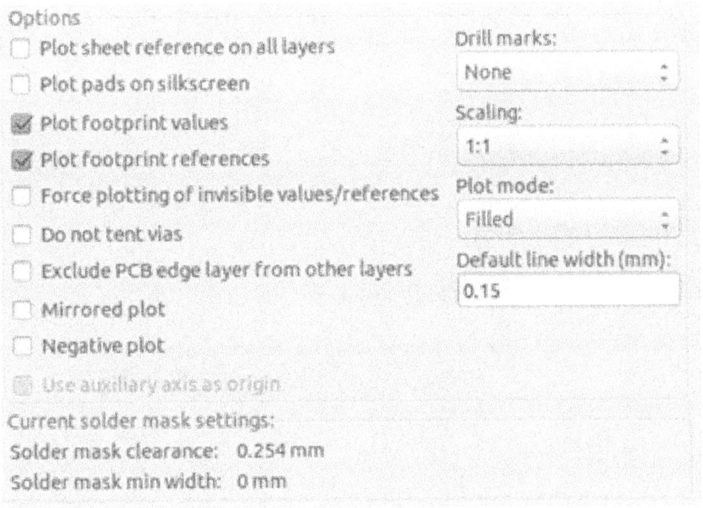

GERBER format specific options:

Use Protel filename extensions	Use .gbl .gtl .gbs .gts .gbp .gtp .gbo .gto instead of .gbr for file name extensions.
Include extended attributes	Output extended attributes to file.
Subtract soldermask from silkscreen	Remove all Silk from solder paste areas.

11.4.4 Other formats

The standard extension depends on the output file type.

Some options are not available for some formats.

The plot can be done at user-selected scales and can be mirrored.

The Print Drill Opt list offers the option of pads that are filled, drilled to the correct diameter or drilled with a small hole (to guide hand drilling).

If the Print Sheet Ref option is active, the sheet cartridge is traced.

11.5 Global clearance settings for the solder stop and the solder paste mask

Mask clearance values can be set globally for the solder mask layers and the solder paste layers. These clearances can be set at the following levels.

- At pads level.
- At footprint level.
- Globally.

And Pcbnew uses by priority order.

- Pad values. If null:
- Footprint values. If null:
- Global values.

11.5.1 Access

The menu option for this is available via the Dimensions menu:

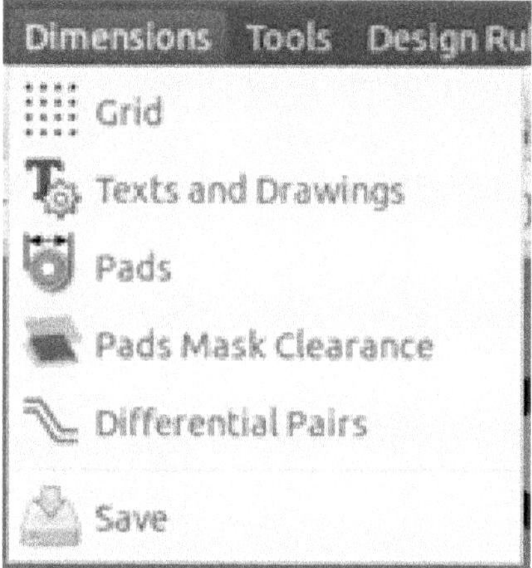

The dialog box is the following:

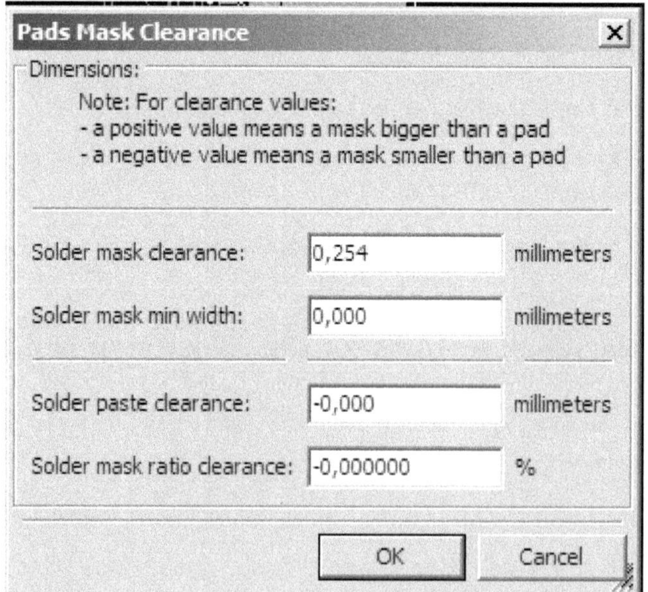

11.5.2 Solder mask clearance

A value near to 0.2 mm is usually good. This value is positive because the mask is usually bigger than the pad.

One can set a minimum value for the solder mask width, between 2 pads.

If the actual value is smaller than the minimum value, the 2 solder mask shapes will be merged.

11.5.3 Solder paste clearance

The final clearance is the sum of the solder paste clearance and a percentage of the pad size.

This value is negative because the mask is usually smaller than the pad.

11.6 Generating drill files

The creation of a drill file xxxx.drl following the EXCELLON standard is always necessary.

One can also produce an optional drill report, and an optional drill map.

- The drill map can be plotted using several formats.
- The drill report is a plain text file.

The generation of these files is controlled via:

- "Create Drill File" button, or
- Files/Fabrication Outputs/Drill file menu selection.

The Drill tools dialog box will be the following:

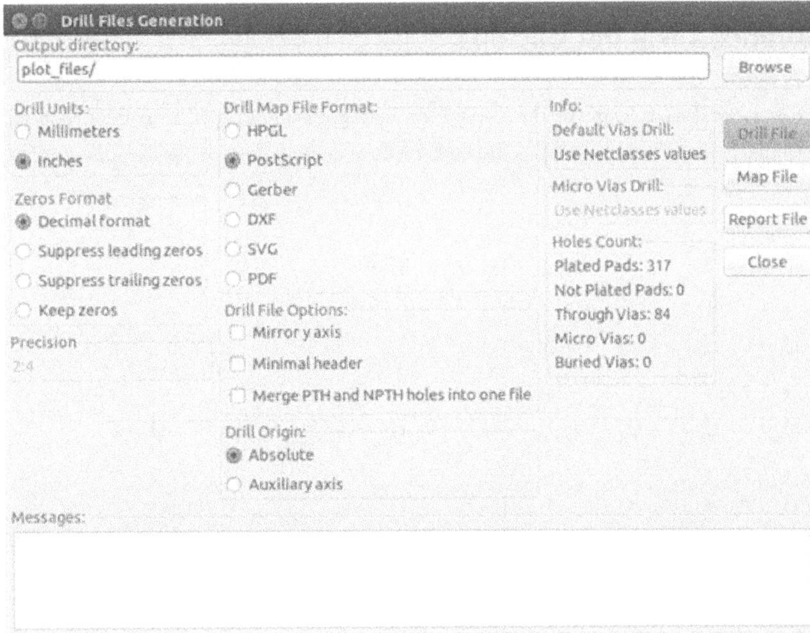

For setting the coordinate origin, the following dialog box is used:

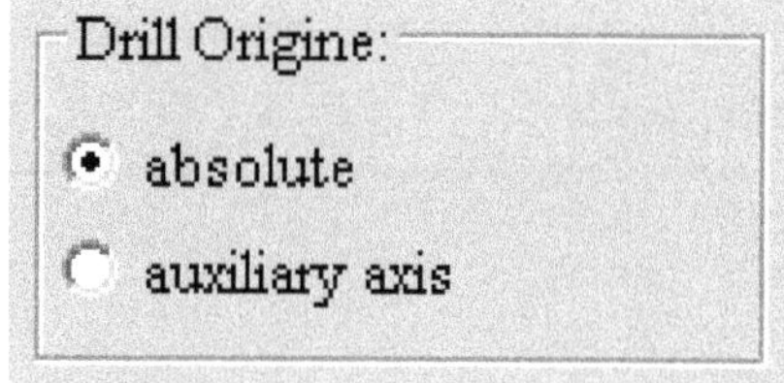

- Absolute: absolute coordinate system is used.
- Auxiliary axis: coordinates are relative to the auxiliary axis, use the icon (right toolbar) to set it.

11.7 Generating wiring documentation

To produce wiring documentation files, the component and copper silkscreen layers can be traced. Usually, just the component-side silkscreen markings are sufficient for wiring a PCB. If the copper-side silkscreen is used, the text it contains should be mirrored in order to be readable.

11.8 Generation of files for automatic component insertion

This option is accessed via the Postprocess/Create Cmp file menu option. However, no file will be generated unless at least one footprint has the Normal+Insert attribute activated (see Editing Footprints). One or two files will be produced, depending upon whether insertable components are present on one or both sides of the PCB. A dialogue box will display the names of the file(s) created.

11.9 Advanced tracing options

The options described below (part of the Files/Plot dialogue) allow for fine-grained control of the tracing process. They are particularly useful when printing the silkscreen markings for wiring documentation.

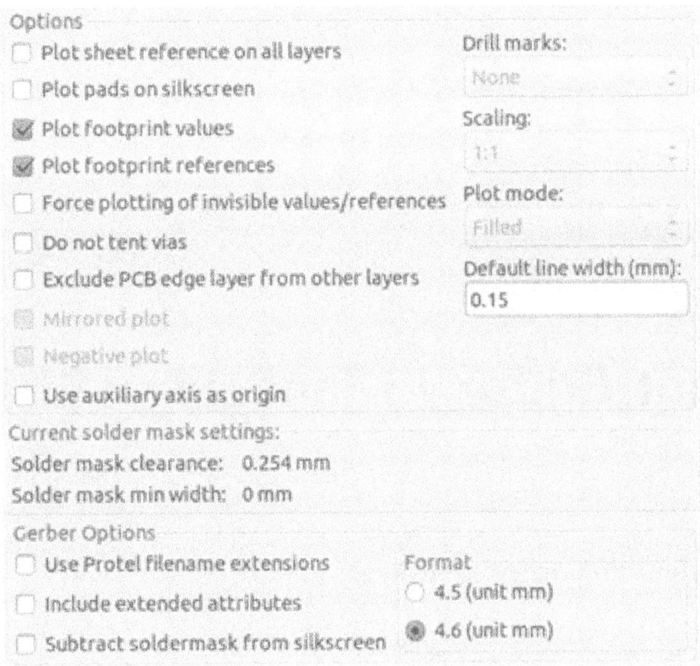

The available options are:

Plot sheet reference on all layers	Trace sheet outline and the cartridge.
Plot pads on silkscreen	Enables/disables printing of pad outlines on the silkscreen layers (if the pads have already been declared to appear on these layers). Prevents any pads from being printed in the disabled mode.
Plot footprint values	Enables printing of VALUE text on the silkscreen.
Plot footprint references	Enables printing of the REFERENCE text on the silkscreen.
Force plotting of invisible values/ references	Forces printing of fields (reference, value) declared as invisible. In combination with *Plot footprint values* and *Plot footprint references*, this option enables production of documents for guiding wiring and repair. These options have proven necessary for circuits using components that are too small (SMD) to allow readable placement of two separate text fields.
Do not tent vias	Delete the mask over the vias.
Exclude PCB edge layer from other layers	GERBER format specific. Do not plot graphic items on edge layer.
Use Protel filename extensions	GERBER format specific. When creating files, use specific extensions for each file. If disabled the Gerber file extension is .gbr.

Chapter 12

Footprint Editor - Managing Libraries

12.1 Overview of Footprint Editor

Pcbnew can simultaneously maintain several libraries. Thus, when a footprint is loaded, all libraries that appear in the library list are searched until the first instance of the footprint is found. In what follows, note that the active library is the library selected within the Footprint Editor, the program will now be described

Footprint Editor enables the creation and the editing of footprints:

- Adding and removing pads.
- Changing pad properties (shape, layer) for individual pads or globally for all pads of a footprint.
- Editing graphic elements (lines, text).
- Editing information fields (value, reference, etc.).
- Editing the associated documentation (description, keywords).

Footprint Editor allows the maintenance of the active library as well by:

- Listing the footprints in the active library.
- Deletion of a footprint from the active library.
- Saving a footprint to the active library.
- Saving all of the footprints contained by a printed circuit.

It is also possible to create new libraries.

The library extension is `.mod`.

12.2 Accessing Footprint Editor

The Footprint Editor can be accessed in two different ways:

- Directly, via the icon 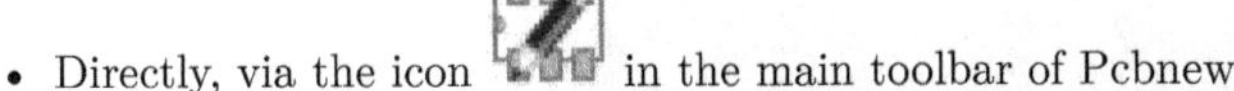 in the main toolbar of Pcbnew.
- In the edit dialog for the active footprint (see figure below: accessed via the context menu), there is the button Footprint Editor.

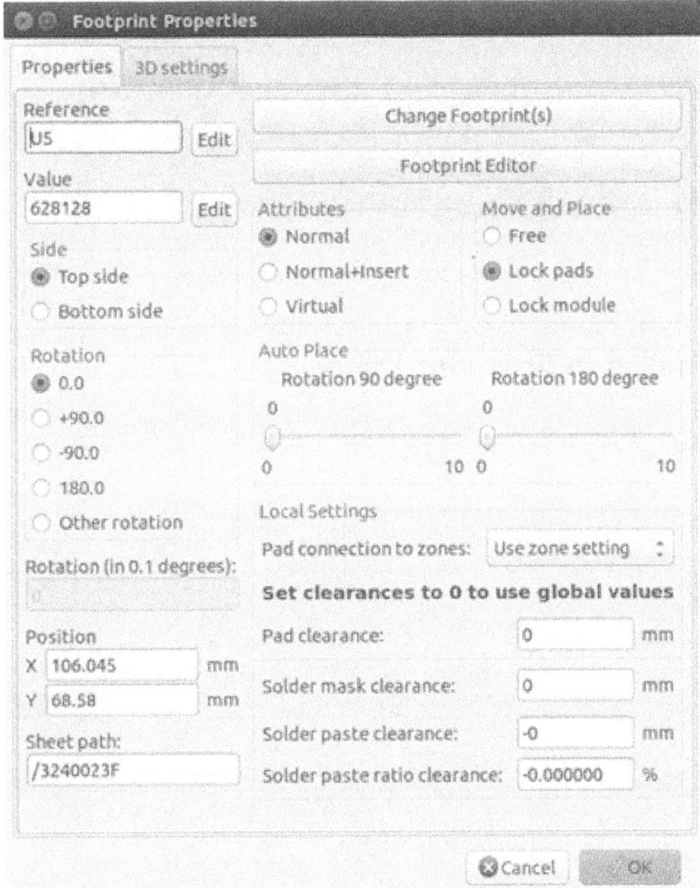

In this case, the active footprint of the board will be loaded automatically in Footprint Editor, enabling immediate editing or archiving.

12.3 Footprint Editor user interface

By calling Footprint Editor the following window will appear:

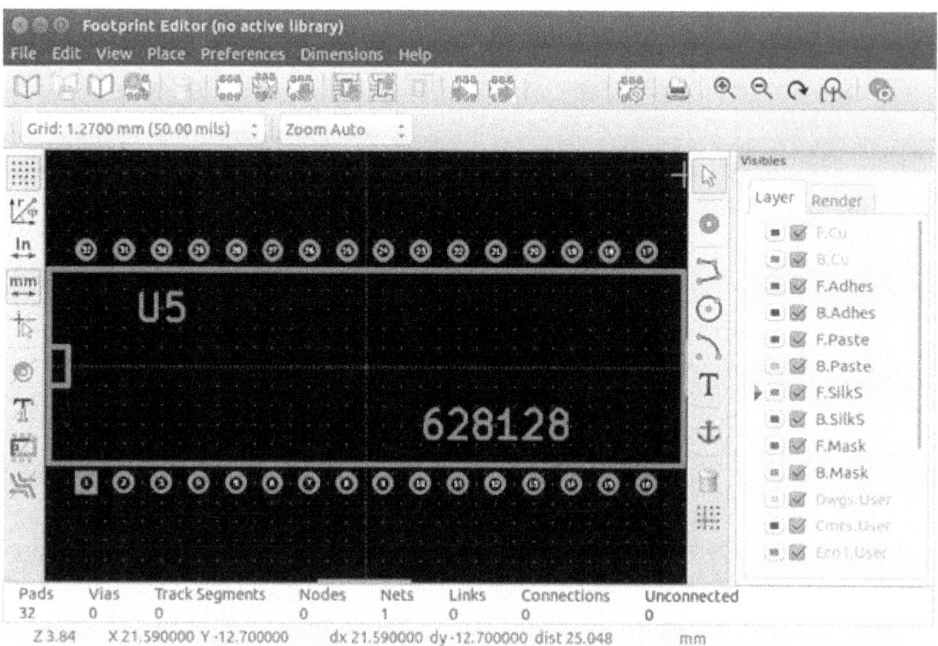

12.4 Top toolbar in Footprint Editor

From this toolbar, the following functions are available:

	Select the active library.
	Save the current footprint to the active library, and write it to disk.
	Create a new library and save the current footprint in it.
	Open the Footprint Viewer
	Access a dialog for deleting a footprint from the active library.
	Create a new footprint.
	Create a footprint using a wizard
	Load a footprint from the active library.
	Load (import) a footprint from the printed circuit board.

	Export the current footprint to the printed circuit board. when the footprint was previously imported from the current board. It will replace the corresponding footprint on the board (i.e., respecting position and orientation).
	Export the current footprint to the printed circuit board. It will be copied on to the printed circuit board at position 0.
	Import a footprint from a file created by the Export command.
	Export a footprint. This command is essentially identical to that for creating a library, the only difference being that it creates a library in the user directory, while creating a library in the standard library directory (usually kicad/modules).
	Undo and Redo
	Invokes the footprint properties dialog.
	Call the print dialog.
	Standard zoom commands.
	Call the pad editor.
	Perform a check of footprint correctness

12.5 Creating a new library

The creation of a new library is done via the button , in this case the file is created by default in the library directory or via the button , in which case the file is created by default in your working directory.

A file-choosing dialog allows the name of the library to be specified and its directory to be changed. In both cases, the library will contain the footprint being edited.

> **Warning**
> If an old library of the same name exists, it will be overwritten without warning.

12.6 Saving a footprint in the active library

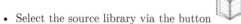

The action of saving a footprint (thereby modifying the file of the active library) is performed using this button . If a footprint of the same name already exists, it will be replaced. Since you will depend upon the accuracy of the library footprints, it is worth double-checking the footprint before saving.

It is recommended to edit either the reference or value field text to the name of the footprint as identified in the library.

12.7 Transferring a footprint from one library to another

- Select the source library via the button .
- Load the footprint via the button 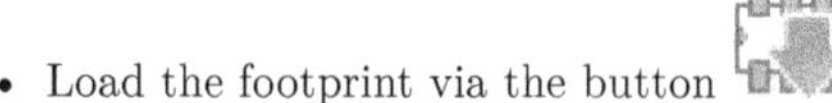.
- Select the destination library via the button 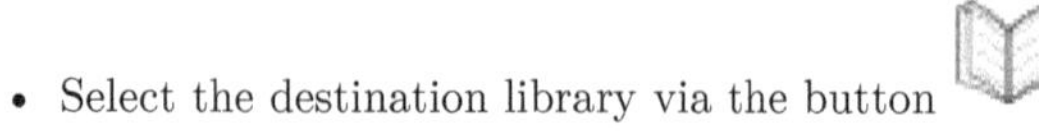.
- Save the footprint via the button 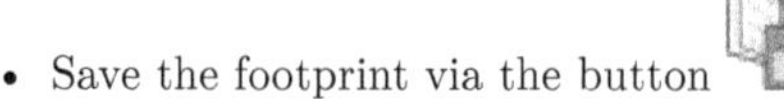

You may also wish to delete the source footprint.

- Reselect the source library with 
- Delete the old footprint via the button

12.8 Saving all footprints of your board in the active library

It is possible to copy all of the footprints of a given board design to the active library. These footprints will keep their current library names. This command has two uses:

- To create an archive or complete a library with the footprints from a board, in the event of the loss of a library.
- More importantly, it facilitates library maintenance by enabling the production of documentation for the library, as below.

12.9 Documentation for library footprints

It is strongly recommended to document the footprints you create, in order to enable rapid and error-free searching.

For example, who is able to remember all of the multiple pin-out variants of a TO92 package? The Footprint Properties dialog offers a simple solution to this problem.

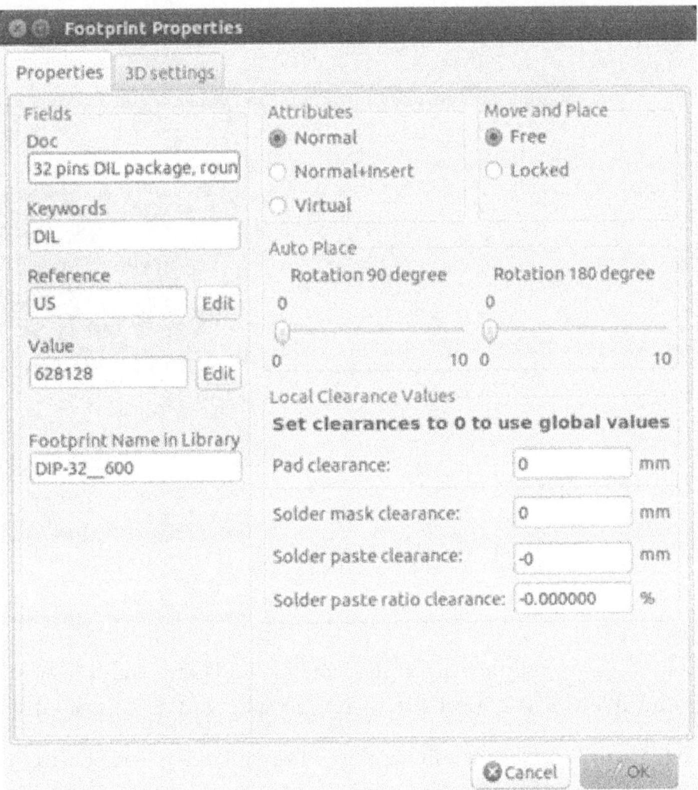

This dialog accepts:

- A one-line comment/description.
- Multiple keywords.

The description is displayed with the component list in Cvpcb and, in Pcbnew, it is used in the footprint selection dialogs.

The keywords enable searches to be restricted to those footprints corresponding to particular keywords.

When directly loading a footprint (the icon of the right-hand Pcbnew toolbar), keywords may be entered in the dialog box. Thus, entering the text `=CONN` will cause the display of the list of footprints whose keyword lists contain the word `CONN`.

12.10 Documenting libraries - recommended practice

It is recommended to create libraries indirectly, by creating one or more auxiliary circuit boards that constitute the source of (part of) the library, as follows: Create a circuit board in A4 format, in order to be able to print easily to scale (scale = 1).

Create the footprints that the library will contain on this circuit board. The library itself will be created with the File/Archive footprints/Create footprint archive command.

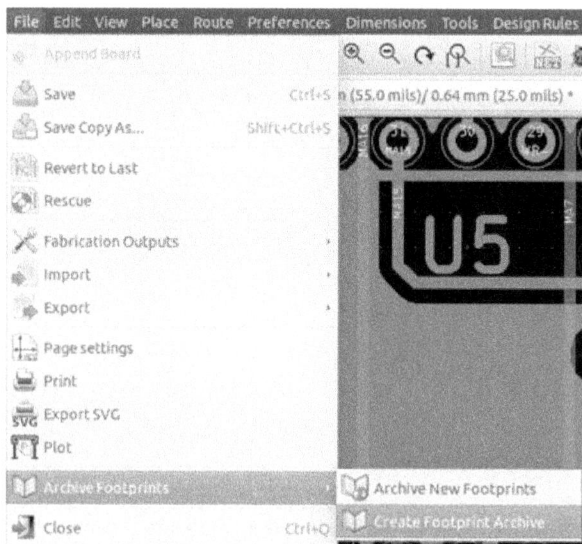

The "true source" of the library will thus be the auxiliary circuit board, and it is on this circuit that any subsequent alterations of footprints will be made. Naturally, several circuit boards can be saved in the same library.

It is generally a good idea to make different libraries for different kinds of components (connectors, discretes,···), since Pcbnew is able to search many libraries when loading footprints.

Here is an example of such a library source:

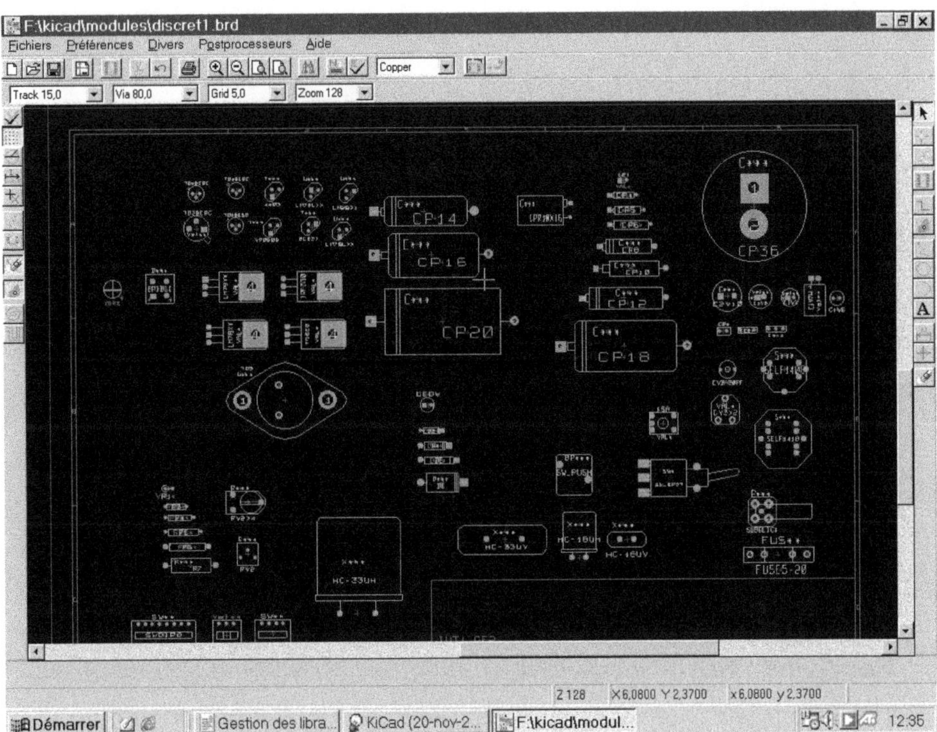

This technique has several advantages:

- The circuit can be printed to scale and serve as documentation for the library with no further effort.
- Future changes of Pcbnew may require regeneration of the libraries, something that can be done very quickly if circuit-board sources of this type have been used. This is important, because the circuit board file formats are guaranteed to remain compatible during future development, but this is not the case for the library file format.

12.11 Footprint Libraries Management

The list of footprint libraries in Pcbnew can be edited using the Footprint Libraries Manager. This allows you to add and remove footprint libraries by hand, and also allows you to invoke the Footprint Libraries Wizard by pressing the "Append With Wizard" button.

The Footprint Libraries Wizard can also be invoked through the Preferences menu, and can automatically add a library (detecting its type) from a file or from a Github URL. The URL for the official libraries is: https://github.com/KiCad

More details about footprint library tables and the Manager and Wizard can be found in the CvPcb Reference Manual in the section *Footprint Library Tables.*

12.12 3D Shapes Libraries Management

The 3D shape libraries can be downloaded by 3D Shape Libraries Wizard. It can be invoked from the menu Preferences → 3D Shapes Libraries Downloader.

Chapter 13

Footprint Editor - Creating and Editing Footprints

13.1 Footprint Editor overview

Footprint Editor is used for editing and creating PCB footprints. This includes:

- Adding and removing pads.
- Changing pad properties (shape, layer), for individual pads or for all the pads in a footprint.
- Adding and editing graphic elements (contours, text).
- Editing fields (value, reference, etc.).
- Editing the associated documentation (description, keywords).

13.2 Footprint elements

A footprint is the physical representation (footprint) of the part to be inserted in the PCB and it must be linked to the relative component in your schematic. Each footprint includes three different elements:

- The pads.
- Graphical contours and text.
- Fields.

In addition, a number of other parameters must be correctly defined if the auto-placement function will be used. The same holds for the generation of auto-insertion files.

13.2.1 Pads

Two pad properties are important:

- Geometry (shape, layers, drill holes).
- The pad number, which is constituted by up to four alphanumeric characters. Thus, the following are all valid pad numbers: 1, 45 and 9999, but also AA56 and ANOD. The pad number must be identical to that of the corresponding pin number in the schematic, because it defines the matching pin and pad numbers that Pcbnew links pins and pads with.

13.2.2 Contours

Graphical contours are used to draw the physical shape of the footprint. Several different types of contour are available: lines, circles, arcs, and text. Contours have no electrical significance, they are simply graphical aids.

13.2.3 Fields

These are text elements associated with a footprint. Two are obligatory and always present: the reference field and the value field. These are automatically read and updated by Pcbnew when a netlist is read during the loading of footprints into your board. The reference is replaced by the appropriate schematic reference (U1, IC3, etc.). The value is replaced by the value of the corresponding part in the schematic (47K, 74LS02, etc.). Other fields can be added and these will behave like graphical text.

13.3 Starting Footprint Editor and selecting a footprint to edit

Footprint Editor can be started in two ways:

- Directly via the icon from the main toolbar of Pcbnew. This allows the creation or modification of a footprint in the library.
- Double-clicking a footprint will launch the *Footprint Properties* menu, which offers a *Go to Footprint Editor* button. If this option is used, the footprint from the board will be loaded into the editor, for modification or for saving.

13.4 Footprint Editor Toolbars

Calling Footprint Editor will launch a new window that looks like this:

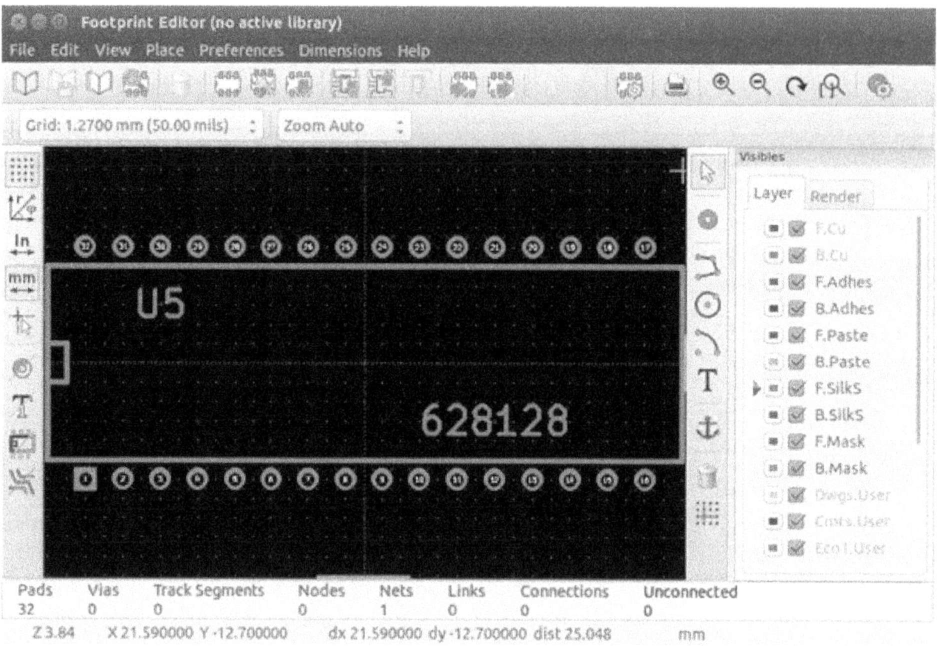

13.4.1 Edit toolbar (right-hand side)

This toolbar contains tools for:

- Placing pads.
- Adding graphic elements (contours, text).
- Positioning the anchor.
- Deleting elements.

The specific functions are the following:

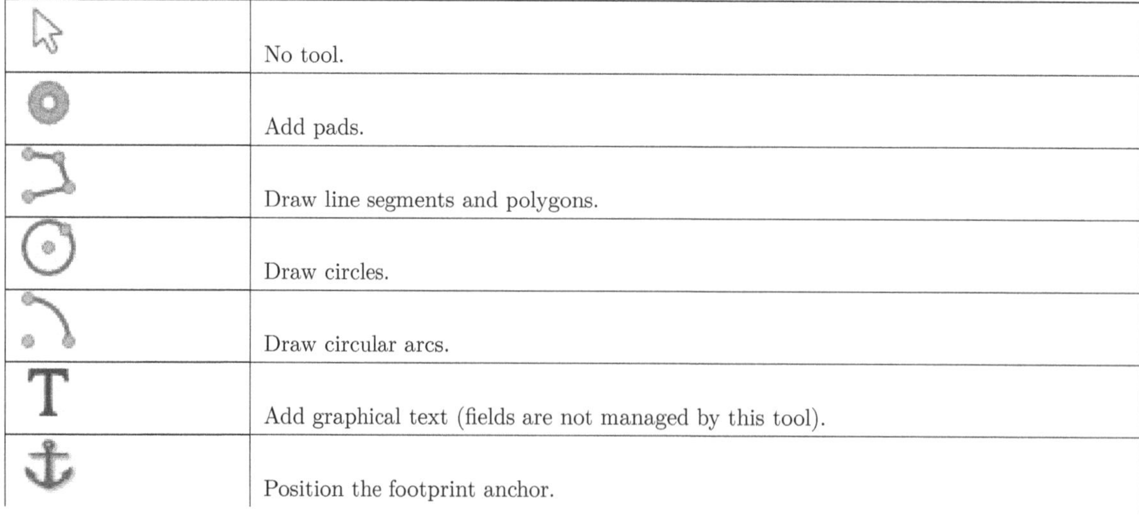

	No tool.
	Add pads.
	Draw line segments and polygons.
	Draw circles.
	Draw circular arcs.
	Add graphical text (fields are not managed by this tool).
	Position the footprint anchor.

	Delete elements.
	Grid origin. (grid offset). Useful for placement of pads. The grid origin can be put on a given location (the first pad to place), and after the grid size can be set to the pad pitch. Placing pads is therefore very easy

13.4.2 Display toolbar (left-hand side)

These tools manage the display options in Footprint Editor:

	Display the grid.
	Display polar coordinates.
mm In	Use units of mm or inch
	Toggle cursor crosshair shape
	Display pad in outline mode.
	Display text in outline mode.
	Display contours in outline mode.
	Toggle high-contrast mode

13.5 Context Menus

The right mouse button calls up menus that depend upon the element beneath the cursor.

The context menu for editing footprint parameters:

The context menu for editing pads:

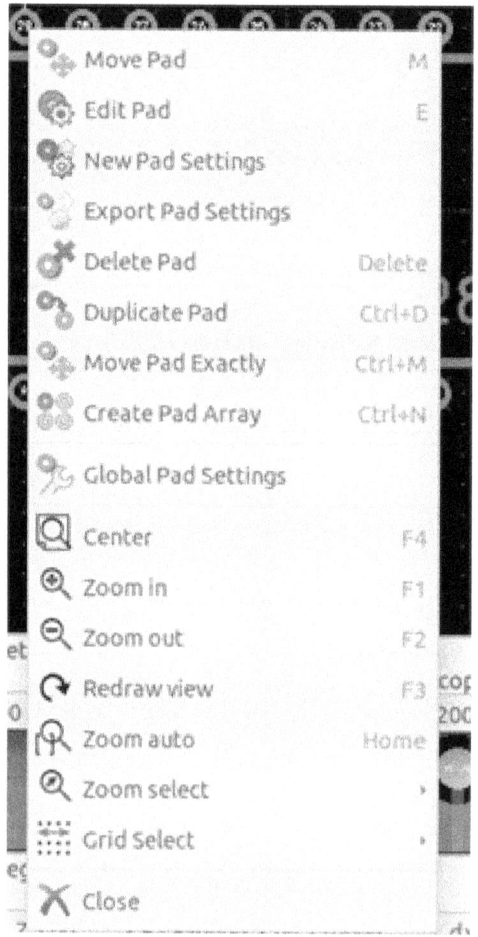

The context menu for editing graphic elements:

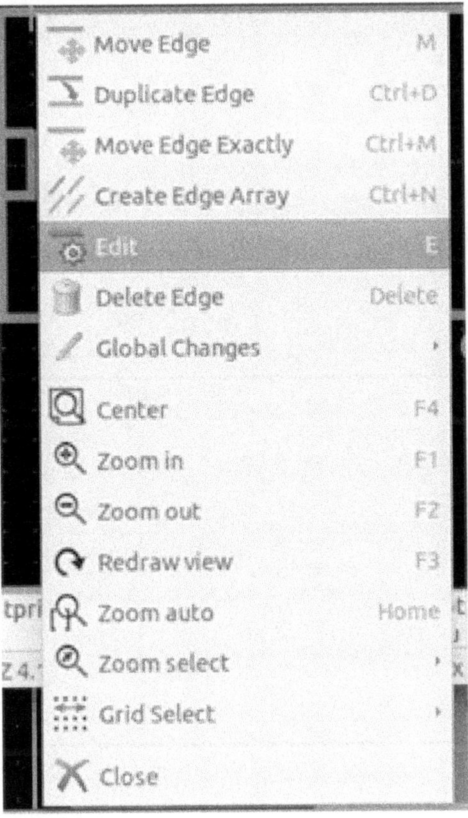

13.6 Footprint properties dialog

This dialog can be launched when the cursor is over a footprint by clicking on the right mouse button and then selecting *Edit Footprint*.

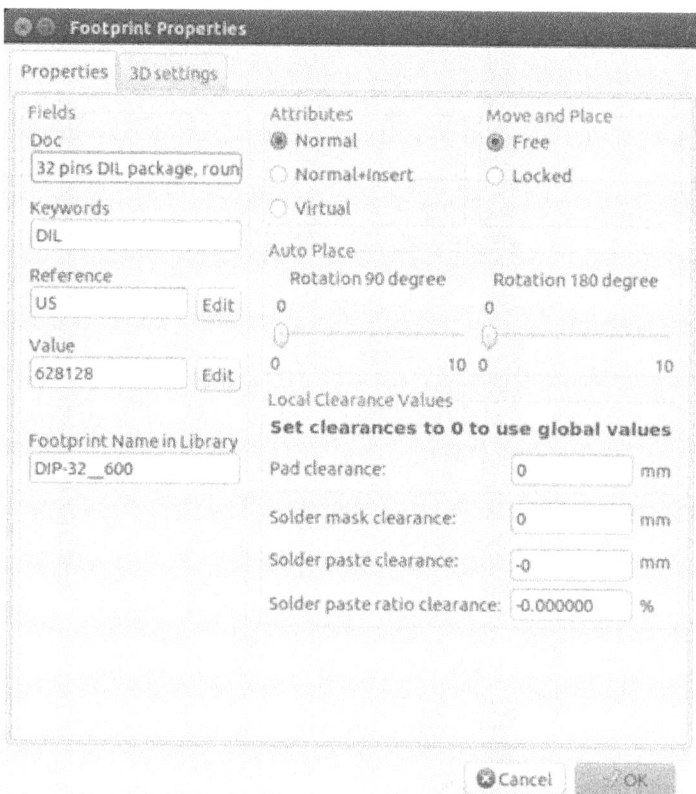

The dialog can be used to define the main footprint parameters.

13.7 Creating a new footprint

A new footprint can be created via the button . The name of the new footprint will be requested. This will be the name by which the footprint will be identified in the library.

This text also serves as the footprint value, which is ultimately replaced by the real value (100 µF_16 V, 100 Ω_0.5 W, …).

The new footprint will require:

- Contours (and possibly graphic text).
- Pads.
- A value (hidden text that is replaced by the true value when used).

Alternative method:

When a new footprint is similar to an existing footprint in a library or a circuit board, an alternative and quicker method of creating the new footprint is as follows:

- Load the similar footprint (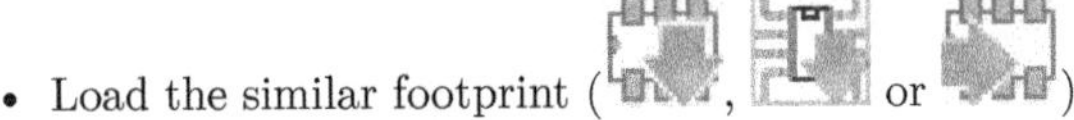).
- Modify the "Footprint Name in Library" field in order to generate a new identifier (name).
- Edit and save the new footprint.

13.8 Adding and editing pads

Once a footprint has been created, pads can be added, deleted or modified. Modification of pads can be local, affecting only the pad under the cursor, or global, affecting all pads of the footprint.

13.8.1 Adding pads

Select the icon from the right hand toolbar. Pads can be added by clicking in the desired position with the left mouse button. Pad properties are predefined in the pad properties menu.

Do not forget to enter the pad number.

13.8.2 Setting pad properties

This can be done in three different ways:

- Selecting the icon from the horizontal toolbar.
- Clicking on an existing pad and selecting *Edit Pad*. The pad' s settings can then be edited.
- Clicking on an existing pad and selecting *Export Pad Settings*. In this case, the geometrical properties of the selected pad will become the default pad properties.

In the first two cases, the following dialog window will be displayed:

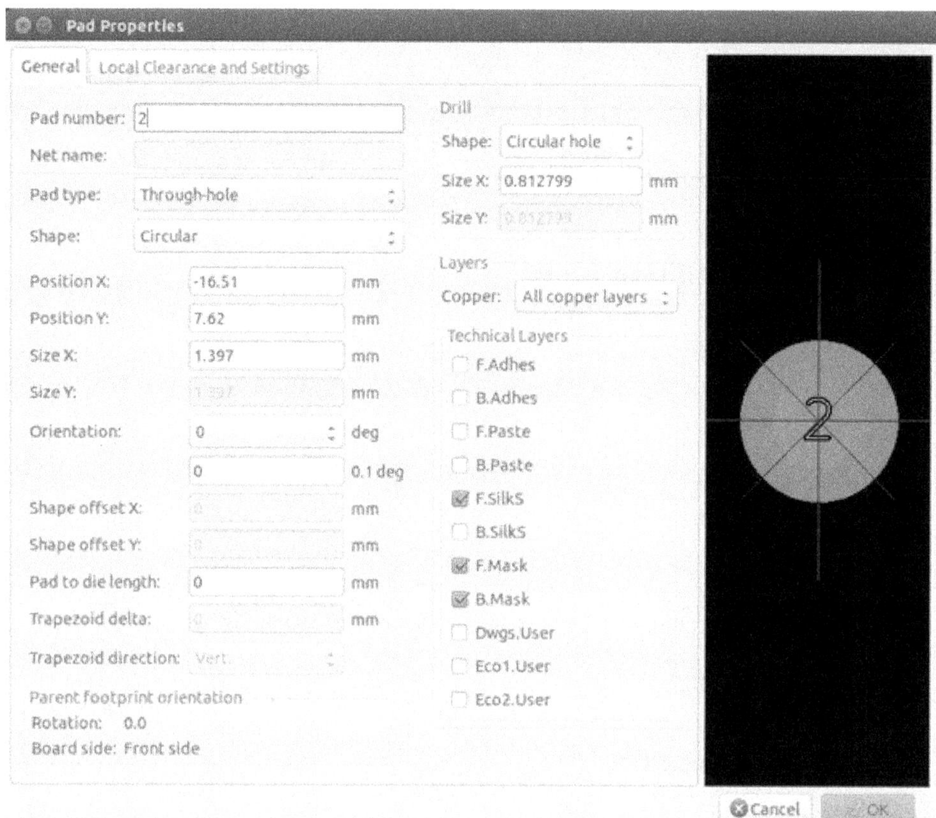

Care should be taken to define correctly the layers to which the pad will belong. In particular, although copper layers are easy to define, the management of non-copper layers (solder mask, solder pads···) is equally important for circuit manufacture and documentation.

The Pad Type selector triggers an automatic selection of layers that is generally sufficient.

13.8.2.1 Rectangular pads

For SMD footprints of the VQFP/PQFP type which have rectangular pads on all four sides (both horizontal and vertical) it is recommended to use just one shape (for example, a horizontal rectangle) and to place it with different orientations (0 for horizontal and 90 degrees for vertical). Global resizing of pads can then be done in a single operation.

13.8.2.2 Rotate pads

Rotations of -90 or -180 are only required for trapezoidal pads used in microwave footprints.

13.8.2.3 Non-plated through hole pads

Pads can be defined as Non-Plated Through Hole pads (NPTH pads).

These pads must be defined on one or all copper layers (obviously, the hole exists on all copper layers).

This requirement allows you to define specific clearance parameters (for instance clearance for a screw).

When the pad hole size is the same as the pad size, for a round or oval pad, this pad is NOT plotted on copper layers in GERBER files.

These pads are used for mechanical purposes, therefore no pad name or net name is allowed. A connection to a net is not possible.

13.8.2.4 Pads not on copper layers

These are unusual pads. This option can be used to create fiducials or masks on technical layers.

13.8.2.5 Offset parameter

Pad 3 has an offset Y = 15 mils:

13.8.2.6 Delta Parameter (trapezoidal pads)

Pad 1 has its parameter Delta X = 10 mils

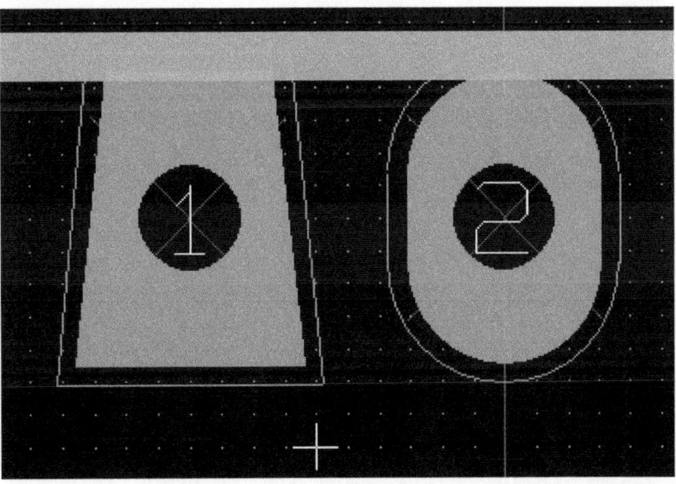

13.8.3 Setting clearance for solder mask and solder paste mask layers

Setting a clearance can be made at 3 levels:

- Global level.
- Footprint level.
- Pad level.

Pcbnew uses the following to calculate clearances:

- Pad settings. If null,
- Footprint settings. If null,
- Global settings.

13.8.3.1 Remarks

The solder mask pad shape is usually bigger than the pad itself. So the clearance value is positive. The solder paste mask pad shape is usually smaller than the pad itself. So the clearance value is negative.

13.8.3.2 Solder paste mask parameters

For solder paste mask there are two parameters:

- A fixed value.
- A percentage of the pad size.

The real value is the sum of these two values.

Footprint level settings:

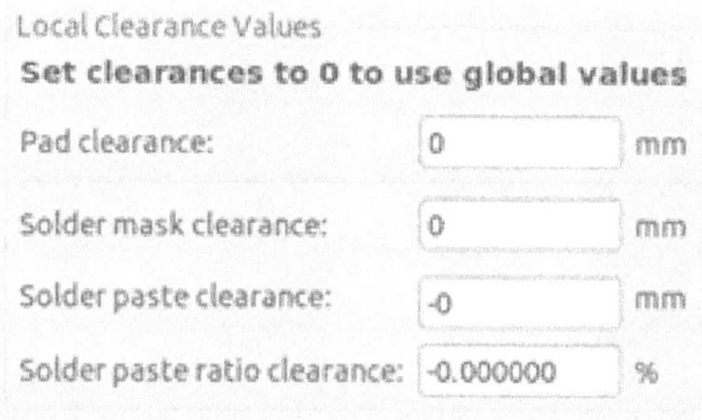

Pad level settings:

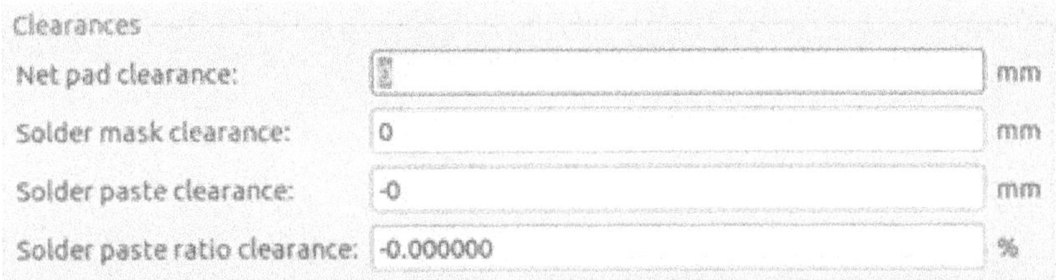

13.9 Fields Properties

There are at least two fields: reference and value.

Their parameters (attribute, size, width) must be updated. You can access the dialog box from the pop-up menu, by double clicking on the field, or by the footprint properties dialog box:

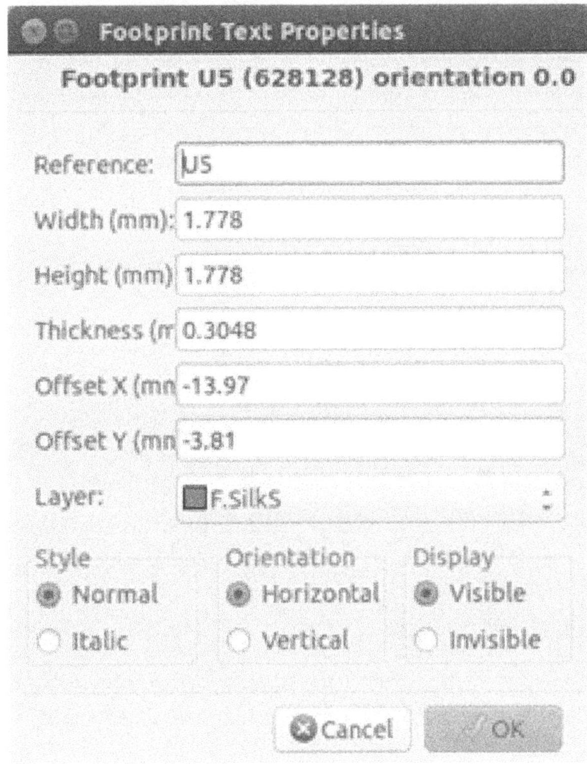

13.10 Automatic placement of a footprint

If the user wishes to exploit the full capabilities of the auto-placement functions, it is necessary to define the allowed orientations of the footprint (Footprint Properties dialog).

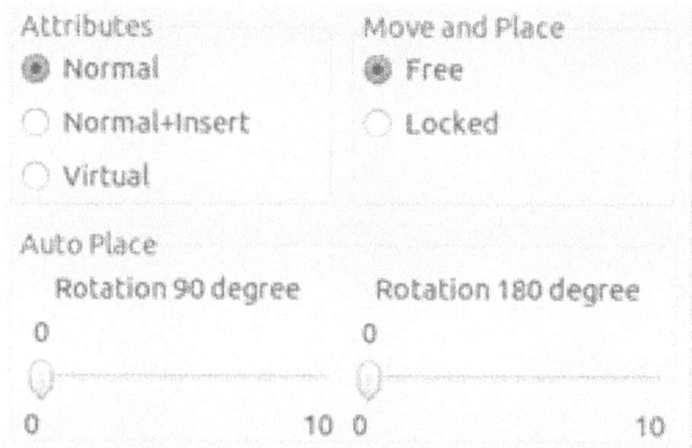

Usually, rotation of 180 degrees is permitted for resistors, non-polarized capacitors and other symmetrical elements.

Some footprints (small transistors, for example) are often permitted to rotate by +/- 90 or 180 degrees. By default, a new footprint will have its rotation permissions set to zero. This can be adjusted according to the following rule:

A value of 0 makes rotation impossible, 10 allows it completely, and any intermediate value represents a limited rotation. For example, a resistor might have a permission of 10 to rotate 180 degrees (unrestrained) and a permission of 5 for a +/- 90 degree rotation (allowed, but discouraged).

13.11 Attributes

The attributes window is the following:

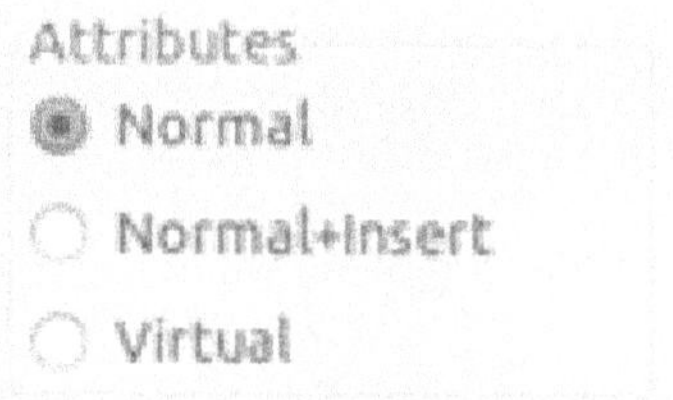

- Normal is the standard attribute.
- Normal+Insert indicates that the footprint must appear in the automatic insertion file (for automatic insertion machines). This attribute is most useful for surface mount components (SMDs).
- Virtual indicates that a component is directly formed by the circuit board. Examples would be edge connectors or inductors created by a particular track shape (as sometimes seen in microwave footprints).

13.12 Documenting footprints in a library

It is strongly recommended to document newly created footprints, in order to facilitate their rapid and accurate retrieval. Who is able to recall the multiple pin-out variants of a TO92 footprint?

The Footprint Properties dialog offers a simple and yet powerful means for documentation generation.

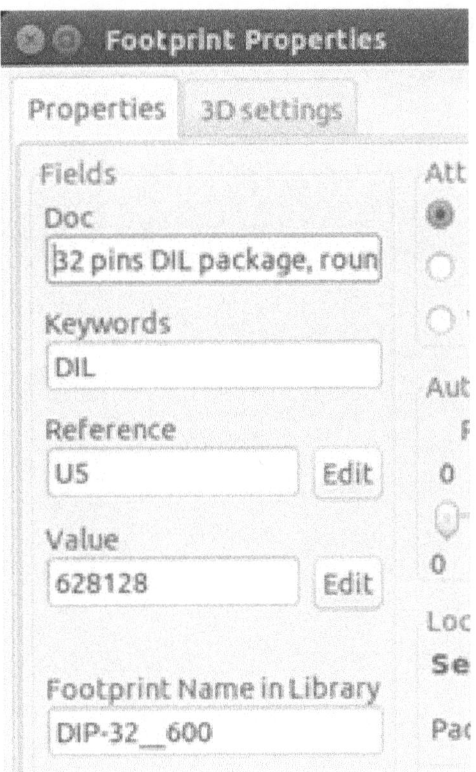

This menu allows:

- The entry of a comment line (description).
- Multiple keywords.

The comment line is displayed with the component list in CvPcb and in the footprint selection menus in Pcbnew. The keywords can be used to restrict searches to those parts possessing the given keywords.

Thus, while using the load footprint command (icon in the right-hand toolbar in Pcbnew), it is possible to type the text `=TO220` into the dialog box to have Pcbnew display a list of the footprints possessing the keyword `TO220`

13.13 3-dimensional visualisation

A footprint may have been associated with a file containing a three-dimensional representation of itself. In order to associate such a file with a footprint, select the 3D Settings tab. The options panel is the following:

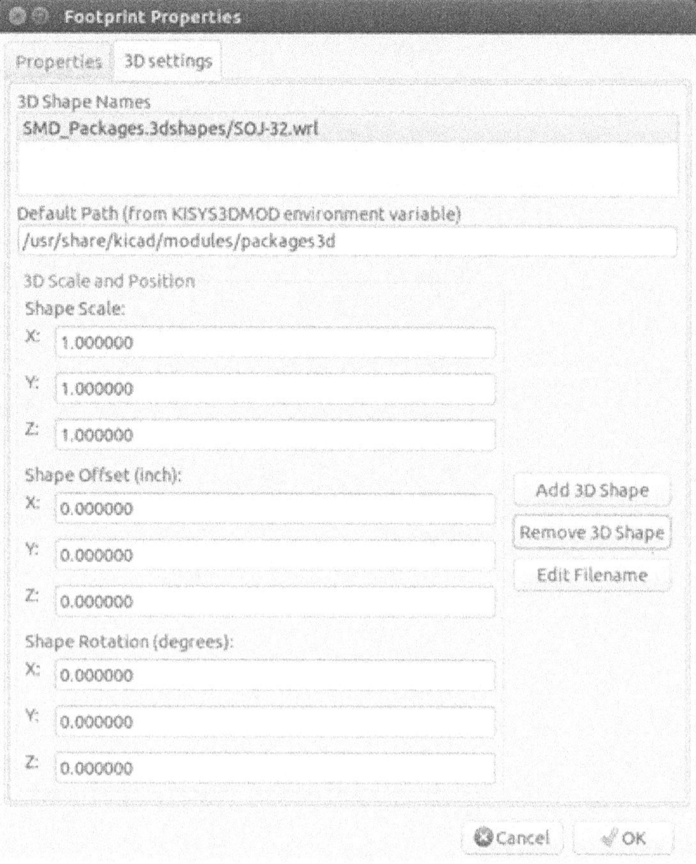

The data information should be provided:

- The file containing the 3D representation (created by the 3D modeler Wings3D, in vrml format, via the export to vrml command).
- The default path is kicad/modules/package3d. In the example, the file name is discret/to_220horiz.wrl, using the default path)
- The x, y and z scales.
- The offset with respect to the anchor point of the footprint (usually zero).
- The initial rotation in degrees about each axis (usually zero).

Setting scale allows:

- To use the same 3D file for footprints which have similar shapes but different sizes (resistors, capacitors, SMD components…)
- For small (or very large) packages, a better use of the Wings3D grid is to scale **0.1 inch in Pcbnew = 1 grid unit** in Wings3D.

If such a file has been specified, it is possible to view the component in 3D.

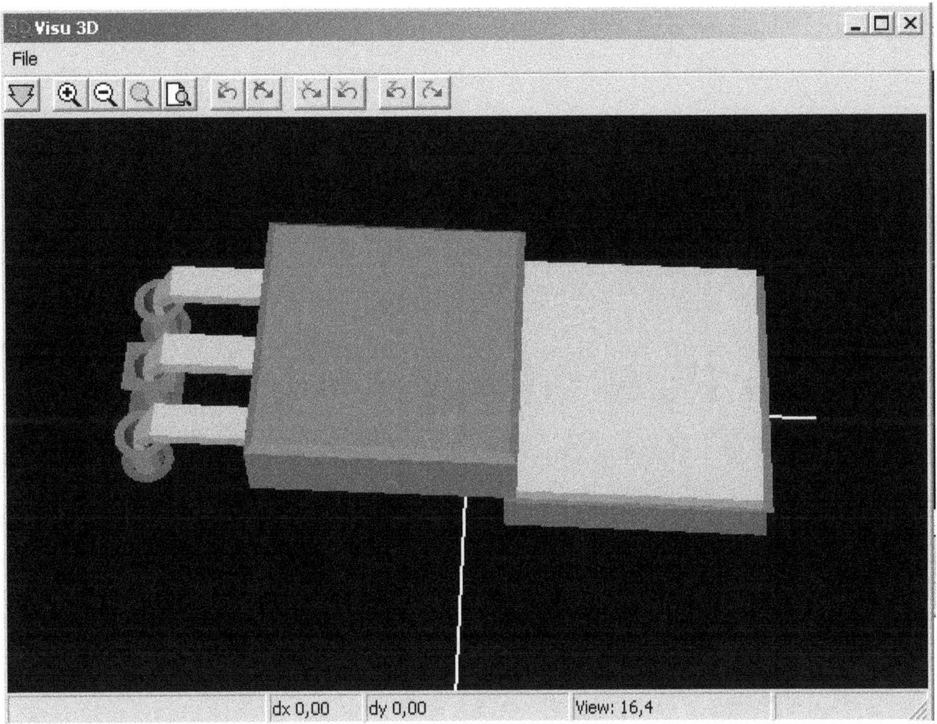

The 3D model will automatically appear in the 3D representation of the printed circuit board.

13.14 Saving a footprint into the active library

The save command (modification of the file of the active library) is activated by the button.

If a footprint of the same name exists (an older version), it will be overwritten. Because it is important to be able to have confidence in the library footprints, it is worth double-checking the footprint for errors before saving.

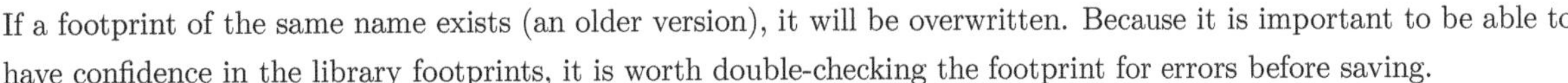

Before saving, it is also recommended to change the reference or value of the footprint to be equal to the library name of the footprint.

13.15 Saving a footprint to the board

If the edited footprint comes from the current board, the button will update this footprint on the board.

Chapter 14

Advanced PCB editing tools

There are some more advanced editing tools available in Pcbnew and Footprint Editor, which can help you to efficiently lay out components on the canvas.

14.1 Duplicating items

Duplication is a method to clone an item and pick it up in the same action. It is broadly similar to copy-and-pasting, but it allows you to "sprinkle" components over the PCB and it allows you to manually lay out components using the "Move Exact" tool (see below) more easily.

Duplication is done by using the hotkey (which defaults to Ctrl-D) or the duplicate item option in the context menu. In the legacy renderer, these appear as below, depending on the item type:

14.2 Moving items exactly

The "Move Exact" tool allows you to move an item (or group of items) by a certain amount, which can be entered in Cartesian or polar formats and which can be entered in any supported units. This is useful when it would otherwise be cumbersome to switch to a different grid, or when a feature is not spaced according to any existing grids.

To use this tool, select the items you wish to move and then use either the hotkey (defaults to Ctrl-M) or the context menu items to invoke the dialog. You can also invoke the dialog with the hotkey when moving or duplicating items, which can make it easy to repeatedly apply an offset to multiple components.

Move exact with Cartesian move vector entry

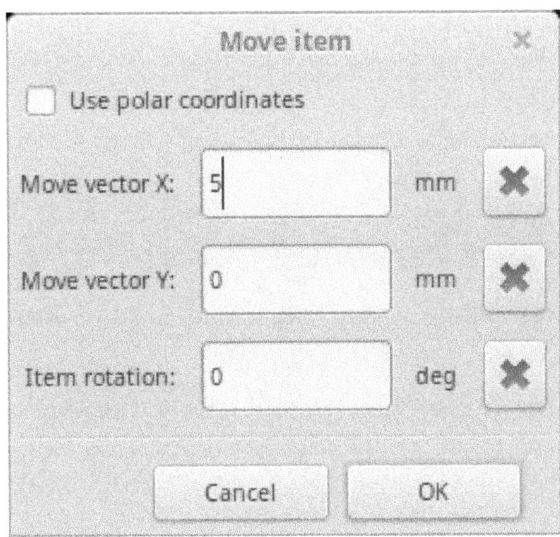

Move exact with polar move vector entry

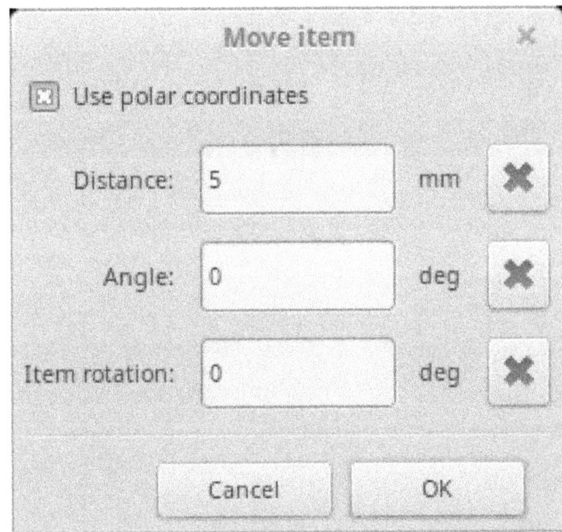

The checkbox allows you to switch between Cartesian and polar co-ordinate systems. Whatever is currently in the form will be converted automatically to the other system.

Then you enter the desired move vector. You can use the units indicated by the labels ("mm" in the images above) or you can specify the units yourself (e.g. "1 in" for an inch, or "2 rad" for 2 radians).

Pressing OK will apply the translation to the selection, and cancel will close the dialog and the items will not be moved. If OK is pressed, the move vector will be saved and pre-filled next time the dialog is opened, which allows repeated application of the same vector to multiple objects.

14.3 Array tools

Pcbnew and the Footprint Editor both have assistants for creating arrays of features and components, which can be used to easily and accurately lay out repetitive elements on PCBs and in footprints.

14.3.1 Activating the array tool

The array tool acts on the component under the cursor, or, in GAL mode, on a selection. It can be accessed either via the context menu for the selection or by a keyboard shortcut (defaults to Ctrl-N). In legacy mode, the context menu icons indicate an array of the selected type:

The array tool is presented as a dialog window, with a pane for the types of arrays. There are two types of arrays supported so far: grid, and circular.

Each type of array can be fully specified on the respective panes. Geometric options (how the grid is laid out) go on the left; numbering options (including how the numbers progress across the grid) on the right.

14.3.2 Grid arrays

Grid arrays are arrays that lay components out according to a 2-dimensional square grid. This kind of array can also produce a linear array by only laying out a single row or column.

The settings dialog for grid arrays look like this:

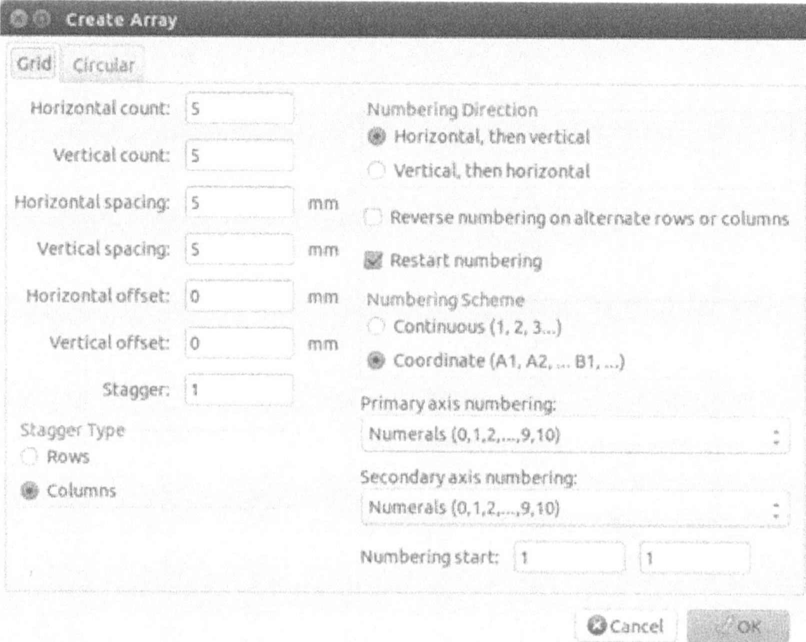

14.3.2.1 Geometric options

The geometric options are as follow:

- **Horrizontal count**: the number of "columns" in the grid.
- **Vertical count**: the number of "rows" in the grid.

- **Horizontal spacing**: the horizontal distance from item to the item in the same row and next column. If this is negative, the grid progresses from right to left.
- **Vertical spacing**: the vertical distance from one item to the item in the same column and the next row. If this is negative, the grid progress bottom to top.
- **Horizontal offset**: start each row this distance to the right of the previous one
- **Vertical offset**: start each column this distance below the previous one

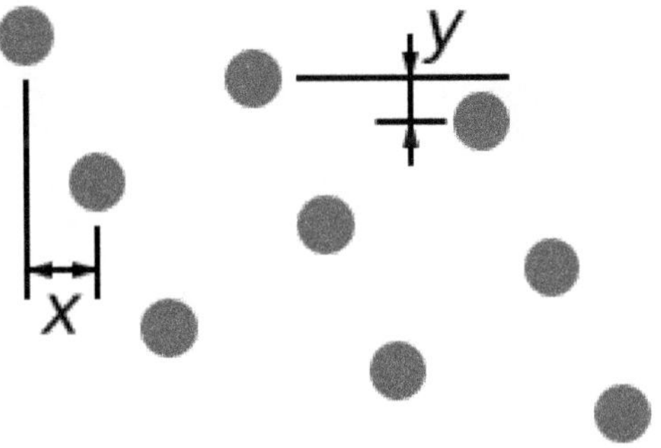

Figure 14.1: 3x3 grid with x and y offsets

- **Stagger**: add an offset to every set of "n" rows/columns, with each row progressing by 1/n′ th of the relevant spacing dimension:

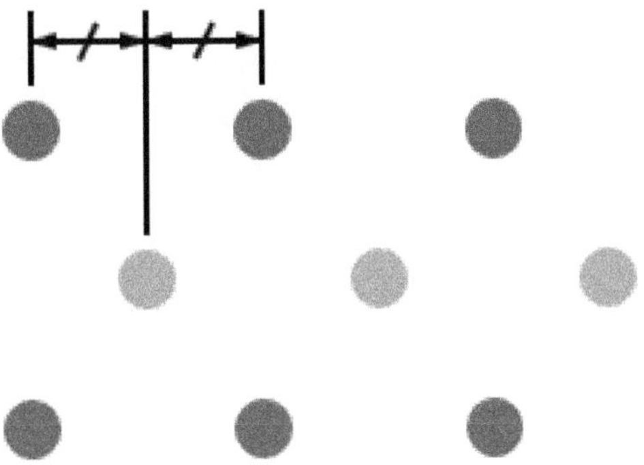

Figure 14.2: 3x3 grid with a row stagger of 2

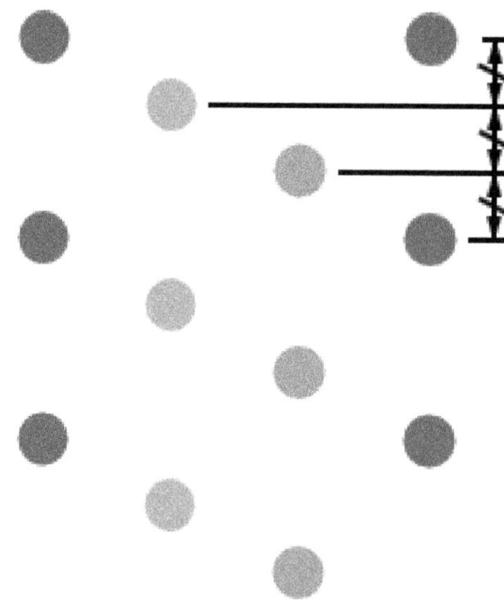

Figure 14.3: 4x3 grid with a column stagger of 3

14.3.2.2 Numbering options

- **Numbering Direction**: Determines whether numbers proceed along rows and then moves to the next row, or down columns and then to the next column. Note that the direction on numbering is defined by the sign of the spacing: a negative spacing will result in right-to-left or bottom-to-top numbering.
- **Reverse numbering on alternate rows or columns**: If selected, the numbering order (left-to-right or right-to-left, for example) on alternate rows or columns. Whether rows or columns alternate depends on the numbering direction. This option is useful for packages like DIPs where the numbering proceeds up one side and down the other.
- **Restart numbering**: if laying out using items that already have numbers, reset to the start, otherwise continue if possible from this item' s number
- **Numbering Scheme**
  - **Continuous**: the numbering just continues across a row/column break - if the last item in the first row is numbered "7", the first item in the second row will be "8".
  - **Coordinate**: the numbering uses a two-axis scheme where the number is made up of the row and column index. Which one comes first (row or column) is determined by the numbering direction.
- **Axis numberings**: what "alphabet" to use to number the axes. Choices are
  - **Numerals** for normal integer indices
  - **Hexadecimal** for base-16 indexing
  - **Alphabetic, minus IOSQXZ**, a common scheme for electronic components, recommended by ASME Y14.35M-1997 sec. 5.2 (previously MIL-STD-100 sec. 406.5) to avoid confusion with numerals.
  - **Full alphabet** from A-Z.

14.3.3 Circular arrays

Circular arrays lay out items around a circle or a circular arc. The circle is defined by the location of the selection (or the centre of a selected group) and a centre point that is specified. Below is the circular array configuration dialog:

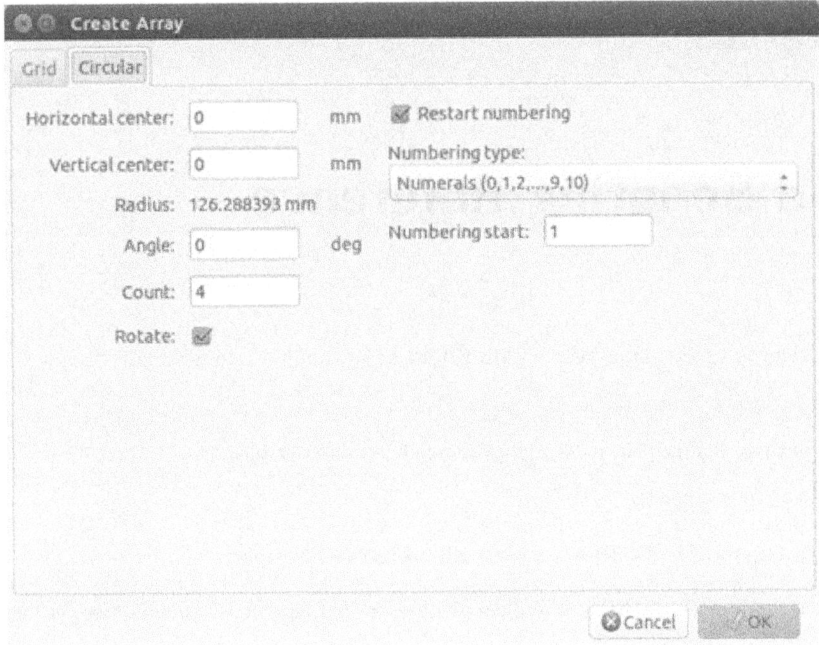

14.3.3.1 Geometric options

- **Horizontal center**, **Vertical center**: The centre of the circle. The radius field below will update automatically when you adjust these.
- **Angle**: The angular difference between two adjacent items in the array. Set this to zero to evenly divide the circle with "count" elements.
- **Count**: Number of items in the array (including the original item)
- **Rotate**: Rotate each item around its own location. Otherwise, the item will be translated but not rotated (for example, a square pad will always remain upright if this option is not set).

14.3.3.2 Numbering options

Circular arrays have only one dimension and a simpler geometry than grids. The meanings of the available options are the same as for grids. Items are numbered clockwise - for an anticlockwise array, specify a negative angle.

Chapter 15

KiCad Scripting Reference

Scripting allows you to automate tasks within KiCad using the Python language.

Also see the doxygen documentation on Python Scripting Reference.

You can see python module help by typing `pydoc pcbnew` on your terminal.

Using scripting you can create:

- **Plugins**: this type of script is loaded when KiCad starts. Examples:
  - **Footprint Wizards**: To help you build footprints easily filling in parameters. See the dedicated section Footprint Wizards below.
  - **File I/O** *(planned)*: To let you write plugins to export/import other filetypes
  - **Actions** *(planned)*: Associate events to scripting actions or register new menus or toolbar icons.
- **Command Line Scripts**: scripts that can be used from the command line, load boards or libraries, modify them, and render outputs or new boards.

It shall be noted that the only KiCad applicaiton that supports scripting is Pcbnew. It is also planned for Eeschema in the future.

15.1 KiCad Objects

The scripting API reflects the internal object structure inside KiCad/pcbnew. BOARD is the main object, that has a set of properties and a set of MODULEs, and TRACKs/VIAs, TEXTE_PCB, DIMENSION, DRAWSEGMENT. Then MODULEs have D_PADs, EDGEs, etc.

- See the BOARD section below.

15.2 Basic API Reference

All the pcbnew API is provided from the "pcbnew" module in Python. GetBoard() method will return the current pcb open at editor, useful for commands written from the integrated scripting shell inside pcbnew or action plugins.

15.3 Loading and Saving a Board

- **LoadBoard(filename):** loads a board from file returning a BOARD object, using the file format that matches the filename extension.
- **SaveBoard(filename,board):** saves a BOARD object to file, using the file format that matches the filename extension.
- **board.Save(filename):** same as above, but it' s a method of BOARD object.

Example that loads a board, hides all values, shows all references

```
#!/usr/bin/env python2.7
import sys
from pcbnew import *

filename=sys.argv[1]

pcb = LoadBoard(filename)
for module in pcb.GetModules():
    print "* Module: %s"%module.GetReference()
    module.Value().SetVisible(False)      # set Value as Hidden
    module.Reference().SetVisible(True)   # set Reference as Visible

pcb.Save("mod_"+filename)
```

15.4 Listing and Loading Libraries

Enumerate library, enumerate modules, enumerate pads

```
#!/usr/bin/python

from pcbnew import *

libpath = "/usr/share/kicad/modules/Sockets.pretty"
print ">> enumerate footprints, pads of",libpath

# Load the suitable plugin to read/write the .pretty library
# (containing the .kicad_mod footprint files)
src_type = IO_MGR.GuessPluginTypeFromLibPath( libpath );
# Rem: we can force the plugin type by using IO_MGR.PluginFind( IO_MGR.KICAD )
plugin = IO_MGR.PluginFind( src_type )

# Print plugin type name: (Expecting "KiCad" for a .pretty library)
print( "Selected plugin type: %s" % plugin.PluginName() )

list_of_footprints = plugin.FootprintEnumerate(libpath)
```

```
for name in list_of_footprints:
    fp = plugin.FootprintLoad(libpath,name)
    # print the short name of the footprint
    print name  # this is the name inside the loaded library
    # followed by ref field, value field, and decription string:
    # Remember ref and value texts are dummy texts, replaced by the schematic values
    # when reading a netlist.
    print "  ->", fp.GetReference(), fp.GetValue(), fp.GetDescription()

    # print pad info: GetPos0() is the pad position relative to the footrint position
    for pad in fp.Pads():
        print "     pad [%s]" % pad.GetPadName(), "at",\
        "pos0", ToMM(pad.GetPos0().x), ToMM(pad.GetPos0().y),"mm",\
        "shape offset", ToMM(pad.GetOffset().x), ToMM(pad.GetOffset().y), "mm"
    print ""
```

15.5 BOARD

Board is the basic object in KiCad pcbnew, it' s the document.

BOARD contains a set of object lists that can be accessed using the following methods, they will return iterable lists that can be iterated using "for obj in list:"

- **board.GetModules():** This method returns a list of MODULE objects, all the modules available in the board will be exposed here.
- **board.GetDrawings():** Returns the list of BOARD_ITEMS that belong to the board drawings
- **board.GetTracks():** This method returns a list of TRACKs and VIAs inside a BOARD
- **board.GetFullRatsnest():** Returns the list of ratsnest (connections still not routed)
- **board.GetNetClasses():** Returns the list of net classes
- **board.GetCurrentNetClassName():** Returns the current net class
- **board.GetViasDimensionsList():** Returns the list of Via dimensions available to the board.
- **board.GetTrackWidthList():** Returns the list of Track Widths available to the board.

Board Inspection Example

```
#!/usr/bin/env python
import sys
from pcbnew import *

filename=sys.argv[1]
```

```
pcb = LoadBoard(filename)

ToUnits = ToMM
FromUnits = FromMM
#ToUnits=ToMils
#FromUnits=FromMils

print "LISTING VIAS:"

for item in pcb.GetTracks():
    if type(item) is VIA:

        pos = item.GetPosition()
        drill = item.GetDrillValue()
        width = item.GetWidth()
        print " * Via:   %s - %f/%f "%(ToUnits(pos),ToUnits(drill),ToUnits(width))

    elif type(item) is TRACK:

        start = item.GetStart()
        end = item.GetEnd()
        width = item.GetWidth()

        print " * Track: %s to %s, width %f" % (ToUnits(start),ToUnits(end),ToUnits(width))

    else:
        print "Unknown type    %s" % type(item)

print ""
print "LIST DRAWINGS:"

for item in pcb.GetDrawings():
    if type(item) is TEXTE_PCB:
        print "* Text:    '%s' at %s"%(item.GetText(), item.GetPosition())
    elif type(item) is DRAWSEGMENT:
        print "* Drawing: %s"%item.GetShapeStr() # dir(item)
    else:
        print type(item)

print ""
print "LIST MODULES:"

for module in pcb.GetModules():
    print "* Module: %s at %s"%(module.GetReference(),ToUnits(module.GetPosition()))

print ""
print "Ratsnest cnt:",len(pcb.GetFullRatsnest())
print "track w cnt:",len(pcb.GetTrackWidthList())
```

```
print "via s cnt:",len(pcb.GetViasDimensionsList())

print ""
print "LIST ZONES:", pcb.GetAreaCount()

for idx in range(0, pcb.GetAreaCount()):
    zone=pcb.GetArea(idx)
    print "zone:", idx, "priority:", zone.GetPriority(), "netname", zone.GetNetname()

print ""
print "NetClasses:", pcb.GetNetClasses().GetCount(),
```

15.6 Examples

15.6.1 Change a component pin' s paste mask margin

We only want to change pins from 1 to 14, 15 is a thermal pad that must be kept as it is.

```
#!/usr/bin/env python2.7
import sys
from pcbnew import *

filename=sys.argv[1]
pcb = LoadBoard(filename)

# Find module U304
u304 = pcb.FindModuleByReference('U304')
pads = u304.Pads()

#  Iterate over pads, printing solder paste margin
for p in pads:
    print p.GetPadName(), ToMM(p.GetLocalSolderPasteMargin())
    id = int(p.GetPadName())
    # Set margin to 0 for all but pad (pin) 15
    if id<15: p.SetLocalSolderPasteMargin(0)

pcb.Save("mod_"+filename)
```

15.7 Footprint Wizards

The footprint wizards are a collection of python scripts that can be accessed from the Footprint Editor. If you invoke the footprint dialog you select a given wizard that allows you to see the footprint rendered, and you have some parameters you can edit.

If the plugins are not properly distributed to your system package, you can find the latest versions in the KiCad source tree at launchpad.

They should be located in for example `C:\Program Files\KiCad\share\kicad\scripting\plugins`.

On linux you can also keep your user plugins in `$HOME/.kicad_plugins`.

Build footprints easily filling in parameters.

```
from __future__ import division
import pcbnew

import HelpfulFootprintWizardPlugin as HFPW


class FPC_FootprintWizard(HFPW.HelpfulFootprintWizardPlugin):

    def GetName(self):
        return "FPC (SMT connector)"

    def GetDescription(self):
        return "FPC (SMT connector) Footprint Wizard"

    def GetValue(self):
        pins = self.parameters["Pads"]["*n"]
        return "FPC_%d" % pins

    def GenerateParameterList(self):
        self.AddParam( "Pads", "n", self.uNatural, 40 )
        self.AddParam( "Pads", "pitch", self.uMM, 0.5 )
        self.AddParam( "Pads", "width", self.uMM, 0.25 )
        self.AddParam( "Pads", "height", self.uMM, 1.6)
        self.AddParam( "Shield", "shield_to_pad", self.uMM, 1.6 )
        self.AddParam( "Shield", "from_top", self.uMM, 1.3 )
        self.AddParam( "Shield", "width", self.uMM, 1.5 )
        self.AddParam( "Shield", "height", self.uMM, 2 )


    # build a rectangular pad
    def smdRectPad(self,module,size,pos,name):
        pad = pcbnew.D_PAD(module)
        pad.SetSize(size)
        pad.SetShape(pcbnew.PAD_SHAPE_RECT)
        pad.SetAttribute(pcbnew.PAD_ATTRIB_SMD)
        pad.SetLayerSet( pad.SMDMask() )
        pad.SetPos0(pos)
        pad.SetPosition(pos)
        pad.SetPadName(name)
        return pad
```

```
def CheckParameters(self):
    p = self.parameters
    self.CheckParamInt( "Pads", "*n" )  # not internal units preceded by "*"


def BuildThisFootprint(self):
    p = self.parameters
    pad_count       = int(p["Pads"]["*n"])
    pad_width       = p["Pads"]["width"]
    pad_height      = p["Pads"]["height"]
    pad_pitch       = p["Pads"]["pitch"]
    shl_width       = p["Shield"]["width"]
    shl_height      = p["Shield"]["height"]
    shl_to_pad      = p["Shield"]["shield_to_pad"]
    shl_from_top    = p["Shield"]["from_top"]

    offsetX         = pad_pitch * ( pad_count-1 ) / 2
    size_pad = pcbnew.wxSize( pad_width, pad_height )
    size_shld = pcbnew.wxSize(shl_width, shl_height)
    size_text = self.GetTextSize()  # IPC nominal

    # Gives a position and size to ref and value texts:
    textposy = pad_height/2 + pcbnew.FromMM(1) + self.GetTextThickness()
    self.draw.Reference( 0, textposy, size_text )

    textposy = textposy + size_text + self.GetTextThickness()
    self.draw.Value( 0, textposy, size_text )

    # create a pad array and add it to the module
    for n in range ( 0, pad_count ):
        xpos = pad_pitch*n - offsetX
        pad = self.smdRectPad(self.module,size_pad, pcbnew.wxPoint(xpos,0),str(n+1))
        self.module.Add(pad)


    # Mechanical shield pads: left pad and right pad
    xpos = -shl_to_pad-offsetX
    pad_s0_pos = pcbnew.wxPoint(xpos,shl_from_top)
    pad_s0 = self.smdRectPad(self.module, size_shld, pad_s0_pos, "0")
    xpos = (pad_count-1) * pad_pitch+shl_to_pad - offsetX
    pad_s1_pos = pcbnew.wxPoint(xpos,shl_from_top)
    pad_s1 = self.smdRectPad(self.module, size_shld, pad_s1_pos, "0")

    self.module.Add(pad_s0)
    self.module.Add(pad_s1)

    # add footprint outline
    linewidth = self.draw.GetLineTickness()
```

```
margin = linewidth

# upper line
posy = -pad_height/2 - linewidth/2 - margin
xstart = - pad_pitch*0.5-offsetX
xend = pad_pitch * pad_count + xstart;
self.draw.Line( xstart, posy, xend, posy )

# lower line
posy = pad_height/2 + linewidth/2 + margin
self.draw.Line(xstart, posy, xend, posy)

# around left mechanical pad (the outline around right pad is mirrored/y axix)
yend = pad_s0_pos.y + shl_height/2 + margin
self.draw.Line(xstart, posy, xstart, yend)
self.draw.Line(-xstart, posy, -xstart, yend)

posy = yend
xend = pad_s0_pos.x - (shl_width/2 + linewidth + margin*2)
self.draw.Line(xstart, posy, xend, posy)

# right pad side
self.draw.Line(-xstart, posy, -xend, yend)

# vertical segment at left of the pad
xstart = xend
yend = posy - (shl_height + linewidth + margin*2)
self.draw.Line(xstart, posy, xend, yend)

# right pad side
self.draw.Line(-xstart, posy, -xend, yend)

# horizontal segment above the pad
xstart = xend
xend = - pad_pitch*0.5-offsetX
posy = yend
self.draw.Line(xstart, posy, xend, yend)

# right pad side
self.draw.Line(-xstart, posy,-xend, yend)

# vertical segment above the pad
xstart = xend
yend = -pad_height/2 - linewidth/2 - margin
self.draw.Line(xstart, posy, xend, yend)

# right pad side
self.draw.Line(-xstart, posy, -xend, yend)
```

```
FPC_FootprintWizard().register()
```

CvPcb

August 24, 2017

Contents

Reference manual

Copyright

Contributors

Jean-Pierre Charras, Fabrizio Tappero, Wayne Stambaugh.

Feedback

Please direct any bug reports, suggestions or new versions to here:

- About KiCad document: https://github.com/KiCad/kicad-doc/issues
- About KiCad software: https://bugs.launchpad.net/kicad
- About KiCad software i18n: https://github.com/KiCad/kicad-i18n/issues

Publication date and software version

Published on may 22, 2015.

1 Introduction to CvPcb

CvPcb is a tool that allows you to associate components in your schematic to component footprints used when laying out the printed circuit board. This association is added to the net list file created by the schematic capture program Eeschema.

The net list file generated by Eeschema specifies which printed circuit board footprint is associated with each component in the schematic only when the footprint field of the component is initialized.

This is the case when component footprints are associated during schematic capture by setting the component' s footprint field, or it is set in the schematic library when loading the symbol.

CvPcb provides a convenient method of associating footprints to components during schematic capture. It provides footprint list filtering, footprint viewing, and 3D component model viewing to help ensure the correct footprint is associated with each component.

Components can be assigned to their corresponding footprints manually or automatically by creating equivalence files (.equ files). Equivalence files are lookup tables associating each component with it' s footprint.

This interactive approach is simpler and less error prone than directly associating the footprints in the schematic editor.

CvPcb allows you to see the list of available footprints and to display them on the screen to ensure you are associating the correct footprint.

It can be run only from Eeschema, from the top toolbar, either when Eeschema is started from the KiCad project manager or when Eeschema is started as a stand alone application.

Running CvPcb from Eeschema lauched from the KiCad Manager is generally better because:

- Cvpcb needs the project config file to know the footprint libraries to load.
- Cvpcb initializes the components footprint fields of the current schematic project. This is possible only if the project file is in the same path as the open schematic.

Lauching CvPcb from an Eeschema launched from the KiCad manager assures automatically all this.

Warning

You actually **can** launch CvPcb from a stand alone Eeschema session though, but please note that any schematic opened that does not have a project file in the same path may be missing components due to missing libraries which will not show up in CvPcb. If there is no fp-lib-table file in the same path as the open schematic, no project specific footprint libraries will be available either.

2 CvPcb Features

2.1 Manual or Automatic Association

CvPcb allows for interactive assignment (manual) as well as automatic assignment via equivalence files.

3 Invoking CvPcb

CvPcb is only invoked from the schematic capture program Eeschema, by the tool:

Eeschema automatically passes the correct data (component list and footprints) to CvPcb. There is no update to do (unless some new components are not yet annotated), just run Cvpcb.

4 CvPcb Commands

4.1 Main Screen

The image below shows the main window of CvPcb.

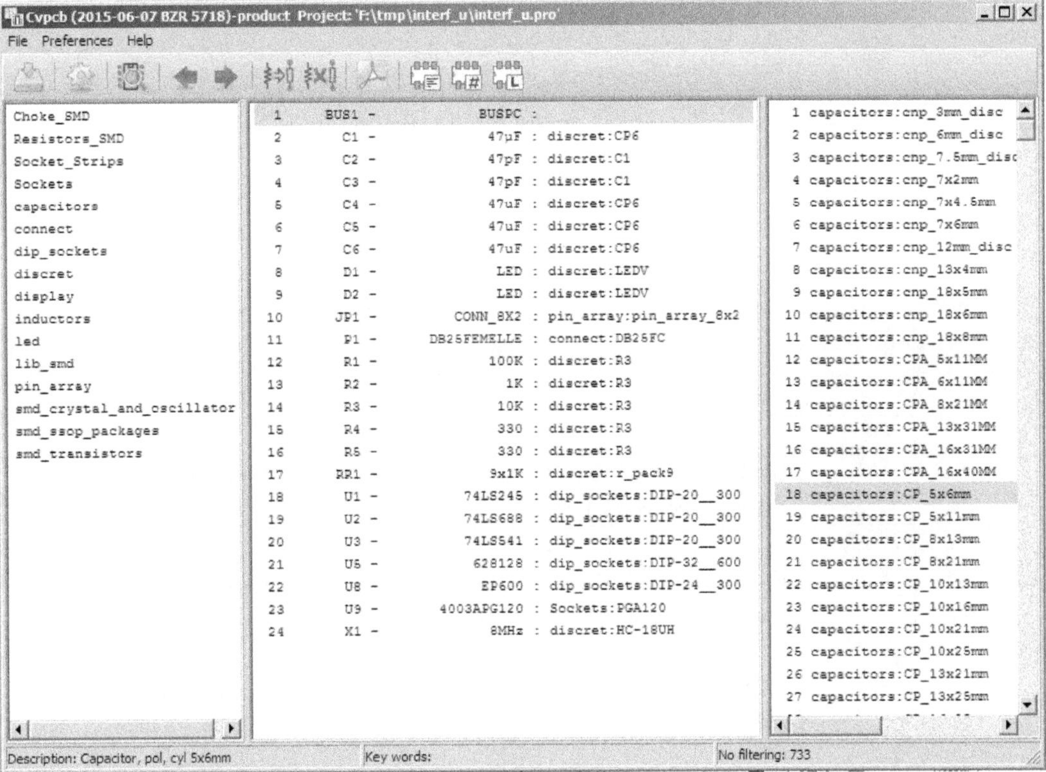

The left pane contains the list of available footprint library file names associated with the project. The center pane contains the list of components loaded from the net list file. The right pane contains the list of available footprints loaded from the project footprint libraries. The component pane will be empty if no netlist file has been loaded and the footprint pane can be also empty if no footprint libraries are found.

4.2 Main Window Toolbar

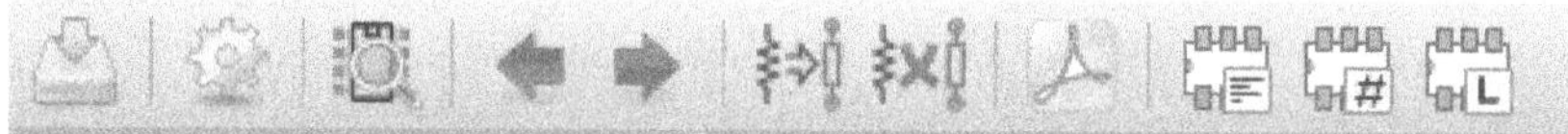

The top toolbar allows for easy access to the following commands:

	Transfer the current footprint association to Eeschema (this is the content of footprint fields).
	Invoke the CvPcb configuration menu.
	Display the footprint of the component selected in the footprint window.
	Automatically select the previous component in the list without a footprint association.
	Automatically select the next component in the list without a footprint association.
	Automatically associate footprints with components starting using an equivalence file.
	Delete all footprint assignments.
	Open the selected footprint documentation pdf file using the default pdf viewer.
	Enable or disable the filtering to limit the list of footprints to the footprint filters of the selected component.
	Enable or disable the filtering to limit the list of footprints using the pin count of the selected component.
	Enable or disable filtering to limit the list of footprints using the selected library.

4.3 Main Window Keyboard Commands

The following table lists the keyboard commands for the main window:

Right Arrow / Tab	Activate the next pane to the right of the currently activated pane. Wrap around to the first pane if the last pane is currently activated.

Left Arrow	Activate the next pane to the left of the currently activated pane. Wrap around to the last pane if the first pane is currently activated.
Up Arrow	Select the previous item of the currently selected list.
Down Arrow	Select the next item of the currently selected list.
Page Up	Select the item up one full page of the currently selected list.
Page Down	Select the item down one full page of the currently selected list.
Home	Select the first item of the currently selected list.
End	Select the last item of the currently selected list.

4.4 CvPcb Configuration

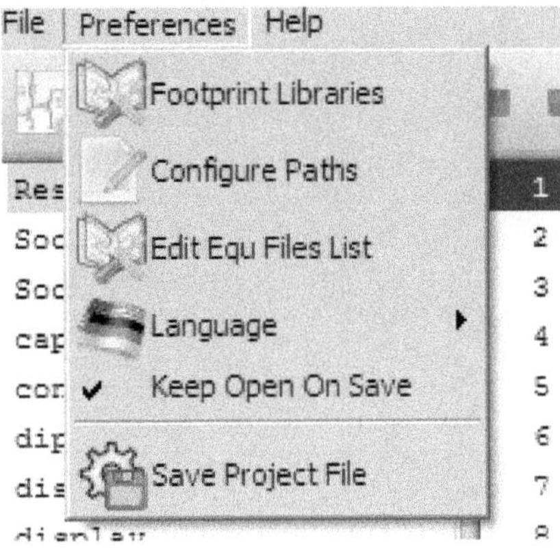

CvPcb can be automatically closed after saving the footprint association file, or not.

Invoking the "Libraries" entry in the "Preferences" menu displays the library configuration dialog.

Depending on the CvPcb version, there are 2 different methods of library management:

- The legacy management, using *.mod files, and a library list of files.
- The new "Pretty" format, using one file by footprint. It uses a folder list. Each folder (*.pretty folder name) is a library. When using this new method of library management, You can also use native libraries originating from GEDA/GPCB or even Eagle xml format files.

5 Footprint Libraries Management

5.1 Important remark:

This section is relevant only for KiCad versions since December 2013

5.2 Footprint Library tables

Since December 2013, Pcbnew and CvPcb uses a new library management tool based on ***footprint library tables*** which allows **direct use of footprint libraries** from

- KiCad Legacy footprint libraries (.mod files)
- KiCad New *.pretty* footprint libraries (on your local disk) (folders with .pretty extension, containing .kicad_mod files)
- KiCad New *.pretty* footprint libraries (on our Github server, or other Github server)
- GEDA libraries (folders containing .fp files)
- Eagle footprint libraries

Note

- you can write only KiCad *.pretty* footprint library folders on your local disk (and the .kicad_mod files inside these folders).
- All other formats are read only.

The image below shows the footprint library table editing dialog which can be opened by invoking the "Footprint Libraries" entry from the "Preferences" menu.

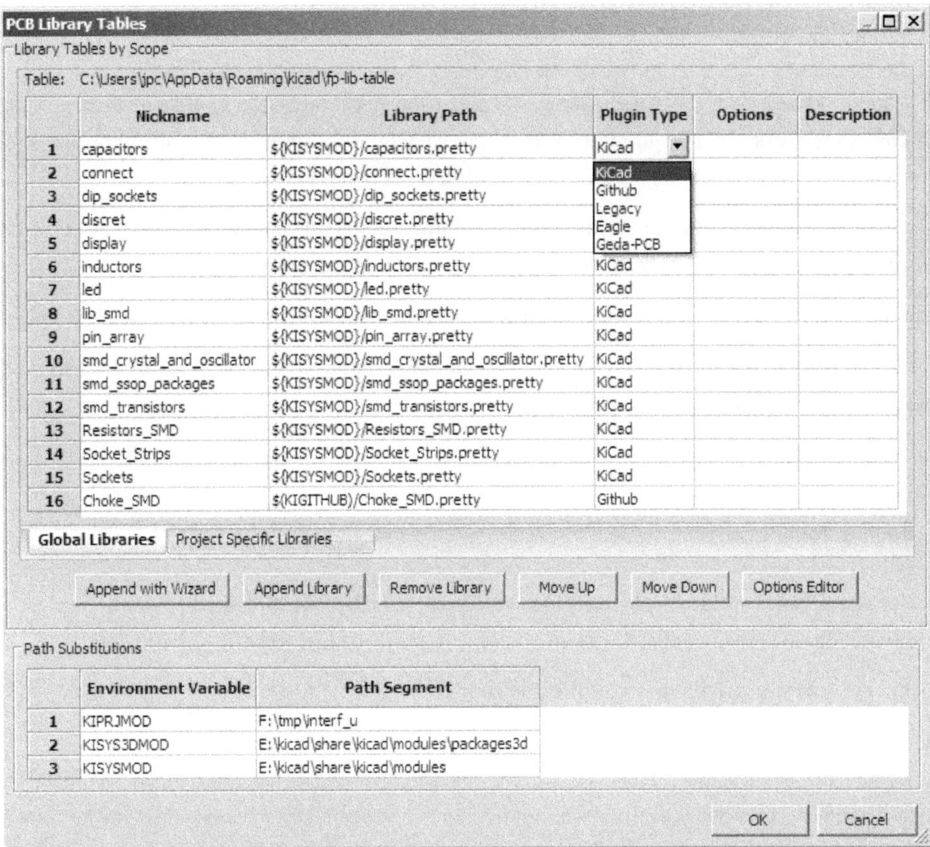

The footprint library table is used to map a footprint library of any supported library type to a library nickname. **This nickname is used to look up footprints** instead of the previous method which depended on library search path ordering.

This allows CvPcb to access footprints with the same name in different libraries by ensuring that the correct footprint is loaded from the appropriate library. It also allows CvPcb to support loading libraries from different PCB editors such as Eagle and GEDA.

5.2.1 Global Footprint Library Table

The global footprint library table contains the list of libraries that are always available regardless of the currently loaded project file. The table is saved in the file fp-lib-table in the user' s home folder. The location of this folder is dependent upon the operating system being used.

5.2.2 Project Specific Footprint Library Table

The project specific footprint library table contains the list of libraries that are available specifically for the currently loaded project file. The project specific footprint library table can only be edited when it is loaded along with the project netlist file. If no project file is loaded or there is no footprint library table file in the project path, an empty table is created which can be edited and later saved along with the footprint assignment file.

5.2.3 Initial Configuration

The first time Pcbnew or CvPcb is run and the global footprint table file **fp-lib-table** is not found in the user′ s home folder, Pcbnew or CvPcb will attempt to copy the default footprint table file fp-lib-table stored in the system′ s KiCad template folder to the file fp-lib-table in the user′ s home folder.

If fp-lib-table cannot be found, an empty footprint library table will be created in the user′ s home folder. If this happens, the user can either copy fp-lib-table manually or configure the table by hand.

The default footprint library table includes many of the standard footprint libraries that are installed as part of KiCad.

Obviously, the **first thing** to do is to modify this table (add/remove entries) according to your work and the libraries you need for all your projects.

(Too many libraries to load is time consuming)

5.2.4 Adding Table Entries

In order to use a footprint library, it must first be added to either the global table or the project specific table. The project specific table is only applicable when you have a net list file open.

Each library entry must have a unique nickname.

This does not have to be related in any way to the actual library file name or path. The colon : character cannot be used anywhere in the nickname. Each library entry must have a valid path and/or file name depending on the type of library. Paths can be defined as absolute, relative, or by environment variable substitution (see section below).

The appropriate plug in type must be selected in order for the library to be properly read. KiCad currently supports reading KiCad legacy, KiCad Pretty, Eagle, and GEDA footprint libraries.

There is also a description field to add a description of the library entry. The option field is not used at this time so adding options will have no effect when loading libraries.

- Please note that you cannot have duplicate library nicknames in the same table. However, you can have duplicate library nicknames in both the global and project specific footprint library table.
- The project specific table entry will take precedence over the global table entry when duplicated names occur. When entries are defined in the project specific table, an fp-lib-table file containing the entries will be written into the folder of the currently open net list.

5.2.5 Environment Variable Substitution

One of the most powerful features of the footprint library table is environment variable substitution. This allows you to define custom paths to where your libraries are stored in environment variables. Environment variable substitution is supported by using the syntax `${ENV_VAR_NAME}` in the footprint library path.

By default, at run time KiCad defines **two environment variables**:

- the **KIPRJMOD** environment variable. This points always the current project directory and cannot be modified.
- the **KISYSMOD** environment variable. This points to where the default footprint libraries that were installed with KiCad are located.

You can override KISYSMOD by defining it yourself in preferences/Configure Path which allows you to substitute your own libraries in place of the default KiCad footprint libraries.

When a project netlist file is loaded, CvPcb defines the KIPRJMOD using the file path (the project path).

Pcbnew also defines this environment variable when loading a board file.

This allows you to store libraries in the project path without having to define the absolute path (which is not always known) to the library in the project specific footprint library table.

5.2.6 Using the GitHub Plugin

The GitHub is a special plugin that provides an interface for read only access to a remote Git Hub repository consisting of pretty (Pretty is name of the KiCad footprint file format) footprints and optionally provides "Copy On Write" (COW) support for editing footprints read from the GitHub repo and saving them locally. Therefore the "Git Hub" plugin is for **read only accessing remote pretty footprint libraries at** https://github.com. To add a GitHub entry to the footprint library table the "Library Path" in the footprint library table row a must be set to a valid GitHub URL.

For example:

https://github.com/liftoff-sr/pretty_footprints

or

https://github.com/KiCad

Typically GitHub URLs take the form:

https://github.com/user_name/repo_name

The "Plugin Type"must be set to "Github". To enable the "Copy On Write"feature the option **allow_pretty_writing_to_** must be added to the "Options" setting of the footprint library table entry. This option is the "Library Path" for local storage of modified copies of footprints read from the GitHub repo. The footprints saved to this path are combined with the read only part of the Git Hub repository to create the footprint library. If this option is missing, then the Git Hub library is read only. If the option is present for a Git Hub library, then any writes to this hybrid library will go to the local *.pretty directory. Note that the github.com resident portion of this hybrid COW library is always read only, meaning you cannot delete anything or modify any footprint in the specified Git Hub repository directly. The aggregate library type remains "Github" in all further discussions, but it consists of both the local read/write portion and the remote read only portion.

The table below shows a footprint library table entry without the option **allow_pretty_writing_to_this_dir**:

Nickname	Library Path	Plugin Type	Options	Descript.
github	https://github.com/liftoff-sr/-pretty_footprints	Github		Liftoff' s GH footprints

The table below shows a footprint library table entry with the COW option given. Note the use of the environment variable ${HOME} as an example only. The github.pretty directory is located in ${HOME}/pretty/ path. Anytime you use the option **allow_pretty_writing_to_this_dir**, you will need to create that directory manually in advance and it must end with the extension **.pretty**.

Nickname	Library Path	Plugin Type	Options	Descript.
github	https://github.com/liftoff-sr/-pretty_footprints	Github	allow_pretty_writing_to_this_dir= ${HOME}/pretty/github.pretty	Liftoff' s GH footprints

Footprint loads will always give precedence to the local footprints found in the path given by the option **allow_pretty_writi**
Once you have saved a footprint to the COW library' s local directory by doing a footprint save in the footprint editor, no Git Hub updates will be seen when loading a footprint with the same name as one for which you' ve saved locally.

Always keep a separate local *.pretty directory for each Git Hub library, never combine them by referring to the same directory more than once.

Also, do not use the same COW (*.pretty) directory in a footprint library table entry. This would likely create a mess.

The value of the option **allow_pretty_writing_to_this_dir** will expand any environment variable using the ${} notation to create the path in the same way as the "Library Path" setting.

What is the point of COW? It is to turbo-charge the sharing of footprints.

If you periodically email your COW pretty footprint modifications to the GitHub repository maintainer, you can help update the Git Hub copy. Simply email the individual *.kicad_mod files you find in your COW directories to the maintainer of the GitHub repository. After you have received confirmation that your changes have been committed, you can safely delete your COW file(s) and the updated footprint from the read only part of Git Hub library will flow down. Your goal should be to keep the COW file set as small as possible by contributing frequently to the shared master copies at https://github.com.

5.2.7 Usage Patterns

Footprint libraries can be defined either globally or specifically to the currently loaded project. Footprint libraries defined in the user' s global table are always available and are stored in the fp-lib-table file in the user' s home folder.

Global footprint libraries can always be accessed even when there is no project net list file opened.

The project specific footprint table is active only for the currently open net list file.

The project specific footprint library table is saved in the file fp-lib-table in the path of the currently open net list . You are free to define libraries in either table.

There are advantages and disadvantages to each method. You can define all of your libraries in the global table which means they will always be available when you need them. The disadvantage of this is that you may have to search through a lot of libraries to find the footprint you are looking for. You can define all your libraries on a project specific basis.

The advantage of this is that you only need to define the libraries you actually need for the project which cuts down on searching.

The disadvantage is that you always have to remember to add each footprint library that you need for every project. You can also define footprint libraries both globally and project specifically.

One usage pattern would be to define your most commonly used libraries globally and the library only require for the project in the project specific library table. There is no restriction on how you define your libraries.

5.3 Using the Footprint Library Table Wizard

A wizard to add footprint libraries to the footprint library tables is available from the *footprint library table editing dialog.*

Note also libraries can be any type of footprint library supported by KiCad.

It can add "local" libraries or libraries from a Github repository.

When libraries are on a Github repository, they can be added as remote libraries, or **downloaded and added as *local libraries*.**

Here, the local libraries option is selected.

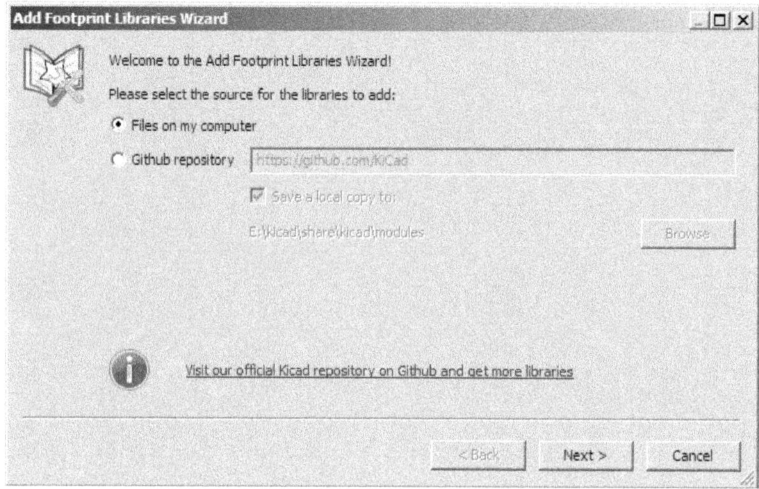

Here, the remote libraries option is selected.

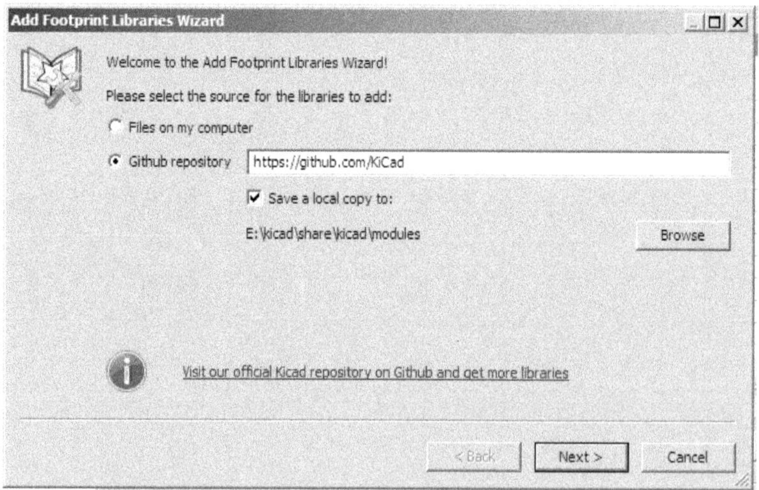

Depending on the selected option, one of these pages will be displayed, to select a list of libraries:

Here, the local libraries option was selected.

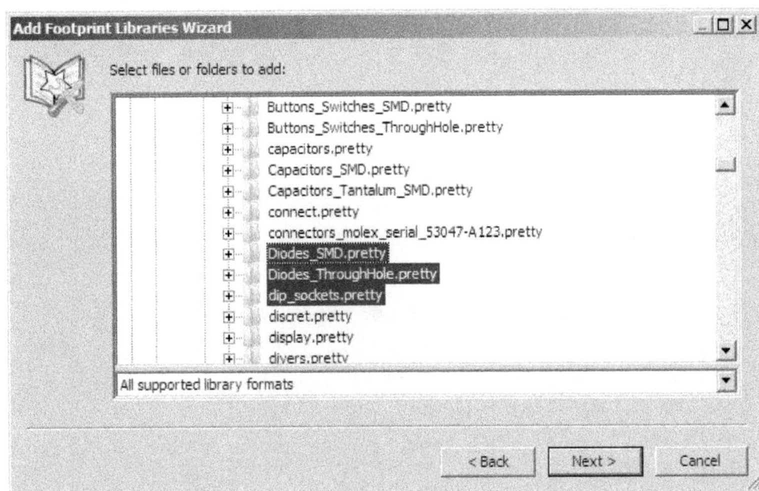

Here, the remote libraries option was selected.

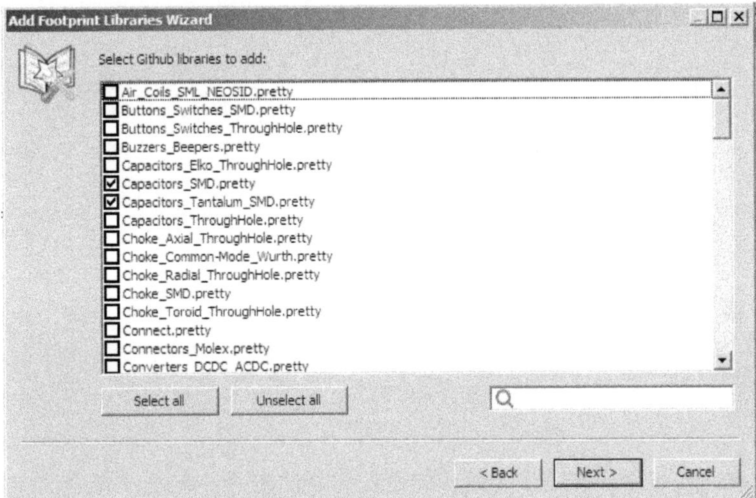

After a set of libraries is selected, the next page validates the choice:

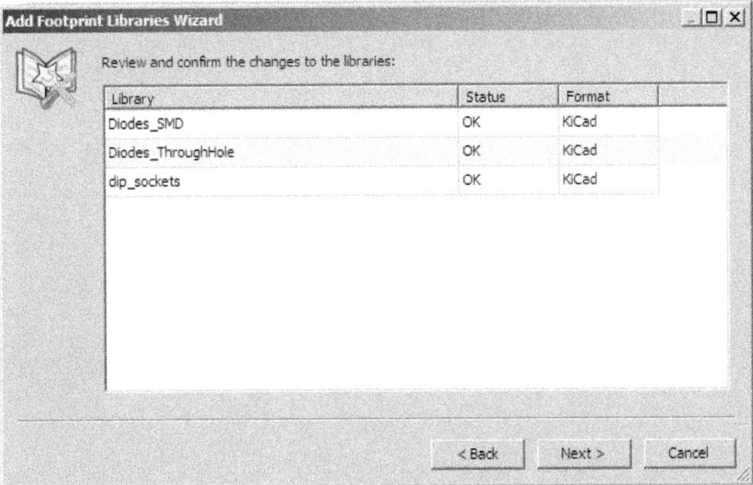

If some selected libraries are incorrect (not supported, not a footprint library ···) they will be flagged as "INVALID"
.

The last choice is the footprint library table to populate:

- the global table
- the local table (the project specific table)

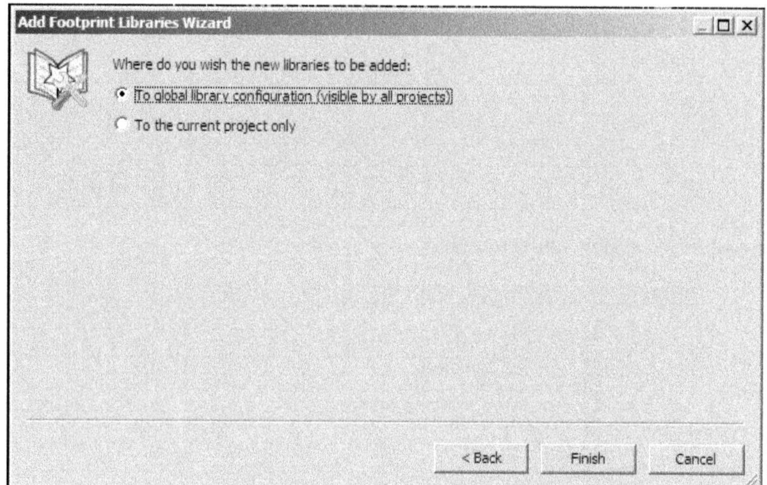

6 Viewing the Current Footprint

6.1 The view footprint command

The view footprint command displays the footprint currently selected in the *footprint* window. A 3D model of the component can be shown if it has been created and assigned to the footprint. Below is the footprint viewer window.

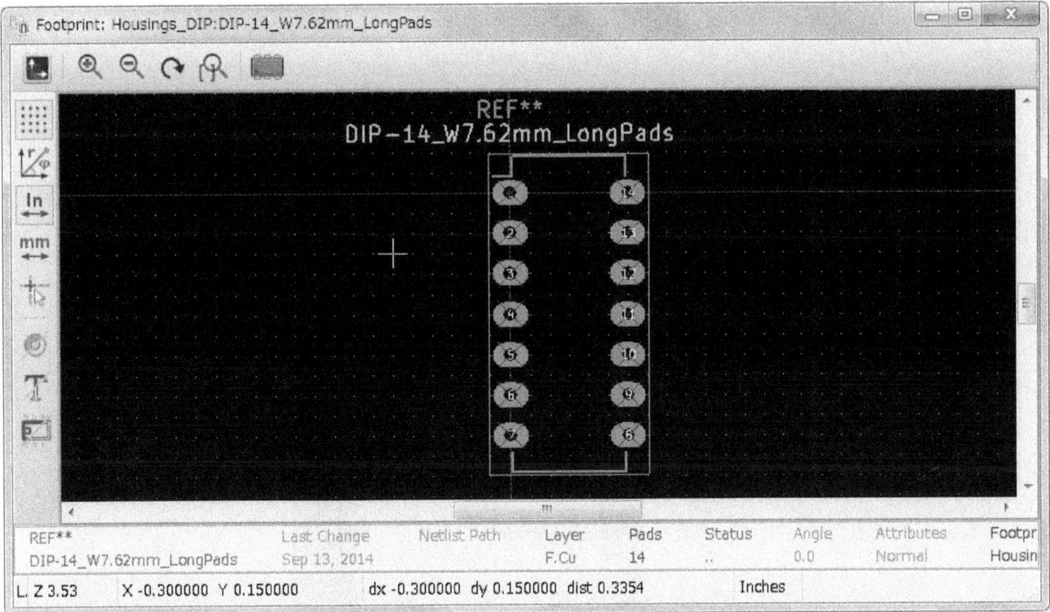

6.1.1 Status Bar Information

The status bar is located at the bottom of the CvPcb new main window and provides useful information to the user. The following table defines the contents of each pane in the status bar.

Left	Component count: total, unassigned
Middle	Filter list of the selected component
Right	Filtering mode and count of available footprints

6.1.2 Keyboard Commands

F1	Zoom In
F2	Zoom Out
F3	Refresh Display
F4	Move cursor to center of display window
Home	Fit footprint into display window
Space Bar	Set relative coordinates to the current cursor position
Right Arrow	Move cursor right one grid position

Left Arrow	Move cursor left one grid position
Up Arrow	Move cursor up one grid position
Down Arrow	Move cursor down one grid position

6.1.3 Mouse Commands

Scroll Wheel	Zoom in and out at the current cursor position
Ctrl + Scroll Wheel	Pan right and left
Shift + Scroll Wheel	Pan up and down
Right Button Click	Open context menu

6.1.4 Context Menu

Displayed by right-clicking the mouse:

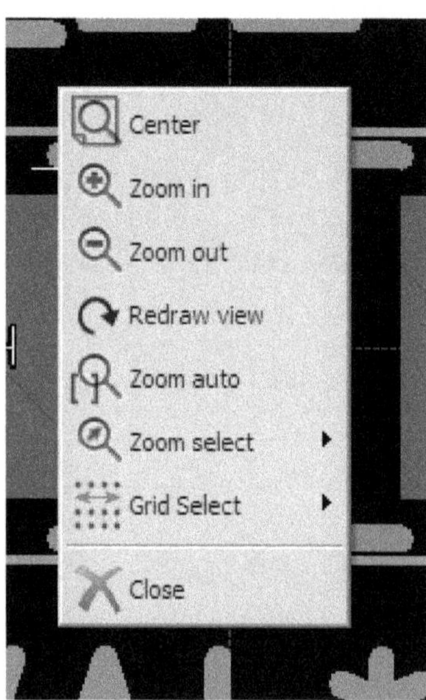

Zoom Selection (Select Zoom)	Direct selection of the display zoom.
Grid Selection (Grid Select)	Direct selection of the grid.

6.1.5 Horizontal Toolbar

	Show display options dialog
	Zoom in
	Zoom out

	Redraw
	Fit drawing in display area
	Open 3D model viewer

6.1.6 Vertical Toolbar

	Show or hide the grid
	Show coordinates in polar or rectangular notation
In	Display coordinates in inches
mm	Display coordinates in millimeters
	Toggle pointer style
	Toggle between drawing pads in sketch or normal mode
	Toggle between drawing text in sketch or normal mode
	Toggle between drawing edges in sketch or normal mode

6.2 Viewing the Current 3D Model

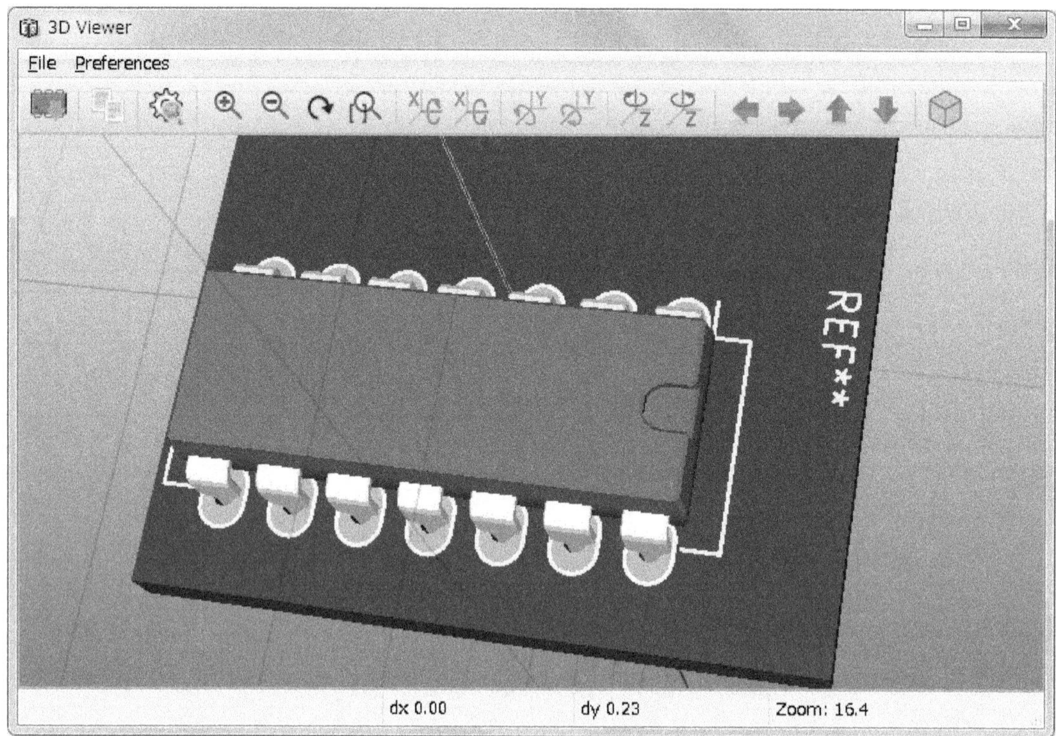

6.2.1 Mouse Commands

Scroll Wheel	Zoom in and out at the current cursor position
Ctrl + Scroll Wheel	Pan right and left
Shift + Scroll Wheel	Pan up and down

6.2.2 Horizontal Toolbar

	Reload the 3D model
	Copy 3D image to clipboard
	Set 3D viewer options
	Zoom in
	Zoom out
	Redraw

	Fit drawing in display area
	Rotate backward along the X axis
	Rotate forward along the X axis
	Rotate backward along the Y axis
	Rotate forward along the Y axis
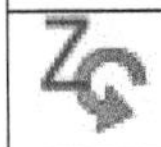	Rotate backward along the Z axis
	Rotate forward along the Z axis
	Pan left
	Pan right
	Pan up
	Pan down
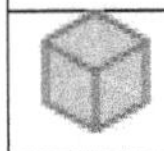	Toggle orthographic projection mode on and off

7 Using CvPcb to Associate Components with Footprints

7.1 Manually Associating Footprints with Components

To manually associate a footprint with a component first select a component in the component pane. Then select a footprint in the footprint pane by double-clicking the left mouse button on the name of the desired footprint. The unassigned next component in the list is automatically selected. Changing the component footprint is performed in the same manner.

7.2 Filtering the Footprint List

If the selected component and/or library is highlighted when the one or more of the filtering option is enabled, the displayed footprint list in CvPcb is filtered accordingly.

The icons enable and disable the filtering feature. When the filtering is not enabled, the full footprint list is shown.

Without filtering:

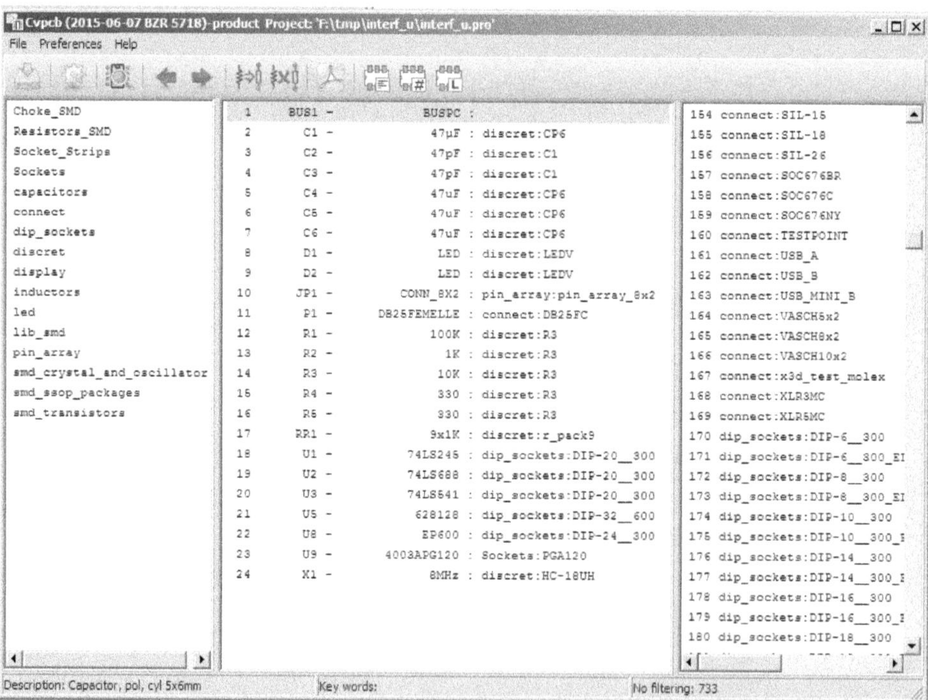

Filtered by list of footprint filters assigned to the selected component. The component filters are listed on the center pane of the status bar at the bottom of the main window.

Filtered by the footprint filter of the selected component:

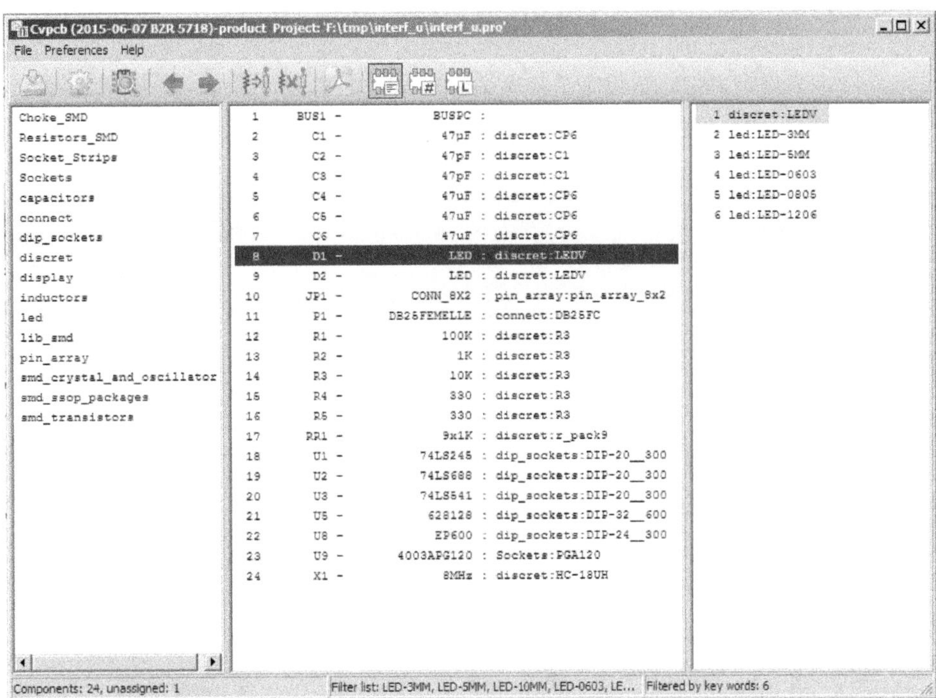

In the component library editor in Eeschema, the footprint list was set using the entries in the footprint filter tab of the component properties dialog as shown below.

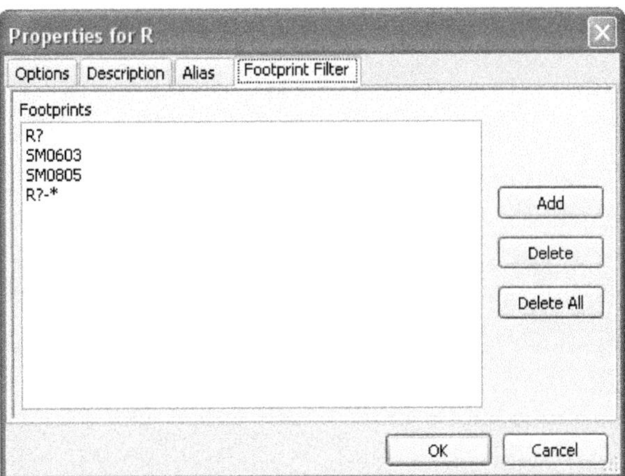

Filtered by the pin count of the selected component:

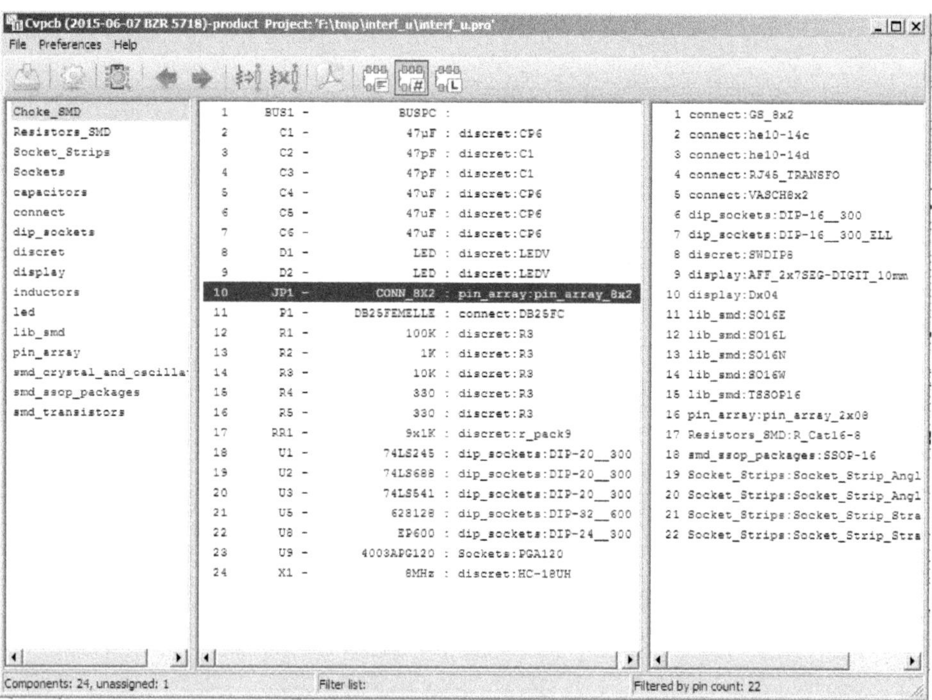

Filtered by the selected library.

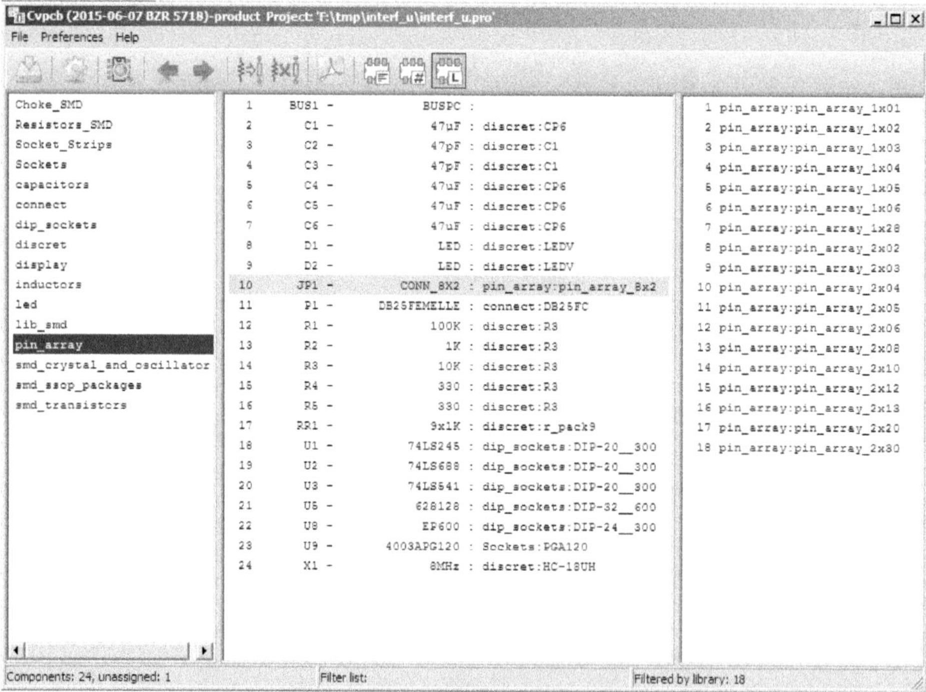

The filtering can be combined to form more complex filtering to help reduce the number of footprints in the footprint pane.

Filtered by the selected component pin count and the component filter:

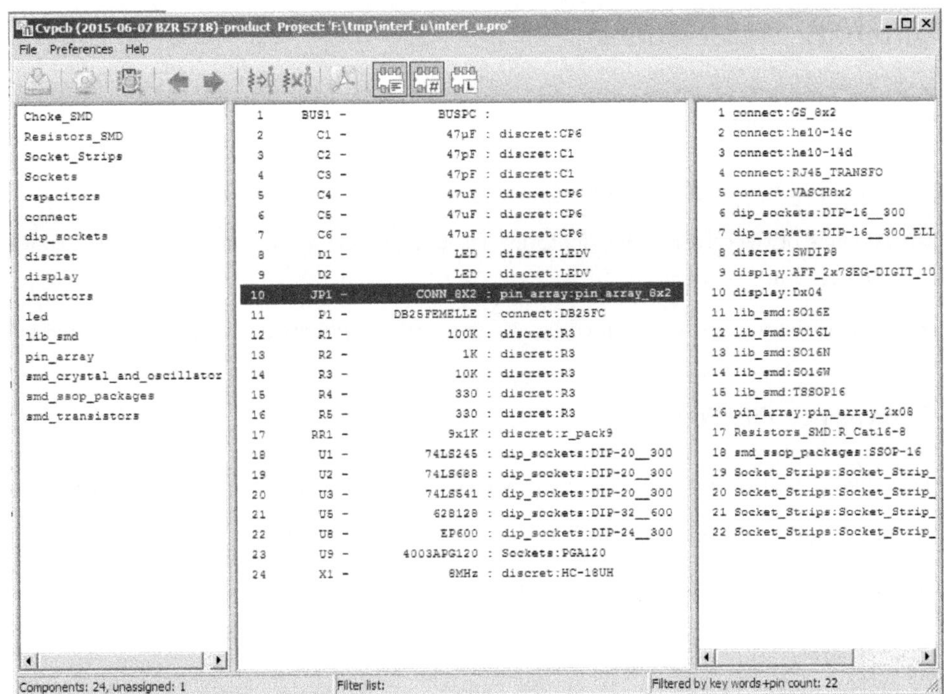
Cvpcb (2015-06-07 BZR 5718)-product Project: 'F:\tmp\interf_u\interf_u.pro'
File Preferences Help
Choke_SMD
Resistors_SMD
Socket_Strips
Sockets
capacitors
connect
dip_sockets
discret
display
inductors
led
lib_smd
pin_array
smd_crystal_and_oscillator
smd_ssop_packages
smd_transistors
1 BUS1 - BUSPC :
2 C1 - 47µF : discret:CP6
3 C2 - 47pF : discret:C1
4 C3 - 47pF : discret:C1
5 C4 - 47uF : discret:CP6
6 C5 - 47uF : discret:CP6
7 C6 - 47uF : discret:CP6
8 D1 - LED : discret:LEDV
9 D2 - LED : discret:LEDV
10 JP1 - CONN_8X2 : pin_array:pin_array_8x2
11 P1 - DB25FEMELLE : connect:DB25FC
12 R1 - 100K : discret:R3
13 R2 - 1K : discret:R3
14 R3 - 10K : discret:R3
15 R4 - 330 : discret:R3
16 R5 - 330 : discret:R3
17 RR1 - 9x1K : discret:r_pack9
18 U1 - 74LS245 : dip_sockets:DIP-20__300
19 U2 - 74LS688 : dip_sockets:DIP-20__300
20 U3 - 74LS541 : dip_sockets:DIP-20__300
21 U5 - 628128 : dip_sockets:DIP-32__600
22 U8 - EP600 : dip_sockets:DIP-24__300
23 U9 - 4003APG120 : Sockets:PGA120
24 X1 - 8MHz : discret:HC-18UH
1 connect:GS_8x2
2 connect:he10-14c
3 connect:he10-14d
4 connect:RJ45_TRANSFO
5 connect:VASCH8x2
6 dip_sockets:DIP-16__300
7 dip_sockets:DIP-16__300_ELL
8 discret:SWDIP8
9 display:AFF_2x7SEG-DIGIT_10
10 display:Dx04
11 lib_smd:SO16E
12 lib_smd:SO16L
13 lib_smd:SO16N
14 lib_smd:SO16W
15 lib_smd:TSSOP16
16 pin_array:pin_array_2x08
17 Resistors_SMD:R_Cat16-8
18 smd_ssop_packages:SSOP-16
19 Socket_Strips:Socket_Strip_
20 Socket_Strips:Socket_Strip_
21 Socket_Strips:Socket_Strip_
22 Socket_Strips:Socket_Strip_
Components: 24, unassigned: 1
Filter list:
Filtered by key words+pin count: 22

8 Automatic Associations

8.1 Equivalence files

Equivalence files allow for automatic assignment of footprints to components.

They list the name of the corresponding footprint according to the name (*value field*) of the component. These files typically have the **.equ** file extension.

They are plain text files and may be edited by using any plain text editor, and must be created by the user.

8.2 Equivalence File Format

Equivalence files consist of one line for each component. Each line has the following structure:

'component value' 'footprint name'

Each name must be single quoted by the ' character and the component and footprint names must be separated by one or more spaces.

Example:

If the U3 component is circuit 14011 and its footprint is 14DIP300, the line is:

`'14011' '14DIP300'`

Any line starting with # is a comment.

Here is an example equivalence file:

```
#integrated circuits (smd):
'74LV14' 'SO14E'
'74HCT541M' 'SO20L'
'EL7242C' 'SO8E'
'DS1302N' 'SO8E'
'XRC3064' 'VQFP44'
'LM324N' 'SO14E'
'LT3430' 'SSOP17'
'LM358' 'SO8E'
'LTC1878' 'MSOP8'
'24LC512I/SM' 'SO8E'
'LM2903M' 'SO8E'
'LT1129_SO8' 'SO8E'
'LT1129CS8-3.3' 'SO8E'
'LT1129CS8' 'SO8E'
'LM358M' 'SO8E'
'TL7702BID' 'SO8E'
'TL7702BCD' 'SO8E'
'U2270B' 'SO16E'
#Xilinx
'XC3S400PQ208' 'PQFP208'
```

```
'XCR3128-VQ100' 'VQFP100'
'XCF08P' 'BGA48'

#upro
'MCF5213-LQFP100' 'VQFP100'

#regulators
'LP2985LV' 'SOT23-5'
```

8.3 Automatically Associating Footprints to Components

Click on the automatic footprint association button on the top toolbar to process an equivalence file.

All components found by their value in the selected equivalence (.equ) file will have their footprint automatically assigned.*

GerbView

August 24, 2017

Contents

Reference manual

Copyright

Contributors

The KiCad Team.

Feedback

Please direct any bug reports, suggestions or new versions to here:

- About KiCad document: https://github.com/KiCad/kicad-doc/issues
- About KiCad software: https://bugs.launchpad.net/kicad
- About KiCad software i18n: https://github.com/KiCad/kicad-i18n/issues

Publication date and software version

Published on February 14, 2015.

1 Introduction to GerbView

GerbView is a Gerber file viewer (RS 274 X format), and is also able to display drill files from Pcbnew (in Excellon format).

It accepts up to 32 files (Gerber and/or Drill files)

Files can be displayed using a transparency mode or stacked mode.

For more information about the Gerber file format please have a read at the specification in The Gerber File Format Specification - Ucamco.

2 Main Screen

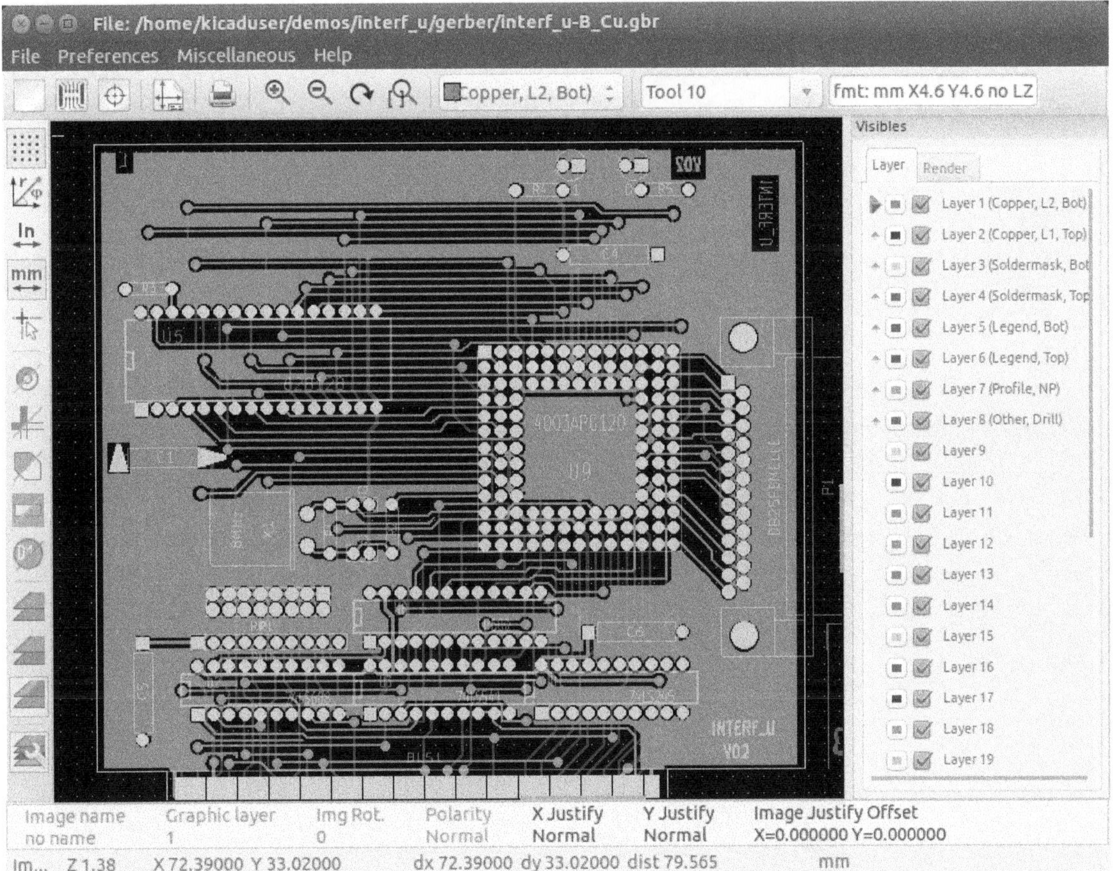

3 Top toolbar

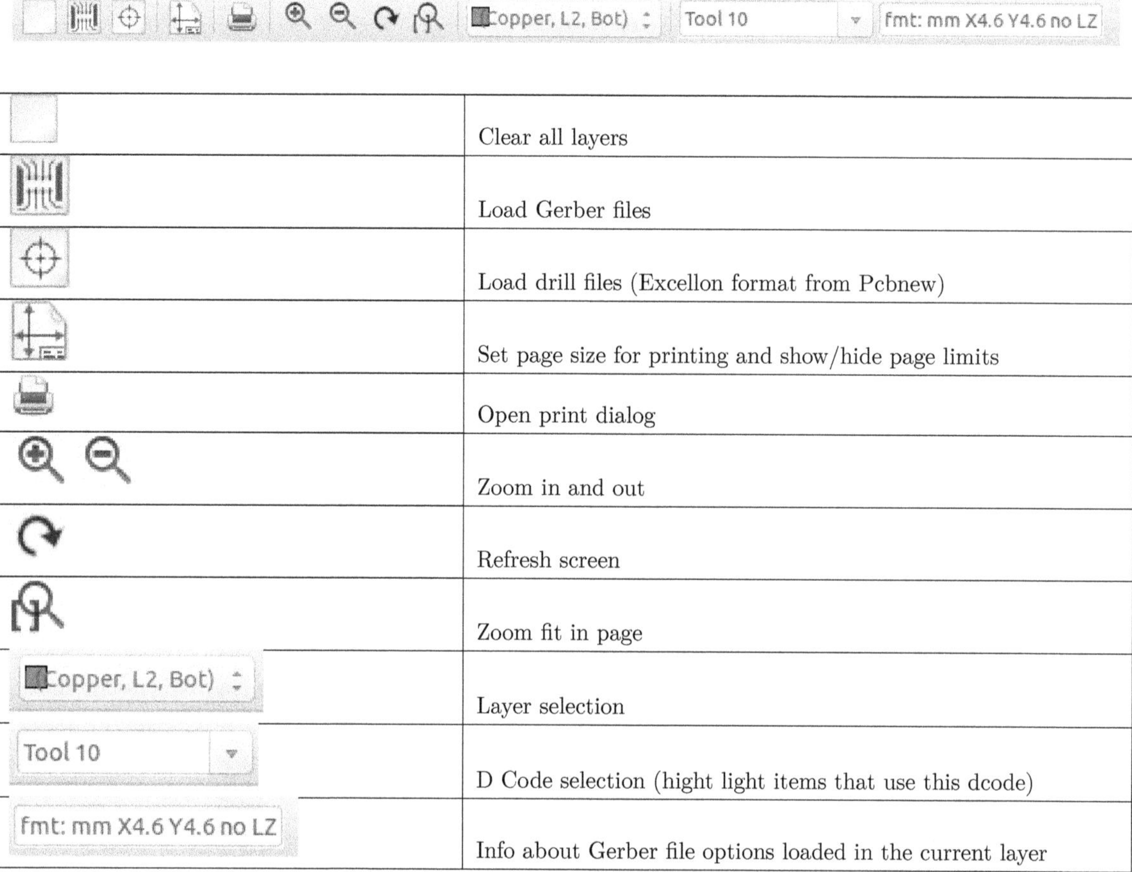

	Clear all layers
	Load Gerber files
	Load drill files (Excellon format from Pcbnew)
	Set page size for printing and show/hide page limits
	Open print dialog
	Zoom in and out
	Refresh screen
	Zoom fit in page
Copper, L2, Bot)	Layer selection
Tool 10	D Code selection (hight light items that use this dcode)
fmt: mm X4.6 Y4.6 no LZ	Info about Gerber file options loaded in the current layer

4 Left toolbar

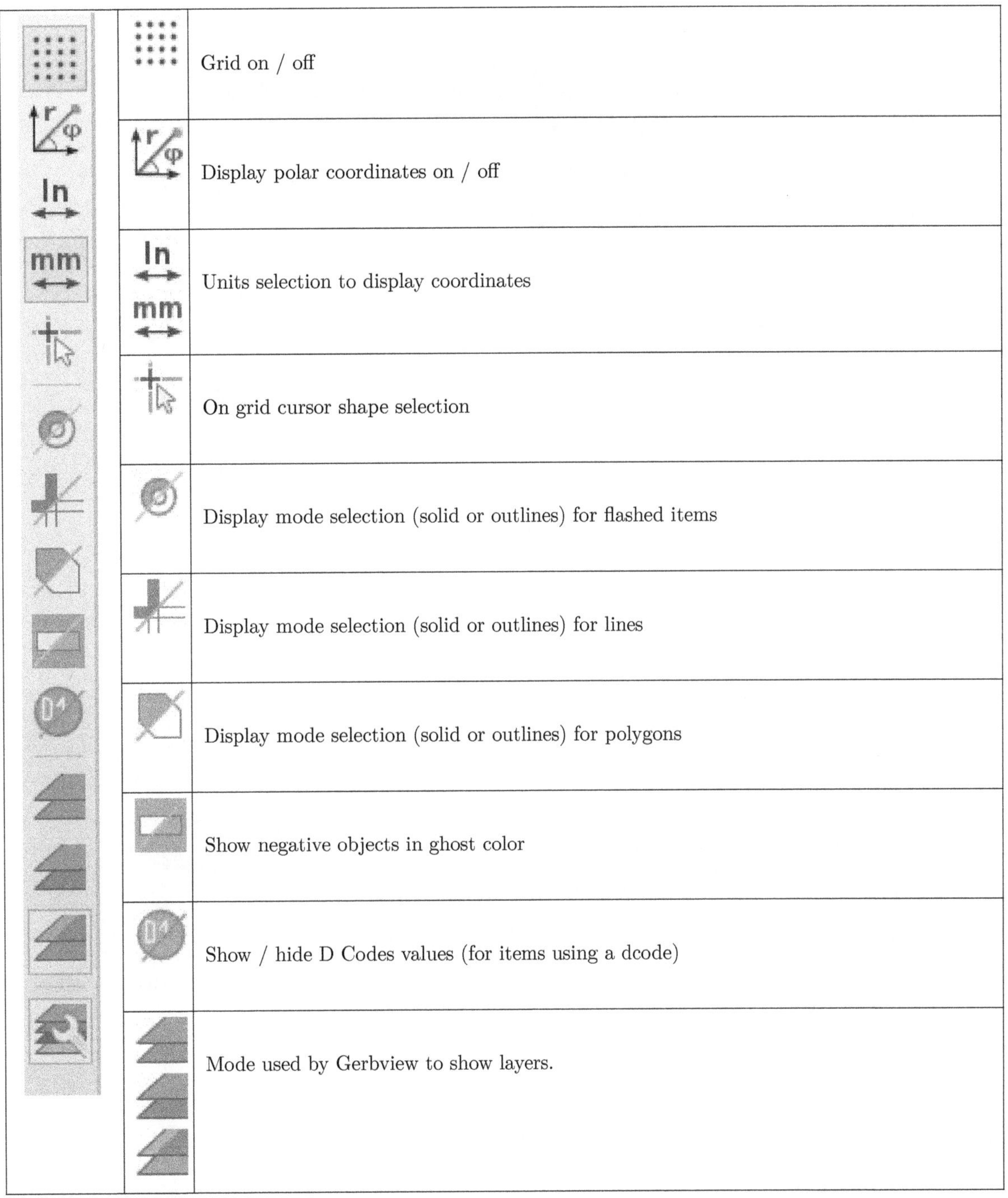

	Grid on / off
	Display polar coordinates on / off
In mm	Units selection to display coordinates
	On grid cursor shape selection
	Display mode selection (solid or outlines) for flashed items
	Display mode selection (solid or outlines) for lines
	Display mode selection (solid or outlines) for polygons
	Show negative objects in ghost color
	Show / hide D Codes values (for items using a dcode)
	Mode used by Gerbview to show layers.

5 Commands in menu bar

5.1 File menu

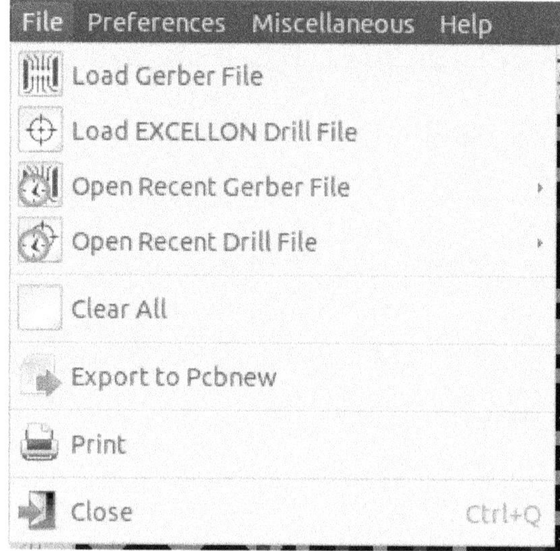

It is possible to load gerber and drill files into Gerbview. There is also an auxiliary option to export gerbers to pcbnew. Previously (a long time ago) it was also possible to load so called Dcodes, but those are now obsolete and is therefore not possible anymore.

5.1.1 Export to Pcbnew

GerbView has a limited capability to export Gerber files to Pcbnew.

The final result depends on what features of RS 274 X format are used in Gerber Files.

RS 274 X format has raster oriented features that cannot be converted (mainly all features relative to negative objects).

Flashed items are converted to vias.

Lines items are converted to track segments (or graphic lines for non copper layers)

So the usability of the converted file is very dependent upon the way each Gerber file was built by the original Pcb tool.

5.2 Preferences menu

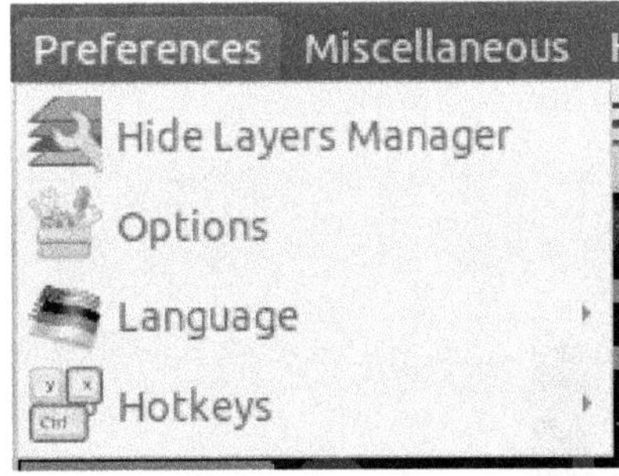

Gives access to the hot keys editor, and some options to display items.

5.3 Miscellaneous menu

- List Dcodes shows the Dcodes in use and some of Dcode parameters.
- Show Source displays the Gerber file contents of the active layer in a text editor.
- Clear Layer erases the contents of the active layer.

6 Layer Manager

The layer manager has 2 purposes:

- Select the active layer
- Show/hide layers

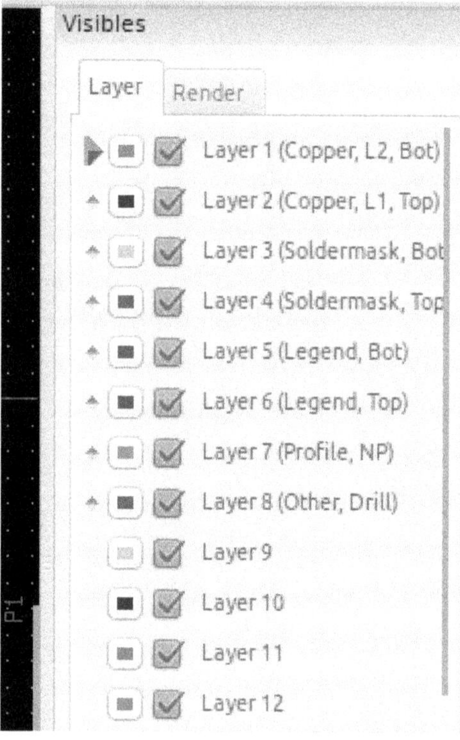

The active layer is drawn after the other layers.

When loading a new file, the active layer is used (the new data replace the previous data)

Note:

- Mouse left click on a line: select the active layer
- Mouse right click on the layer manager: show/hide all layers
- Mouse middle click on a icon: select the layer color.

6.1 Modes to show Gerber layers

- Raw mode 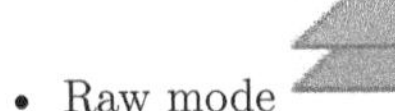

Each gerber file and each item in files are drawn in the order files are loaded.

However the **active layer** is draw last.

When Gerber files have negative items (drawn in black) artefacts are visible on already drawn layers

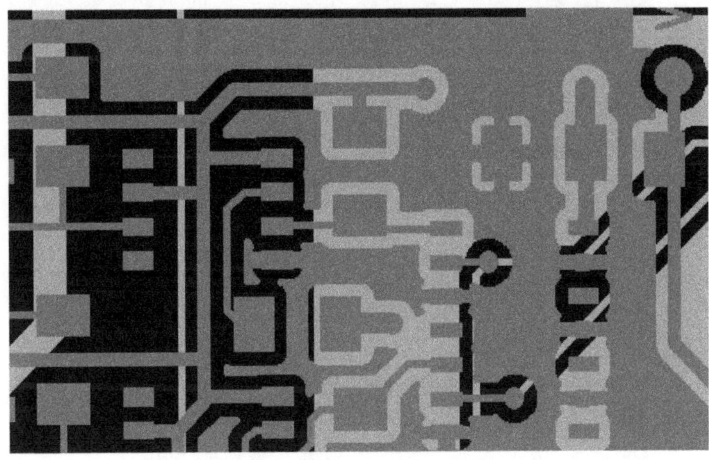

- Stacked mode 

Each gerber file is drawn in the order files are loaded.

The **active layer** is draw last.

When Gerber files have negative items (drawn in black) there are no artefacts on already drawn layers, because this mode draws each file in a local buffer before it is shown on screen. Negative items do not create artefacts.

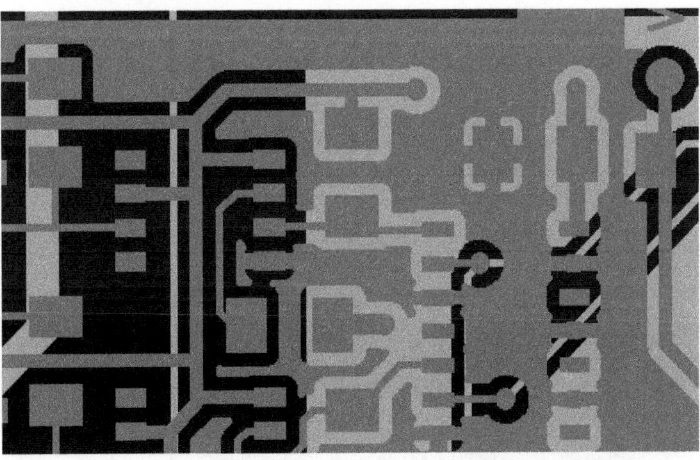

- Transparency mode

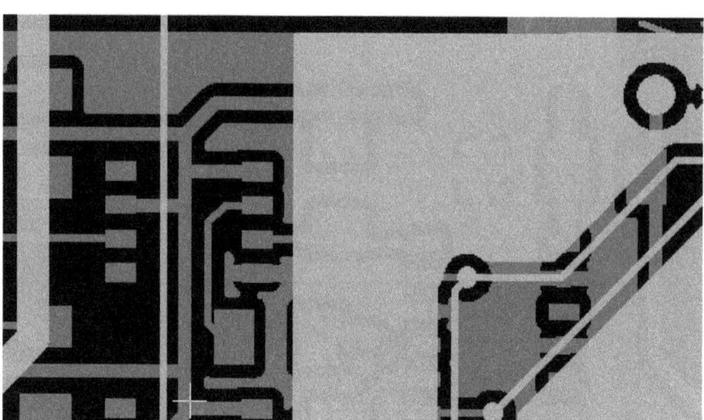

6.2 Effect of layer selection for drawings

This effect is visible only in raw or stacked mode.

The layer 1 (green layer) is drawn after the layer 2

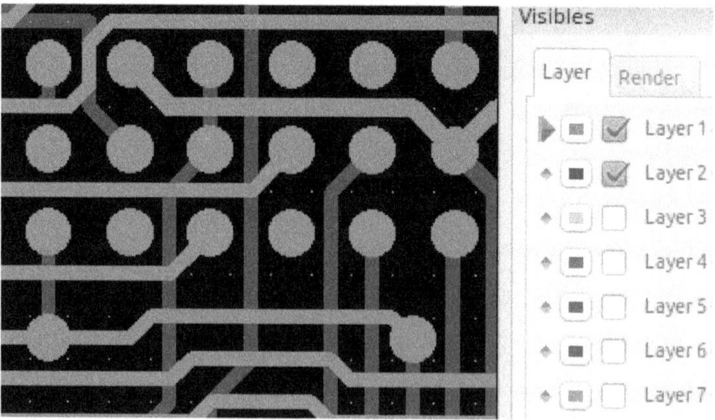

The layer 2 (blue layer) is drawn after the layer 1

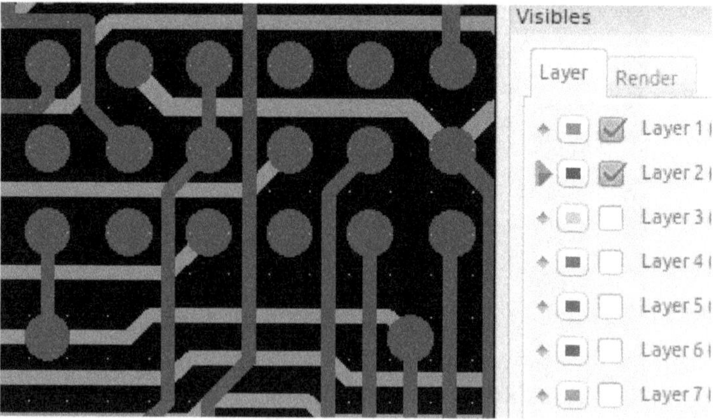

7 Print layers

7.1 Print dialog access

To print layers, use the tool, or the main menu (files)

Caution

But be sure items are inside the printable area (select by a suitable page format).
Do not forget photoplotters can use a large plottable area, much bigger than the page sizes used by printers)
Moving (by block move command) the entire layers is often needed.

7.2 Move block command

You can move items by selecting them (drag the mouse with left button down) and then moving the selected area on screen.

Click the left button to finally place the area you are moving.

Pl_Editor

August 24, 2017

Contents

Reference manual

Copyright

Contributors

Jean-Pierre Charras.

Feedback

Please direct any bug reports, suggestions or new versions to here:

- About KiCad document: https://github.com/KiCad/kicad-doc/issues
- About KiCad software: https://bugs.launchpad.net/kicad
- About KiCad software i18n: https://github.com/KiCad/kicad-i18n/issues

Publication date and software version

may 23, 2015.

1 Introduction to Pl_Editor

Pl_Editor is a page layout editor tool to create custom title blocks, and frame references.

The title block, associated to frame references, and other graphic items (logos) is called here a page layout.

Basic page layout items are:

- **Lines**
- **Rectangles**
- **Texts** (with format symbols, that will be replaced by the actual text, like the date, page number…) in Eeschema or Pcbnew.
- **Poly-polygons** (mainly to place logos and special graphic shapes)
- **Bitmaps**.

Warning
Bitmaps can be plotted only by few plotters (PDF and PS only) Therefore, for other plotters, only a bounding box will be plotted.

- Items can be repeated, and texts and poly_polygons can be rotated.

2 Pl_Editor files

2.1 Input file and default title block

Pl_Editor reads or writes page layout description files *.kicad_wks (KiCad worksheet).

An internal default page layout description to display the default KiCad title block is used until a file is read.

2.2 Output file

The current page layout description can be written in a ***.kicad_wks** file, using the S-expression format, which is widely used in KiCad.

This file can be used to show the custom page layout in Eeschema and/or Pcbnew.

3 Theory of operations

3.1 Basic page layout items properties:

Basic page layout items are:

- **Lines**
- **Rectangles**
- **Texts** (with format symbols, with will be replaced by the actual text, like the date, page number···) in Eeschema or Pcbnew.
- **Poly-polygons** (mainly to place logos and special graphic shapes). These poly polygons are created by **Bitmap2compon** and cannot be built inside pl_editor, because it is not possible to create such shapes by hand.
- **Bitmaps** to place logos.

Warning
Bitmaps can be plotted only by few plotters: PDF and PS only.

Therefore:

- **Texts, poly-polygons** and **bitmaps** are defined by a position, and can be rotated.
- **Lines** (in fact segments) and **rectangles** are defined by two points: a start point and a end point. They cannot be rotated (this is useless for segments).

These basic items can be repeated.

Texts which are repeated accept also an increment value for labels (has meaning only if the text is one letter or one digit).

3.2 Coordinates definition

Each position, start point and end point of items is always relative to a page corner.

This feature ensure you can define a page layout which is not dependent on the paper size.

3.3 Reference corners and coordinates:

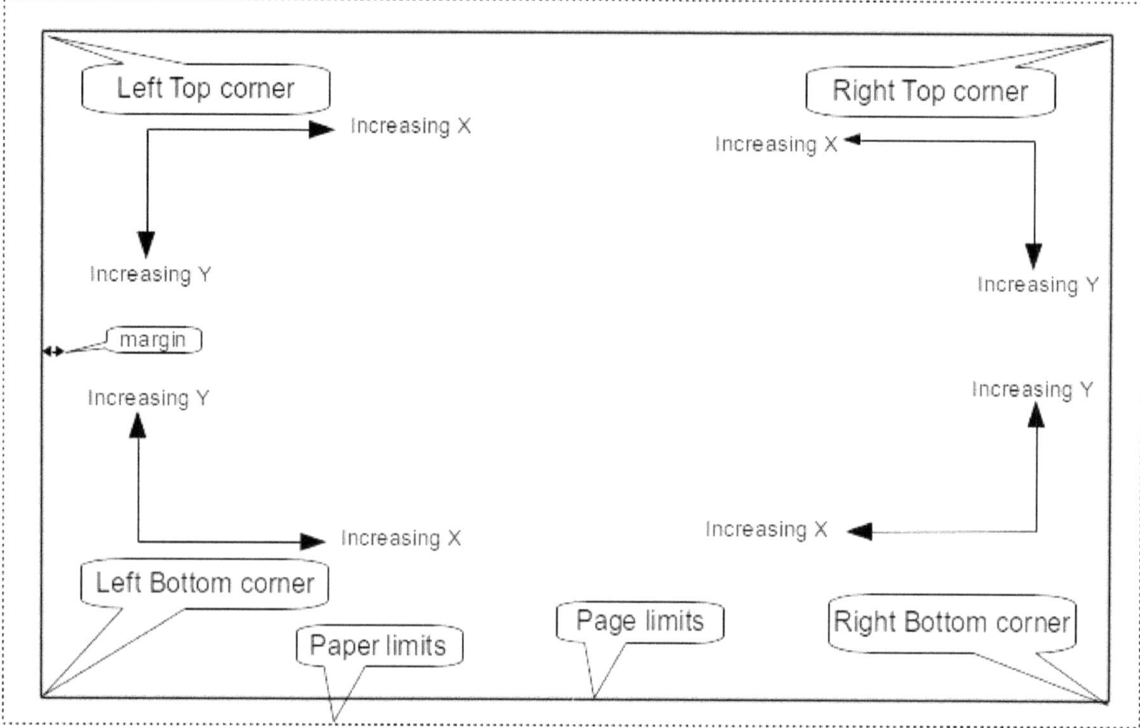

- When the page size is changed, the position of the item, relative to its reference corner does not change.
- Usually, title blocks are attached to the right bottom corner, and therefore this corner is the default corner, when creating an item.

For rectangles and segments, which have two defined points, each point has its reference corner.

3.4 Rotation

Items which have a position defined by just one point (texts and poly-polygons) can be rotated:

Normal: Rotation = 0

Rotated: Rotation = 20 and 10 degrees.

3.5 Repeat option

Items can be repeated:

This is useful to create grid and grid labels.

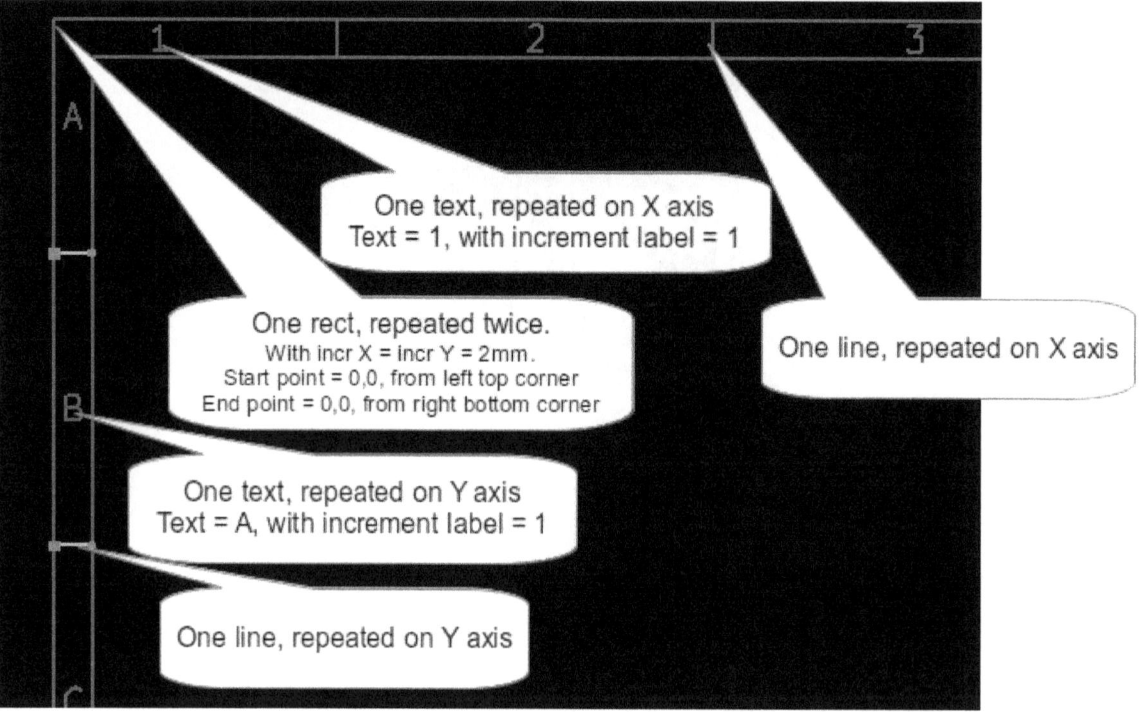

4 Texts and formats

4.1 Format symbols:

Texts can be simple strings or can include format symbols.

Format symbols are replaced by the actual values in Eeschema or Pcbnew.

They are like format symbols in printf function.

A format symbol is **%** followed by 1 letter.

The **%C** format has one digit (comment identifier).

Formats symbols are:

%% = replaced by %

%K = KiCad version

%Z = paper format name (A4, USLetter ···)

%Y = company name

%D = date

%R = revision

%S = sheet number

%N = number of sheets

%Cx = comment (x = 0 to 9 to identify the comment)

%F = filename

%P = sheet path (sheet full name, for Eeschema)

%T = title

Example:

"Size: %Z" displays "Size: A4" or "Size: USLetter"

User display mode:  activated. Title block displayed like in Eeschema and Pcbnew

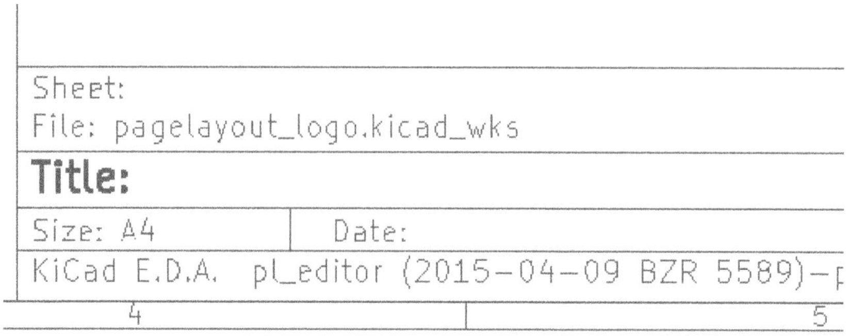

Sheet:
File: pagelayout_logo.kicad_wks
Title:
Size: A4 Date:
KiCad E.D.A. pl_editor (2015-04-09 BZR 5589)-
4 5

"Native" display mode:  activated. The native texts entered in Pl_Editor, with their format symbols.

%Y
Sheet: %P
File: %F
Title: %T
Size: %Z Date: %D
%K
4 5

4.2 Multi-line texts:

Texts can be multi-line.

There are 2 ways to insert a new line in texts:

1. Insert the "\n" 2 chars sequence (mainly in Page setup dialog in KiCad).
2. Insert a new line in Pl_Editor Design window.

Here is an example:

Setup

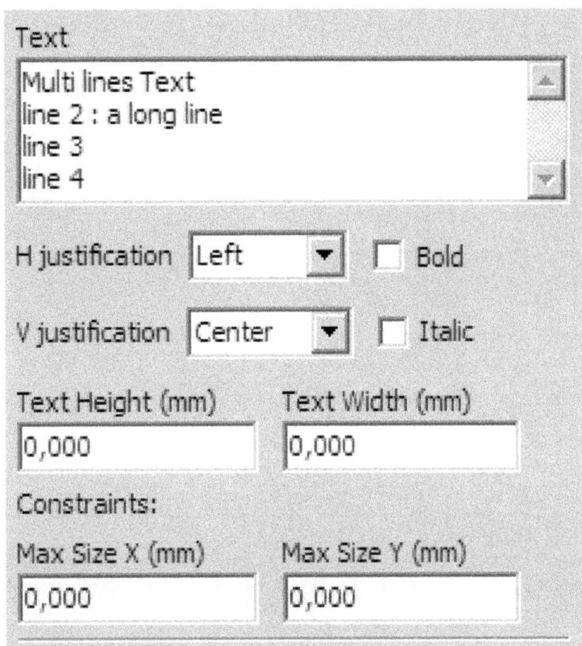

Output

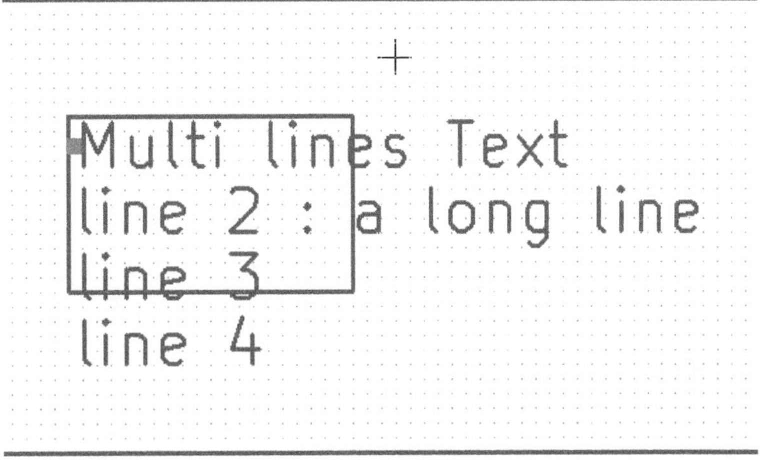

4.3 Multi-line texts in Page Setup dialog:

In the page setup dialog, text controls do not accept a multi-line text.

The "\n" 2 chars sequence should be inserted to force a new line inside a text.

Here is a two lines text, in *comment 2* field:

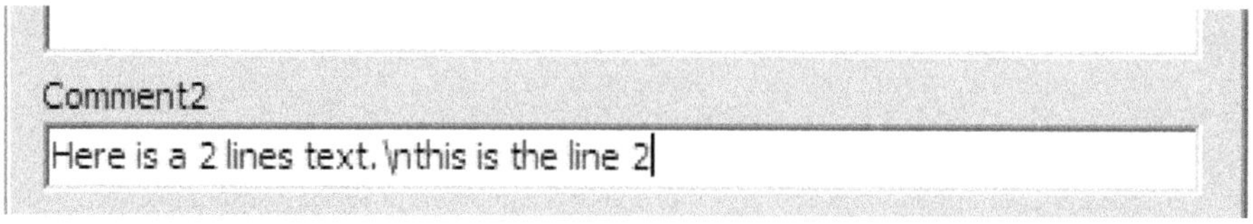

Comment2

Here is a 2 lines text.\nthis is the line 2

Here is the actual text:

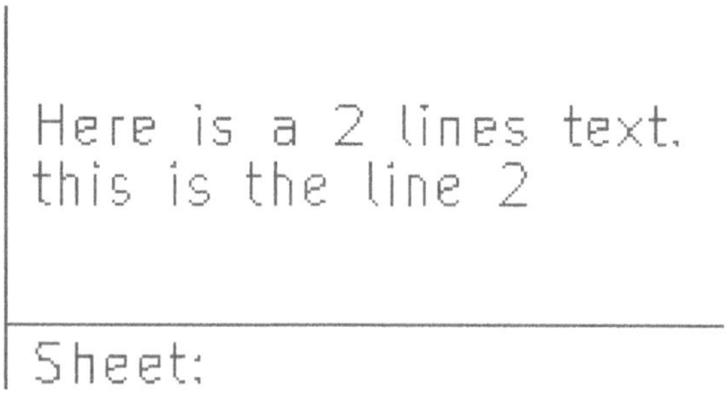

Here is a 2 lines text.
this is the line 2

Sheet:

However, if you really want the "\n" inside the text, enter "\\n".

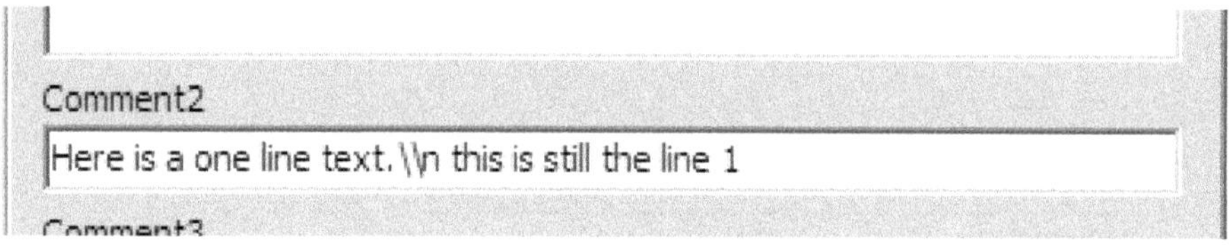

Comment2

Here is a one line text.\\n this is still the line 1

And the displayed text:

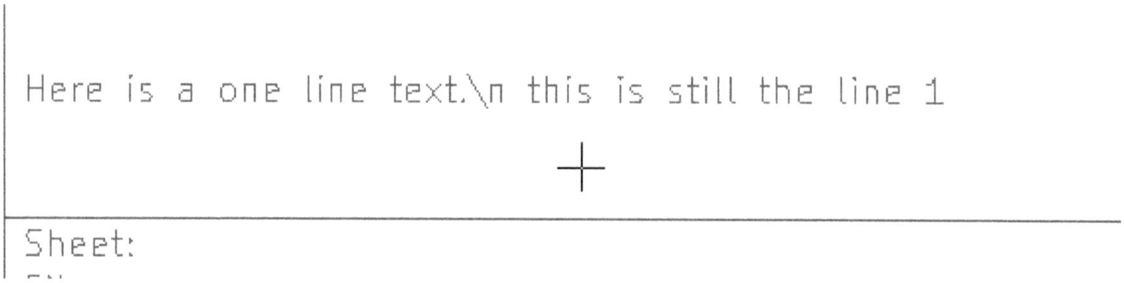

Here is a one line text.\n this is still the line 1

Sheet:

5 Constraints

5.1 Page 1 constraint

When using Eeschema, the full schematic often uses more than one page.

Usually page layout items are displayed on all pages.

But if a user want some items to be displayed only on page 1, or not on page 1, the "page 1 option" this is possible by setting this option:

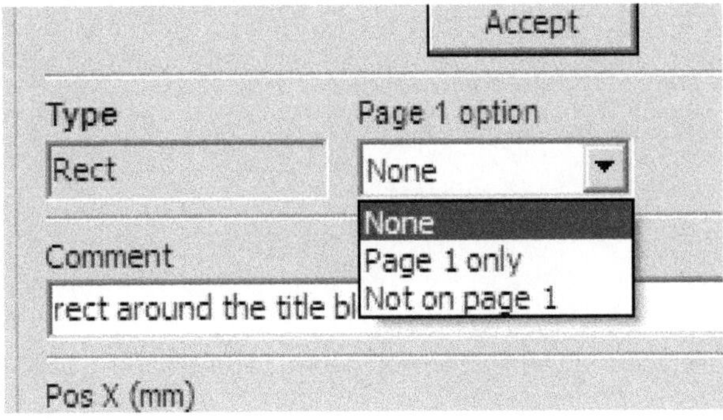

Page 1 option:

- None: no constraint.
- Page 1 only: the items is visible only on page 1.
- Not on page 1: the items is visible on all pages but the page 1.

5.2 Text full size constraint

Text
Multi lines Text
line 2 : a long line
line 3
line 4
H justification Left Bold
V justification Center Italic
Text Height (mm) Text Width (mm)
10,000 0
Constraints:
Max Size X (mm) Max Size Y (mm)
10,000 5

Only for texts, one can set 2 parameters :

- the max size X
- the max size Y

which define a bounding box.

When these parameters are not 0, when displaying the text, the actual text height and the actual text width are dynamically modified if the full text size is bigger than the max size X and/or the max size Y, to fit the full text size with this bounding box.

When the actual full text size is smaller than the max size X and/or the max size Y, the text height and/or the text width is not modified.

The text with no bounding box. Max size X = 0,0 Max size Y = 0,0

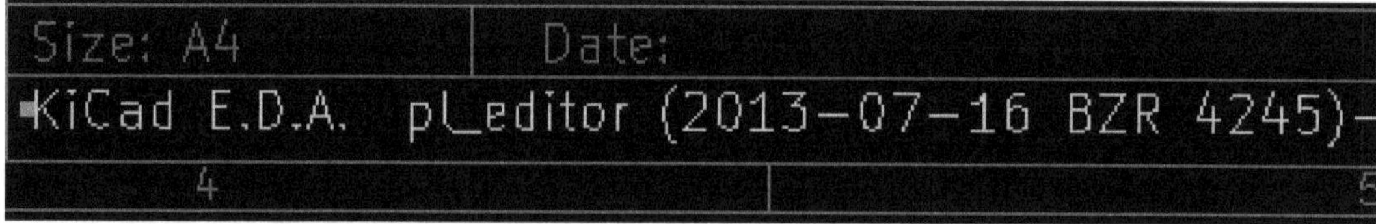

The **same** text with constraint. Max size X = 40,0 Max size Y = 0,0

A multi line text, constrained:

Setup

Text

Multi lines Text
line 2 : a long line
line 3
line 4

H justification: Left — Bold

V justification: Center — Italic

Text Height (mm): 10,000 — Text Width (mm): 0

Constraints:

Max Size X (mm): 10,000 — Max Size Y (mm): 5

Output

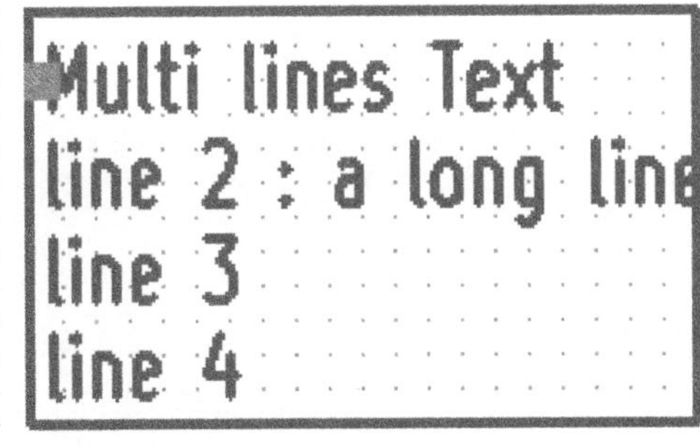

6 Invoking Pl_Editor

Pl_Editor is typically invoked from a command line, or from the KiCad manager.

From a command line, the syntax is pl_editor <*.kicad_wks file to open>.

7 Pl_Editor Commands

7.1 Main Screen

The image below shows the main window of Pl_Editor.

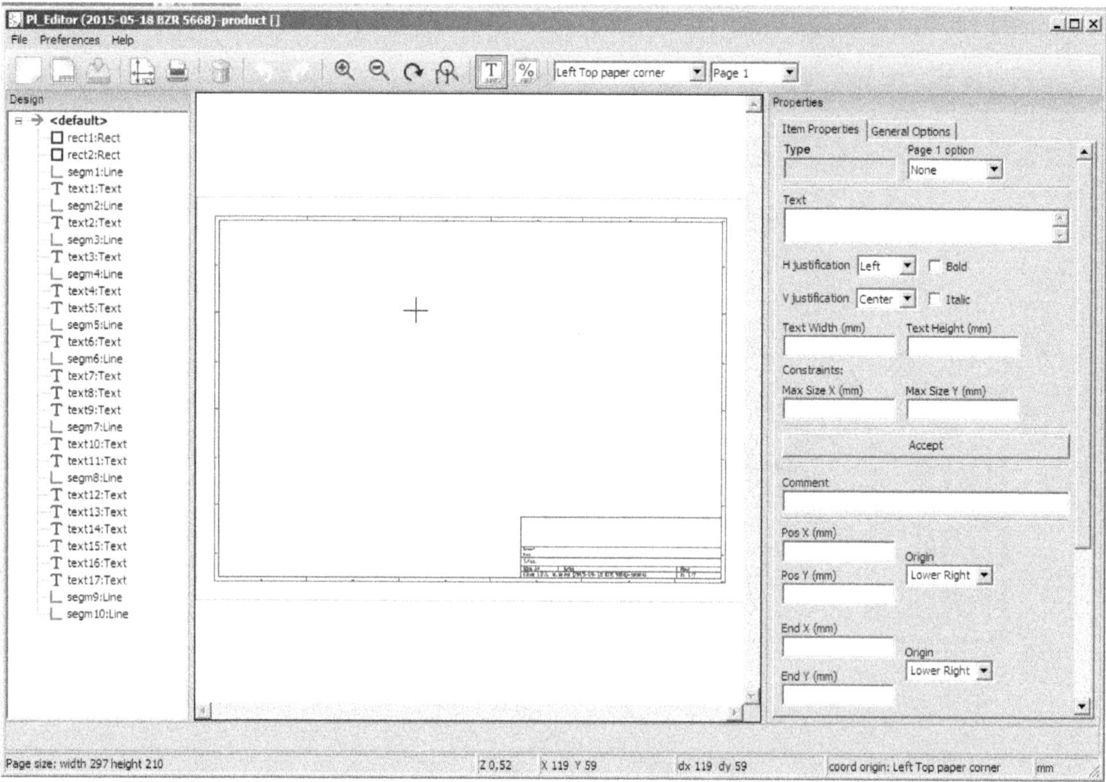

The left pane contains the list of basic items.

The right pane is the item settings editor.

7.2 Main Window Toolbar

The top toolbar allows for easy access to the following commands:

	Select the net list file to be processed.
	Load a page layout description file.
	Save the current page layout description in a .kicad_wks file.
	Display the page size selector and the title block user data editor.
	Prints the current page.
	Delete the currently selected item.
	Undo/redo tools.
	Zoom in, out, redraw and auto, respectively.
	Show the page layout in user mode: texts are shown like in Eeschema or Pcbnew: text format symbols are replaced by the user texts.
	Show the page layout in native mode: texts are displayed "as is", with the contained formats, without any replacement.
	Reference corner selection, for coordinates displayed to the status bar.
	Selection of the page number (page & or other pages). This selection has meaning only if some items than have a page option, are not shown on all pages (in a schematic for instance, which contains more than one page).

7.3 Commands in drawing area (draw panel)

7.3.1 Keyboard Commands

F1	Zoom In
F2	Zoom Out
F3	Refresh Display
F4	Move cursor to center of display window
Home	Fit footprint into display window
Space Bar	Set relative coordinates to the current cursor position
Right Arrow	Move cursor right one grid position
Left Arrow	Move cursor left one grid position
Up Arrow	Move cursor up one grid position
Down Arrow	Move cursor down one grid position

7.3.2 Mouse Commands

Scroll Wheel	Zoom in and out at the current cursor position
Ctrl + Scroll Wheel	Pan right and left
Shift + Scroll Wheel	Pan up and down
Right Button Click	Open context menu

7.3.3 Context Menu

Displayed by right-clicking the mouse:

- Add Line
- Add Rectangle
- Add Text
- Append Page Layout Descr File

Are commands to add a basic layout item to the current page layout description.

- Zoom selection: direct selection of the display zoom.
- Grid selection: direct selection of the grid.

Note

Append Page Layout Descr File is intended to add poly polygons to make logos.

Because usually a logo it needs hundred of vertices, you cannot create a polygon by hand. But you can append a description file, created by Bitmap2Component.

7.4 Status Bar Information

The status bar is located at the bottom of the Pl_Editor and provides useful information to the user.

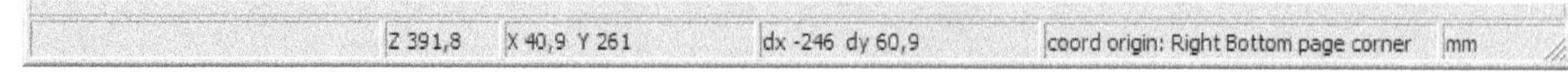

Coordinates are **always relative to the corner** selected as **reference**.

8 Left window

The left windows shows the list of layout items.

One can select a given item (left clicking on the line) or, when right clicking on the line, display a pop up menu.

This menu allows basic operations: add a new item, or delete the selected item.

→ **A selected item is also drawn in a different color on draw panel.**

Design tree: the item 19 is selected, and shown in highlighted on the draw panel.

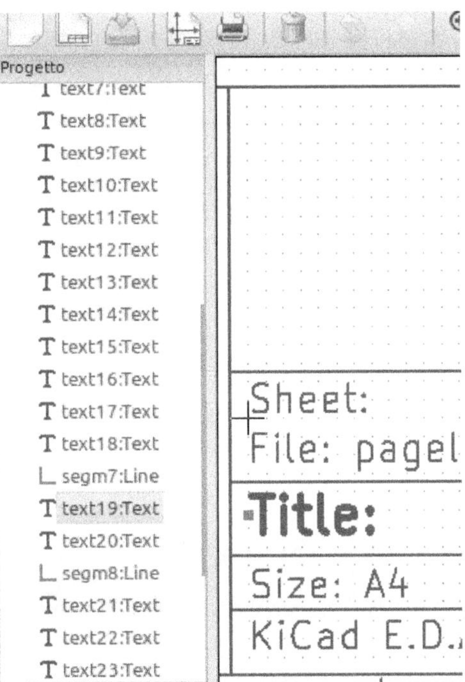

9 Right window

The right window is the edit window.

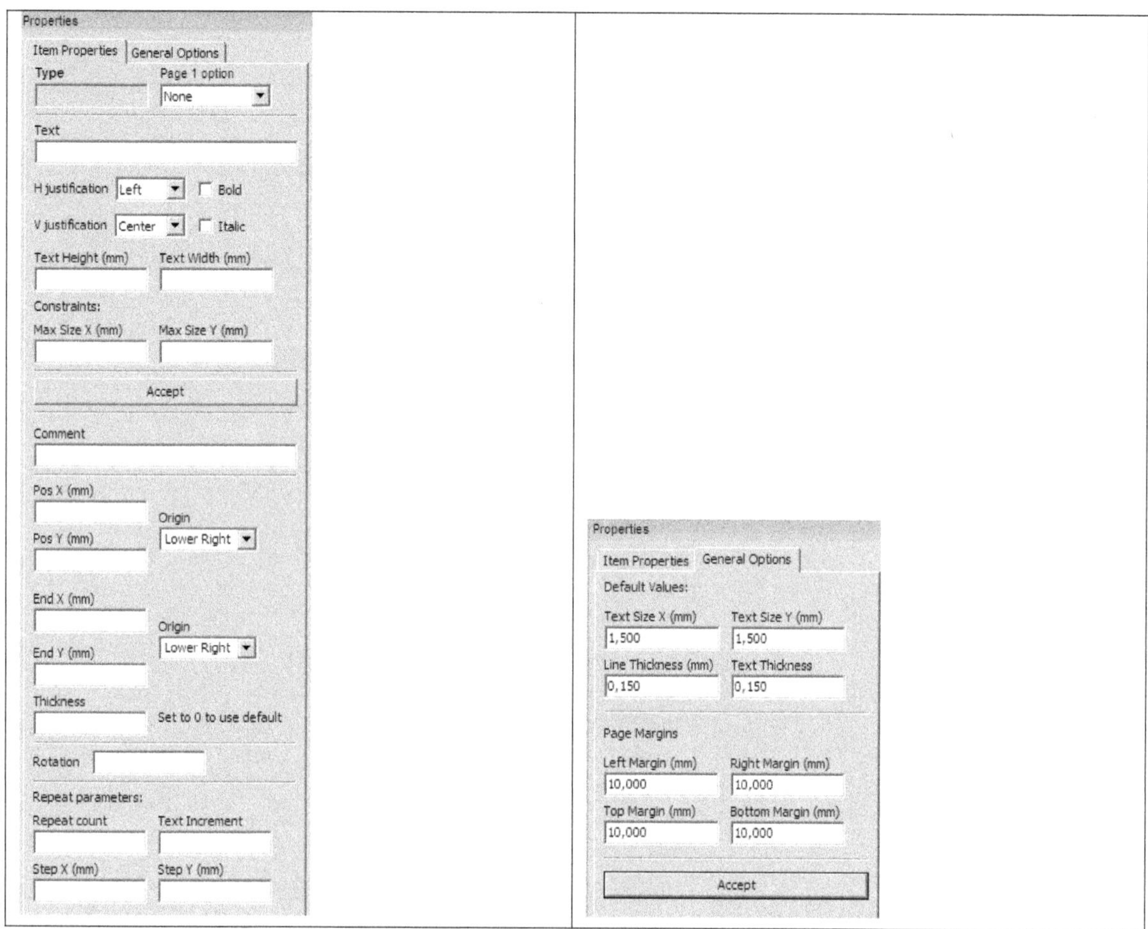

On this dialog you can set the page property and the item property of the current item.

Displayed settings depend on the selected item:

Settings for lines and rectangles	Settings for texts
Accept Type: Line Page 1 option: None Comment Pos X (mm): 50,000 Origin: Upper Left Pos Y (mm): 2,000 End X (mm): 50,000 Origin: Upper Left End Y (mm): 0,000 Thickness: 0,000 Set to 0 to use default Repeat parameters: Repeat count: 30 Step X (mm): 50,000 Step Y (mm): 0,000	Accept Type: Text Page 1 option: None Text: %K H justification: Left Bold V justification: Center Italic Text Height (mm): 0,000 Text Width (mm): 0,000 Constraints: Max Size X (mm): 0,000 Max Size Y (mm): 0,000 Comment Pos X (mm): 109,000 Origin: Lower Right Pos Y (mm): 4,100 Thickness: 0,000 Set to 0 to use default Rotation: 0,000 Repeat parameters: Repeat count: 1 Text Increment: 1 Step X (mm): 0,000 Step Y (mm): 0,000
Settings for poly-polygons	Setting for bitmaps
Accept Type: Poly Page 1 option: Page 1 only Comment Pos X (mm): 136,002 Origin: Lower Right Pos Y (mm): 18,002 Thickness: 0,010 Rotation: 20,000 Repeat parameters: Repeat count: 1 Step X (mm): 0,000 Step Y (mm): 0,000	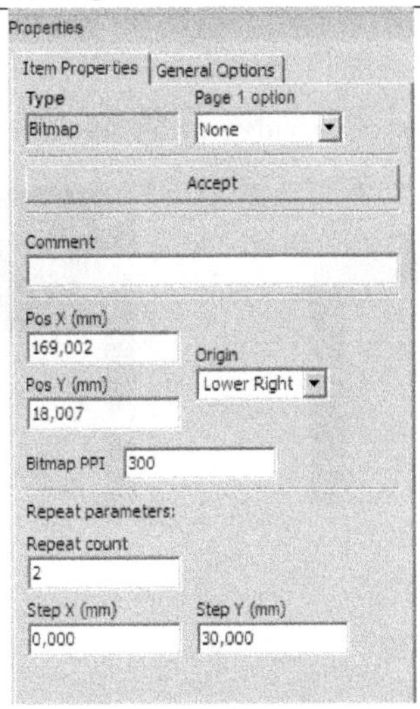 Properties Item Properties | General Options Type: Bitmap Page 1 option: None Accept Comment Pos X (mm): 169,002 Origin: Lower Right Pos Y (mm): 18,007 Bitmap PPI: 300 Repeat parameters: Repeat count: 2 Step X (mm): 0,000 Step Y (mm): 30,000

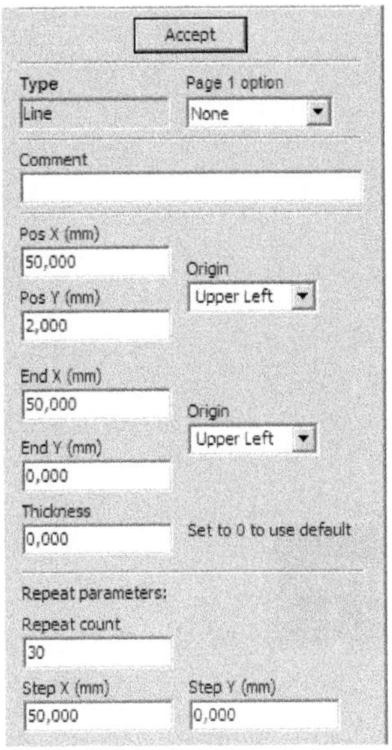

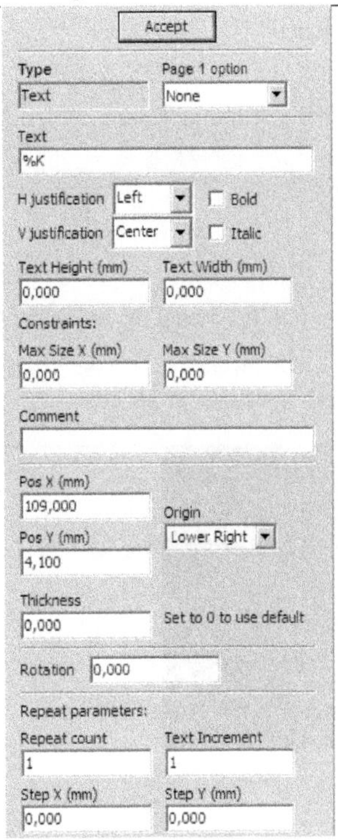

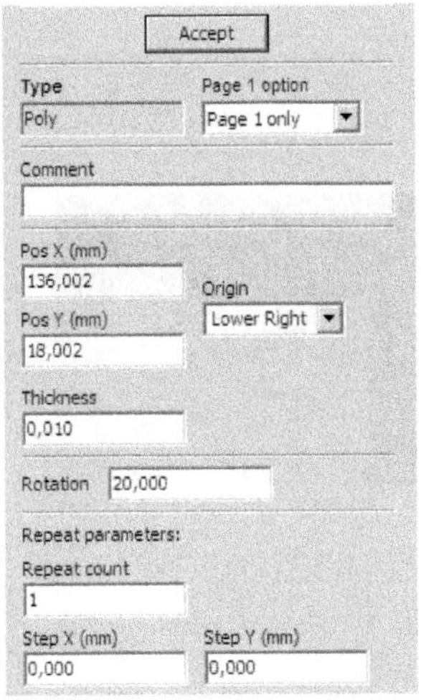

10 Interactive edition

10.1 Item selection

An item can be selected:

- From the Design tree.
- By Left clicking on it.
- By Right clicking on it (and a pop up menu will be displayed).

When selected, this item is drawn in yellow.

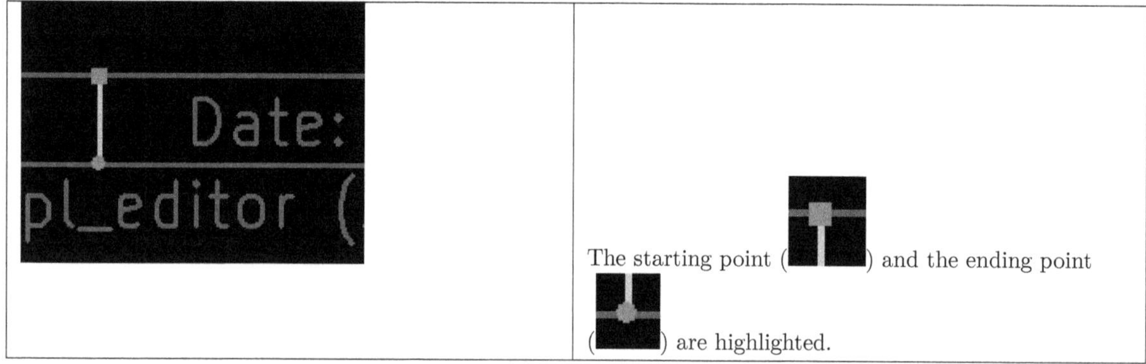

The starting point ( ) and the ending point ( ) are highlighted.

When right clicking on the item, a pop-up menu is displayed.

The pop menu options slightly depend on the selection:

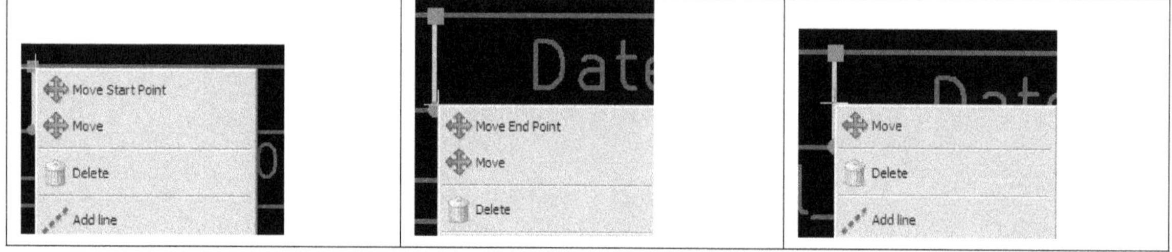

If more than one item is found, a menu clarification will be shown, to select the item:

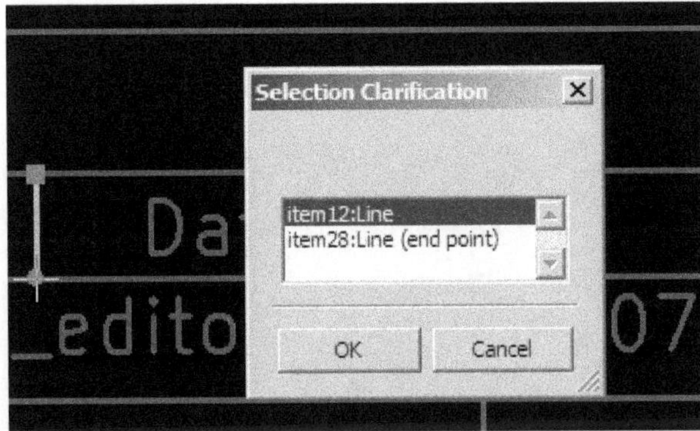

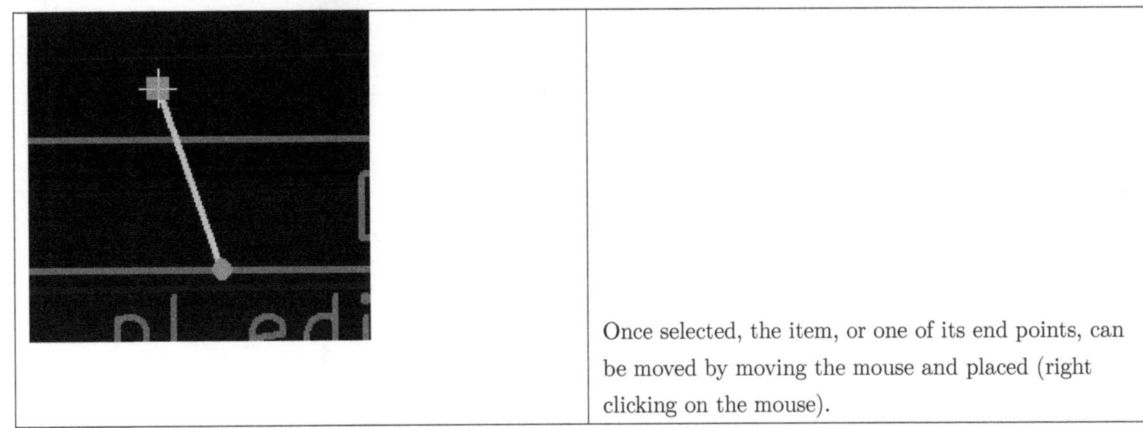

Once selected, the item, or one of its end points, can be moved by moving the mouse and placed (right clicking on the mouse).

10.2 Item creation

To add a new item, right click the mouse button when the cursor is on the left window or the draw area.

A popup menu is displayed:

Pop up menu in left window

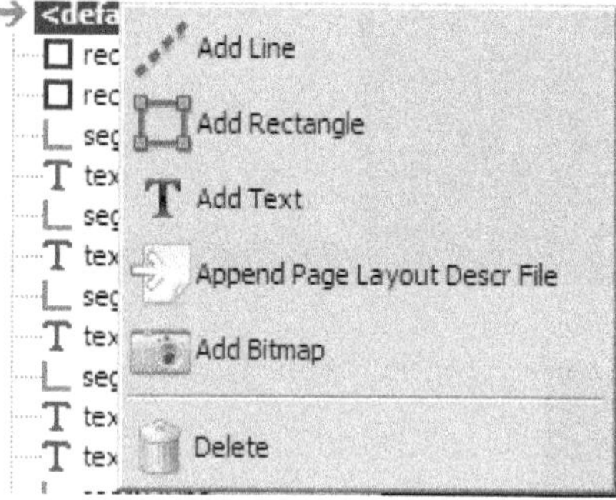

Pop up menu in draw area.

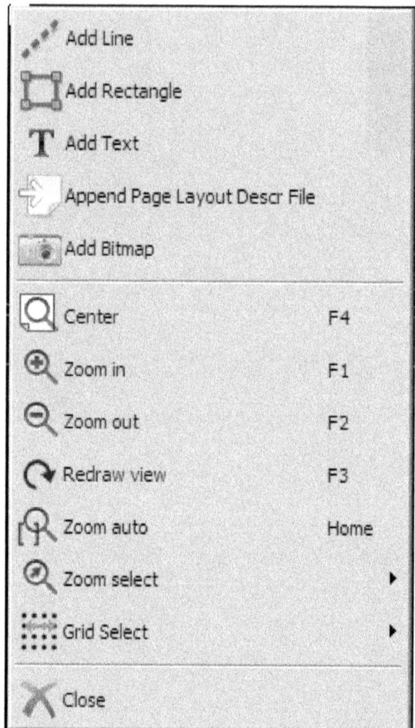

Lines, rectangles and texts are added just by clicking on the corresponding menu item.

Logos must first be created by Bitmap2component, which creates a page layout description file.

The Append Page Layout Descr File option append this file, to insert the logo (a poly polygon).

10.3 Adding lines, rectangles and texts

When clicking on the option, a dialog is opened:

Adding line or rectangle

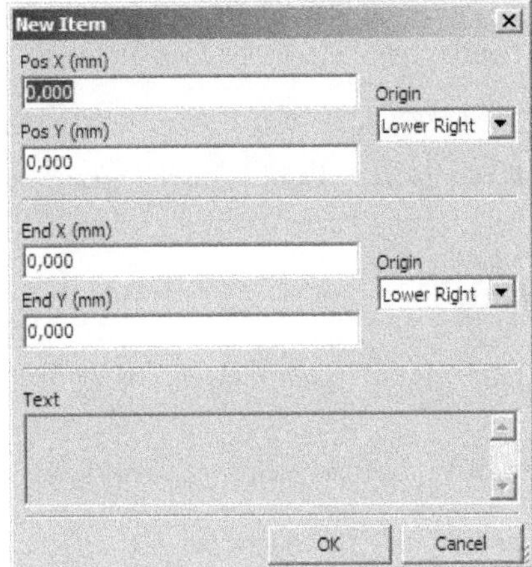

Adding text

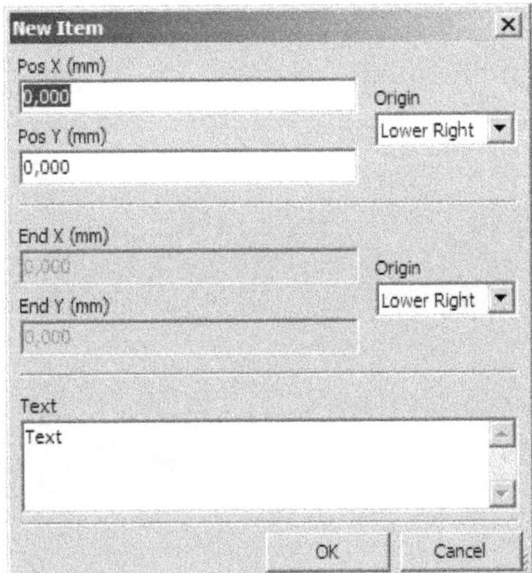

Position of end points, and corner reference can be defined here.

However they can be defined later, from the right window, or by moving the item, or one of its end points.

Most of time the corner reference is the same for both points.

If this is not the case, define the corner reference at creation is better, because if a corner reference is changed later, the geometry of the item will be a bit strange.

When an item is created, if is put in move mode, and you can refine its position (this is very useful for texts and small lines or rectangles)

10.4 Adding logos

To add a logo, a poly polygon (the vectored image of the logo) must be first created using Bitmap2component.

Bitmap2component creates a page layout description file which is append to the current design, using the **Append Page Layout Descr File** option.

Bitmap2component creates a page layout description file which contains only one item: a poly polygon.

However, this command can be used to append any page layout description file, which is merged with the current design.

Once a poly polygon is inserted, it can be moved and its parameters edited.

10.5 Adding image bitmaps

You can add an image bitmap using most of bitmap formats (PNG, JPEG, BMP ···).

- When a bitmap is imported, its PPI (pixel per inch) definition is set to 300PPI.
- This value can be modified in panel Properties (right panel).
- The actual size depend on this parameter.
- Be aware that using higher definition values brings larger output files, and can have a noticeable draw or plot time.

A bitmap can be repeated, **but not rotated.**

IDF Exporter

August 24, 2017

Contents

Reference manual

Copyright

Contributors

Cirilo Bernardo

Feedback

Please direct any bug reports, suggestions or new versions to here:

- About KiCad document: https://github.com/KiCad/kicad-doc/issues
- About KiCad software: https://bugs.launchpad.net/kicad
- About KiCad software i18n: https://github.com/KiCad/kicad-i18n/issues

Publication date and software version

Published on January 26, 2014.

1 Introduction to the IDFv3 exporter

The IDF exporter exports an IDFv3 [1] compliant board (.emn) and library (.emp) file for communicating mechanical dimensions to a mechanical CAD package. The exporter currently exports the board outline and cutouts, all pad and mounting thru-holes including slotted holes, and component outlines; this is the most basic set of mechanical data required for interaction with mechanical designers. All other entities described in the IDFv3 specification are currently not exported.

2 Specifying component models for use by the exporter

The IDF exporter makes use of the 3D model file attribute which was originally used by the 3D viewer. Since the 3D viewer, IDF, and possible future mechanical CAD exporters are generally interested in different types of file format, it is possible to use the 3D model file attribute to specify models for multiple exporters.

From within the Footprint Editor or Pcbnew, edit the footprint parameters and click on the 3D settings tab (see figure 1), click on Add 3D Shape, and select the filter "IDFv3 component files (*.idf)" (see figure 2). Select the desired outline file and enter any necessary values for the offset and rotation. Note that only the offset values and the Z rotation value are used by the IDF exporter; all other values are ignored. The offsets must be specified using the IDF board output units (mm or thou) and in the IDF coordinate system, that is a right-hand coordinate system with +Z moving towards the viewer, +X is to the viewer' s right, and +Y is up. The rotation must be in degrees and a positive rotation is a counter-clockwise rotation as described in the IDFv3 specification. Multiple outlines may be combined with appropriate offsets to represent simple assemblies such as a DIP package in a socket. [**BUG:** in discussions it has been decided that the unit of the Z offset should be inches, which is consistent with the units of the VRML model offset. It may also be useful not to ignore the (X,Y) offset values. The behavior mentioned here will change at some point in the future.]

Once models have been specified for all desired components, from within pcbnew select the **File** menu then **Export** and finally **IDFv3 Export**. A dialog box will pop up (see figure 3) which allows the output filename and IDF output units (mm or mils) to be set. The exported IDF files can be viewed in the free mechanical CAD software FreeCAD or converted to VRML using the idf2vrml tool and viewed with any suitable VRML viewer.

[1] http://www.simplifiedsolutionsinc.com/images/idf_v30_spec.pdf

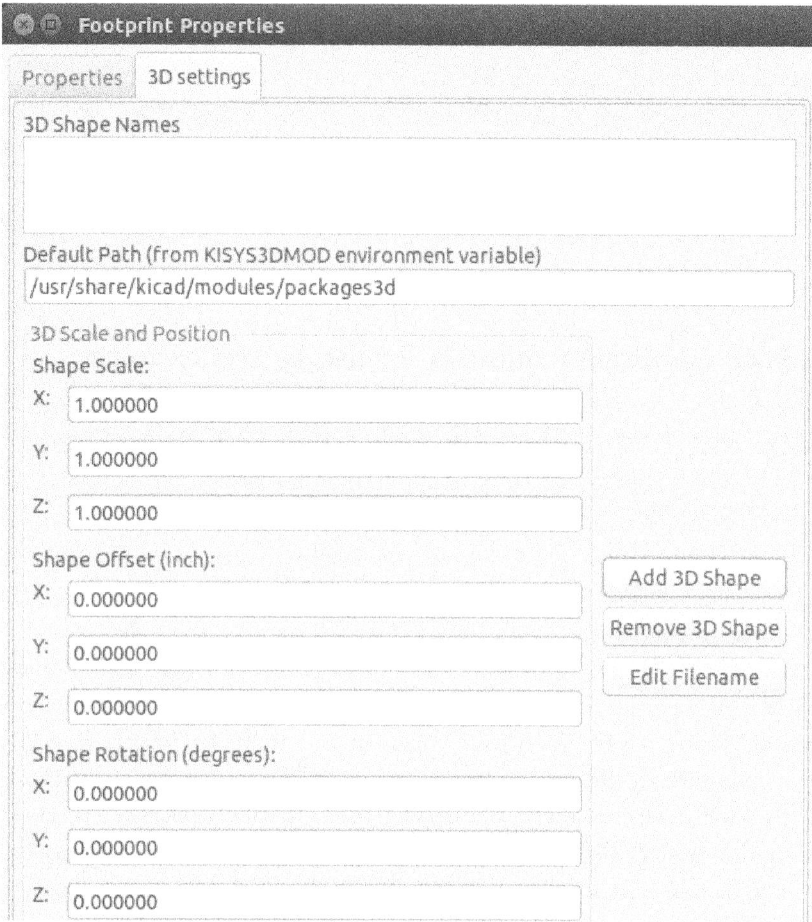

Figure 1: Footprint properties, 3D settings

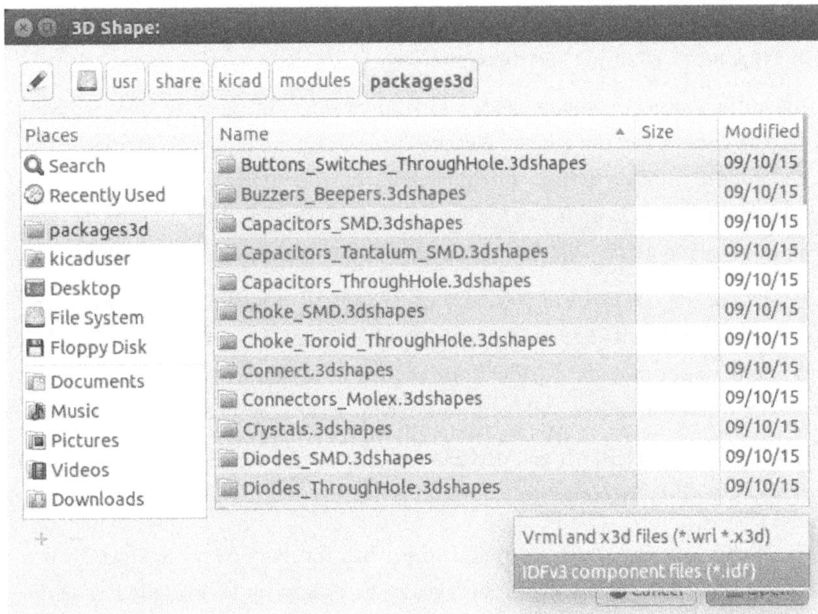

Figure 2: IDF component outline selection

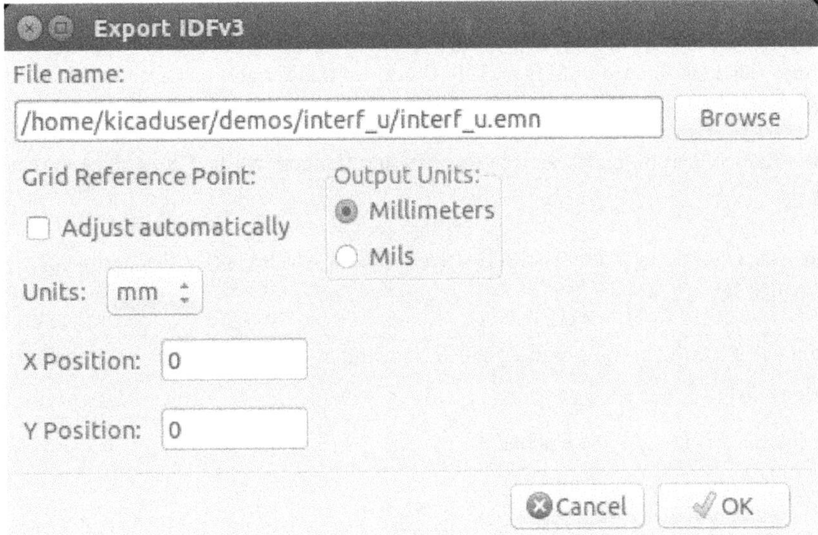

Figure 3: IDF output settings

3 Creating a component outline file

The component outline file (*.idf) consists of a single .ELECTRICAL or .MECHANICAL section as described in the specification document. The section may be preceded by any number of comment lines; the comment lines are copied by the exporter into the library file and can be used to track metadata such as references to the documents used to determine the component' s outline and dimensions.

The component outline section contains fields which are strings, integers, or floating point numbers. A string is a combination of characters which may include spaces; if a string contains spaces then it must be quoted. Quotation marks must not appear within a string. Floating point numbers may be represented using decimal or exponential notations but decimal notation is preferred for human readability. The decimal point must be a dot and not a comma. The IDF file must consist only of 7-bit ASCII characters; use of 8-bit characters will result in undefined behavior.

An IDF file consists of SECTIONS which consist of RECORDS which consist of FIELDS. For the IDF outline files only one type of section may exist and must be one of .ELECTRICAL or .MECHANICAL. A record is a single line of text and may contain one or more fields. Fields are sequences of characters separated by one or more spaces which do not appear between quotation marks. All fields of a record must appear on a single line; records may not span lines.

The section heading (.ELECTRICAL or .MECHANICAL) is considered the first record (Record 1) of the section. Record 1 must be followed by Record 2 which has four fields:

1. Geometry Name: a string which in combination with the Part Number must form a unique identifier for the component outline. For standardized packages, the package name is a good value for the geometry name, for example "SOT-23". For unique packages the manufacturer' s part number is a good choice for the geometry name.
2. Part Number: although obviously intended for the part number, for example BS107, it is better to use this string to help describe the package. For example if the geometry name is "TO-92", the part number entry may be used to describe the layout of the pads or the orientation of this particular TO-92 outline file.
3. IDF Unit: this must be one of MM or THOU and it applies only to the units describing this single component outline.
4. Height: this is a floating point number representing the nominal height of the component using units specified in Field 3.

Record 2 must be followed by a number of Record 3 entries which specify the outline of the component. Record 3 consists of four fields:

1. Loop Index: 0 (outline points are specified in counter-clockwise order) or 1 (outline points are specified in clockwise order)
2. X coordinate: a floating point number
3. Y coordinate: a floating point number
4. Included Angle: a floating point number. If the value is 0 then a straight line segment is drawn from the previous point to this point. If the value is 360 then the previous point specifies the center of a circle and this point specifies a point on the circle; never specify a circle using a value of -360 as at least one major mechanical CAD package does not behave well in that situation. If the value is negative then a clockwise arc is drawn from the previous point to this point and if the value is positive then a counter-clockwise arc is drawn.

Only one closed loop is permitted and it is not possible to specify a cutout. The last point specified must be the same as the first point unless the outline is a circle.

Example IDF File 1:

```
# a simple cylinder - this could represent an electrolytic capacitor
.ELECTRICAL
    "cylinder" "5mm OD, 5mm height" MM 5
    0 0 0 0
    0 2.5 0 360
.END_ELECTRICAL
```

Example IDF File 2:

```
# an upside-down T
# a comment added for the sake of adding comments
.ELECTRICAL
    "Capital T" "5x8x10mm, upside down" MM 10
    0 -0.5 8 0
    0 -0.5 0.5 0
    0 -2.5 0.5 0
    0 -2.5 -0.5 180
    0 2.5 -0.5 0
    0 2.5 0.5 180
    0 0.5 0.5 0
    0 0.5 8 0
    0 -0.5 8 180
.END_ELECTRICAL
```

4 Guidelines for creating outlines

When creating outlines, and especially when sharing the work with others, consistency in the design and naming of files helps people locate files quicker and place the components with minimal hassles.

4.1 Package naming

Try to make some information about the outline available in the filename to give the user a general idea of what the outline is. For example axial leaded cylindrical packages may represent some types of capacitors as well as some types of resistors, so it makes sense to identify an outline as a horizontal or vertical axial leaded device and to add some extra information on the relevant dimensions: diameter, length, and pitch are the most important. If a device has a unique outline, the manufacturer' s part number and a prefix to indicate the class of device are adequate.

4.2 Comments

Use comments in the IDF file to give users more information about the outline, for example a reference to the source used for dimensional information.

4.3 Geometry and Part Number entries

Think carefully about the values to give to the Geometry and Part Number entries. Taken together, these strings act as a unique identifier for the MCAD system. The values of the strings will ideally have some meaning to a user, but this is not necessary: the values are primarily intended for the MCAD system to use as a unique ID. Ideally the values chosen will be unique within any large collection of outlines; choosing values well will result in fewer clashes especially in complex boards.

4.4 Pin orientation and positioning

For through-hole components there are no widely accepted schemes for determining the pin orientation and component center in 3D models. For consistency, if there are only 2 pins they must be in a horizontal arrangement (see figure 4) along the X axis and for 3 pins try to keep 2 in a horizontal arrangement on the X axis. Polarized devices such as electrolytic or tantalum capacitors must have the positive lead on Pin 1 and diodes must have the cathode on Pin 1; this is to maintain compatibility of the schematic symbols with the orientation defined for SMT devices; however, note that many existing KiCad schematics and footprints place the anode at Pin 1.

Note

In the latest revision of the KiCad footprints on github the anode is now Pin 2 for THT as well as SMT components.

For DIP devices the center of the outline must be at the center of the rectangle described by the pin locations and Pin 1 is preferably at the top left corner; this will maintain some consistency with the standardized orientation of SMT components; however, such a model will be rotated -90 degrees relative to most existing KiCad component footprints and VRML models. For items such as a horizontal radial leaded capacitor or a horizontal TO-220 package, prefer to place the leads in a row on the X axis and with the body of the device extending upwards (see figure 4). Non-polarized vertical axial leaded components must have the wire on the right hand side; polarized vertical axial leaded components may have the wire on either side, depending on whether Pin 1 is on the lower end (wire on right) or on the upper end (wire on left).

Note

In the current revision of the KiCad footprint modules the THT components are being organized with pins along the Y axis rather than the X axis and Pin 1 of the device is at the origin rather than at the center of the package. Orient and position the component outline to suit your specific footprints; this will avoid the need to specify a non-zero rotation for the IDF component outlines. Since the IDF exporter currently ignores the (X,Y) offset values it is vital that you use the correct origin in the IDF component outline.

For SMT components the orientation, package center, and outline are defined by various standards. Use the standard appropriate to your work. Also keep in mind that many devices do not conform to any standard; in such cases the offending device is probably best identified by using the manufacturer' s part number in the outline file name. In general, an SMT outline is a rectangle encompassing the component package and including the leads; the package is oriented such that Pin 1 is as close as possible to the top left corner and the top left corner is usually chamfered for visual reference.

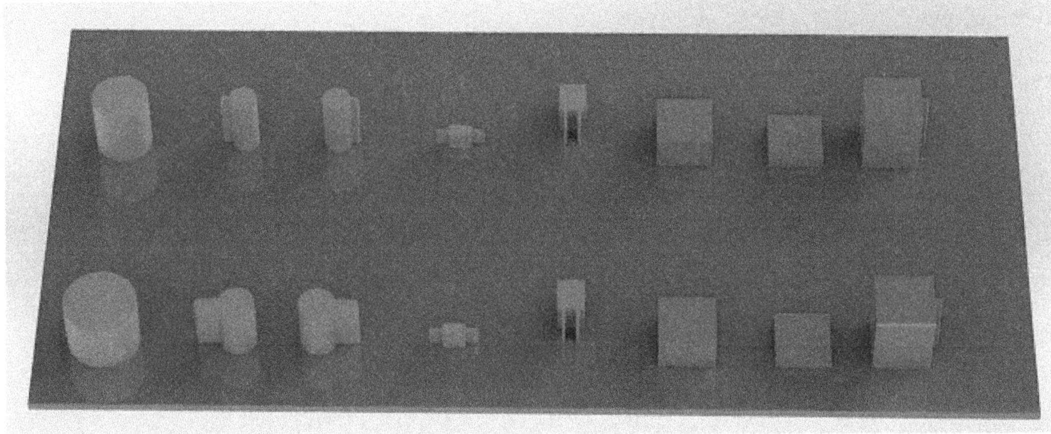

Figure 4: Sample outlines generated by the programs idfcyl and idfrect and rendered by SolidWorks.

From left to right are (a) vertical radial leaded cylinder, (b) vertical axial leaded cylinder with wire on left, (c) vertical axial leaded cylinder with wire on right, (d) horizontal axial leaded cylinder, (e) horizontal radial leaded cylinder, (f) square outline, plain, (g) square outline with chamfer, (h) square outline with axial lead on right. The top outlines were specified in units of millimeters while the bottom outlines were specified in units of inches.

4.5 Tips on dimensions

The purpose served by the extruded outlines is to give the mechanical designer some idea of the location and physical space occupied by each component. In a typical scenario the mechanical designer will replace some of the crude outlines with more detailed mechanical models, for example when checking to ensure that a right-angle mounted LED will fit into a hole on a panel. In most situations the accuracy of an outline doesn' t matter, but it is good practice to create outlines which convey the best mechanical information possible. In a few instances a user may wish to fit the component into a case with very little excess space, for example in a portable music player. In such a situation, if most extruded outlines are a good enough representation of components then the mechanical designer may only have to replace very few models while designing the case. If the outlines are not a reliable reflection of reality then the mechanical designer will waste a lot of time replacing models to ensure a good fit. After all, if you put garbage in you can expect garbage to come out. If you put in good information, you can be confident of good results.

5 IDF Component Outline Tools

A number of command-line tools are available to help generate IDF component outlines. The tools are:

1. **idfcyl:** creates an outline of a cylinder in vertical or horizontal orientation and with axial or radial leads
2. **idfrect:** creates an outline of a rectangle which may have either an axial lead or a chamfer in the top left corner
3. **dxf2idf:** converts a drawing in DXF format into an IDF component outline

5.1 idfcyl

When **idfcyl** is invoked with no arguments it prints out a usage note and a summary of its inputs:

```
idfcyl: This program generates an outline for a cylindrical component.
    The cylinder may be horizontal or vertical.
    A horizontal cylinder may have wires at one or both ends.
    A vertical cylinder may have at most one wire which may be
    placed on the left or right side.

Input:
    Unit: mm, in (millimeters or inches)
    Orientation: V (vertical)
    Lead type: X, R (axial, radial)
    Diameter of body
    Length of body
    Board offset
    *   Wire diameter
    *   Pitch
    **  Wire side: L, R (left, right)
    *** Lead length
    File name (must end in *.idf)

    NOTES:
        *   only required for horizontal orientation or
            vertical orientation with axial leads

        **  only required for vertical orientation with axial leads

        *** only required for horizontal orientation with radial leads
```

The notes can be suppressed by entering any arbitrary argument on the command line. A user can manually enter information at the command line or create scripts to generate outlines. The following script creates a single cylinder axial leaded outline with the lead on the right hand side:

```
#!/bin/bash
# Generate a cylindrical IDF outline for test purposes
# vertical 5mm cylinder, nominal length 8mm + 3mm board offset,
# axial wire on right, 0.8mm wire dia., 3.5mm pitch
idfcyl - 1 > /dev/null << _EOF
mm
v
x
5
8
3
0.8
3.5
r
```

```
cylvmm_1R_D5_L8_Z3_WD0.8_P3.5.idf
_EOF
```

5.2 idfrect

When **idfrect** is invoked with no arguments it prints out a usage note and a summary of its inputs:

```
idfrect: This program generates an outline for a rectangular component.
    The component may have a single lead (axial) or a chamfer on the
    upper left corner.
Input:
    Unit: mm, in (millimeters or inches)
    Width:
    Length:
    Height:
    Chamfer: length of the 45 deg. chamfer
    *  Leaded: Y,N (lead is always to the right)
    ** Wire diameter
    ** Pitch
    File name (must end in *.idf)

    NOTES:
        *   only required if chamfer = 0

        **  only required for leaded components
```

The notes can be suppressed by entering any arbitrary argument on the command line. A user can manually enter information at the command line or create scripts to generate outlines. The following script creates a chamfered rectangle and an axial leaded outline:

```
#!/bin/bash
# Generate various rectangular IDF outlines for test purposes
# 10x10, 1mm chamfer, 2mm height
idfrect - 1 > /dev/null <<  _EOF
mm
10
10
2
1
rectMM_10x10x2_C0.5.idf
_EOF
# 10x10x12,  0.8mm lead on 6mm pitch
idfrect - 1 > /dev/null <<  _EOF
mm
10
10
12
```

```
0
Y
0.8
6
rectLMM_10x10x12_D0.8_P6.0.idf
_EOF
```

5.3 dxf2idf

The DXF file used to specify the component outline can be prepared with the free software LibreCAD for best compatibility. When **dxf2idf** is invoked with no arguments it prints out a usage note and a summary of its inputs:

```
dxf2idf: this program takes line, arc, and circle segments
    from a DXF file and creates an IDF component outline file.

Input:
    DXF filename: the input file, must end in '.dxf'
    Units: mm, in (millimeters or inches)
    Geometry Name: string, as per IDF version 3.0 specification
    Part Name: as per IDF version 3.0 specification of Part Number
    Height: extruded height of the outline
    Comments: all non-empty lines are comments to be added to
        the IDF file. An empty line signifies the end of
        the comment block.
    File name: output filename, must end in '.idf'
```

The notes can be suppressed by entering any arbitrary argument on the command line. A user can manually enter information at the command line or create scripts to generate outlines. The following script creates a 5mm high outline from a DXF file *test.dxf*:

```
#!/bin/bash
# Generate an IDF outlines from a DXF file
dxf2idf - 1 > /dev/null << _EOF
test.dxf
mm
DXF TEST GEOMETRY
DXF TEST PART
5
This is an IDF test file produced from the outline 'test.dxf'
This is a second IDF comment to demonstrate multiple comments

test_dxf2idf.idf
_EOF
```

6 idf2vrml

The idf2vrml tool reads a set of one IDF Board (.emn) and one IDF Component file (.emp) and produces a VRML file which can be viewed with a VRML viewer. This feature is useful for visualization of the board assembly in cases where the user does not have access to MCAD software. Invoking idf2vrml without any arguments will result in the display of a usage message:

```
>./idf2vrml
Usage: idf2vrml -f input_file.emn -s scale_factor {-k} {-d} {-z} {-m}
flags:
   -k: produce KiCad-friendly VRML output; default is compact VRML
   -d: suppress substitution of default outlines
   -z: suppress rendering of zero-height outlines
   -m: print object mapping to stdout for debugging purposes
example to produce a model for use by KiCad: idf2vrml -f input.emn -s 0.3937008 -k
>
```

[**BUG:** The idf2vrml tool currently does not correctly render **OTHER_OUTLINE** entities in an emn file if that entity is specifies on the back layer of the PCB; however you will not notice this bug using files exported by KiCad since there is no mechanism to specify such an entity. Essentially this bug is only an issue in rare instances where you might render a third party emn file which does employ the entity on the back side of a board.]

Kicad Plugins

January 3, 2018

Contents

KiCad Plugin System

Copyright

Contributors

Cirilo Bernardo

Feedback

Please direct any bug reports, suggestions or new versions to here:

- About KiCad document: https://github.com/KiCad/kicad-doc/issues
- About KiCad software: https://bugs.launchpad.net/kicad
- About KiCad software i18n: https://github.com/KiCad/kicad-i18n/issues

Publication date and software version

Published on January 29, 2016.

1 Introduction to the KiCad plugin system

The KiCad plugin system is a framework for extending the capabilities of KiCad using shared libraries. One of the main advantages of using a plugin is that it is not necessary to rebuild the KiCad suite while developing a plugin; in fact, plugins can be built with the aid of a very small set of headers from the KiCad source tree. Removing the requirement to build KiCad during plugin development greatly increases productivity by ensuring that the developer only compiles code directly related to the plugin which is being developed and thus reducing the time required for each build and test cycle.

Plugins were initially developed for the 3D model viewer to make it possible to support more types of 3D models without requiring major changes to the KiCad source for each new model type supported. The plugin framework was later generalized so that in the future developers can create different classes of plugins. Currently only 3D plugins are implemented within KiCad but it is envisioned that a PCB plugin will eventually be developed to make it possible for users to implement data Importers and Exporters.

1.1 Plugin Classes

Plugins are divided into Plugin Classes since each plugin addresses problems in a specific domain and therefore requires an interface unique to that domain. For example, the 3D model plugins load 3D model data from files and translate that data into a format which can be displayed by the 3D viewer. A PCB Import/Export plugin would take PCB data and export to other electrical or mechanical data formats, or translate a foreign format into a KiCad PCB. At the moment only the 3D Plugin Class has been developed and it will be the focus of this document.

Implementing a Plugin Class requires creating code within the KiCad source tree which manages the loading of plugin code. Within the KiCad source tree, the file `plugins/ldr/pluginldr.h` declares the base class for all plugin loaders. This class declares the most basic functions which we would expect to find in any KiCad plugin (boilerplate code) and its implementation provides basic checks on version compatibility between the plugin loader and the available plugins. The header `plugins/ldr/3d/pluginldr3D.h` declares a loader for the 3D Plugin Class. The loader is responsible for loading a given plugin and making its functions available to KiCad. Each instance of a plugin loader represents an actual plugin implementation and acts as a transparent bridge between KiCad and the plugin' s features. The loader is not the only code required within KiCad to support plugins: we also need code to discover the plugins and code to invoke the functions of the plugins via the plugin loader. In the case of the 3D plugins the discovery and invocation functions are all contained within the S3D_CACHE class.

Plugin developers do not need to be concerned with the details of KiCad' s internal code for managing plugins unless a new Plugin Class is being developed; a plugin only needs to define the functions declared by their specific plugin class.

The header `include/plugins/kicad_plugin.h` declares the generic functions required of all KiCad plugins; these functions identify the Plugin Class, provide the name of the specific plugin, provide version information for the Plugin Class API, provide version information for the specific plugin, and provide a basic version compatibility check on the Plugin Class API. In brief, these functions are:

```
/* Return a UTF-8 string naming the Plugin Class */
char const* GetKicadPluginClass( void );

/* Return version information for the Plugin Class API */
```

```
void GetClassVersion( unsigned char* Major, unsigned char* Minor,
     unsigned char* Patch, unsigned char* Revision );

/*
   Return true if the version check implemented in the plugin
   determines that the given Plugin Class API is compatible.
 */
bool CheckClassVersion( unsigned char Major,
    unsigned char Minor, unsigned char Patch, unsigned char Revision );

/* Return the name of the specific plugin, for example "PLUGIN_3D_VRML" */
const char* GetKicadPluginName( void );

/* Return version information for the specific plugin */
void GetPluginVersion( unsigned char* Major, unsigned char* Minor,
     unsigned char* Patch, unsigned char* Revision );
```

1.1.1 Plugin Class: PLUGIN_3D

The header `include/plugins/3d/3d_plugin.h` declares the functions which must be implemented by all 3D plugins and defines a number of functions which are required by the plugin and which the user must not reimplement. The defined functions which the user must not reimplement are:

```
/* Returns the Plugin Class name "PLUGIN_3D" */
char const* GetKicadPluginClass( void );

/* Return version information for the PLUGIN_3D API */
void GetClassVersion( unsigned char* Major, unsigned char* Minor,
     unsigned char* Patch, unsigned char* Revision );

/*
   Performs basic version checks enforced by the developers of
   the loader for the PLUGIN_3D class and returns true if the
   checks pass
 */
bool CheckClassVersion( unsigned char Major, unsigned char Minor,
     unsigned char Patch, unsigned char Revision );
```

The functions which the user must implement are as follows:

```
/* Return the number of extension strings supported by the plugin */
int GetNExtensions( void );

/*
   Return the requested extension string; valid values are 0 to
   GetNExtensions() - 1
 */
char const* GetModelExtension( int aIndex );
```

```
/* Return the total number of file filters supported by the plugin */
int GetNFilters( void );

/*
   Return the file filter requested; valid values are 0 to
   GetNFilters() - 1
 */
char const* GetFileFilter( int aIndex );

/*
    Return true if the plugin can render this type of 3D model.
    In some cases a plugin may not yet provide a visual model
    and must return false.
 */
bool CanRender( void );

/* Load the specified model and return a pointer to its visual model data */
SCENEGRAPH* Load( char const* aFileName );
```

2 Tutorials: 3D Plugin Class

This section contains a description of two very simple plugins of the PLUGIN_3D class and walks the user through the setup and building of the code.

2.1 Basic 3D Plugin

This tutorial walks the user through the development of a very basic 3D plugin named "PLUGIN_3D_DEMO1". The purpose of this tutorial is only to demonstrate the construction of a very basic 3D plugin which does nothing other than provide a few filter strings which permit the KiCad user to filter file names while browsing for 3D models. The code demonstrated here is the absolute minimum requirement for any 3D plugin and can be used as a template for creating more advanced plugins.

In order to build the demo project we require the following:

- CMake
- KiCad plugin headers
- KiCad Scene Graph library `kicad_3dsg`

To automatically detect the KiCad headers and library we shall use a CMake FindPackage script; the script supplied in this tutorial should work on Linux and Windows if the relevant header files are installed to `${KICAD_ROOT_DIR}/kicad` and the KiCad Scene Graph library is installed in `${KICAD_ROOT_DIR}/lib`.

To start let's create a project directory and the FindPackage script:

```
mkdir demo && cd demo
export DEMO_ROOT=${PWD}
mkdir CMakeModules && cd CMakeModules
cat > FindKICAD.cmake << _EOF
find_path( KICAD_INCLUDE_DIR kicad/plugins/kicad_plugin.h
    PATHS ${KICAD_ROOT_DIR}/include $ENV{KICAD_ROOT_DIR}/include
    DOC "Kicad plugins header path."
    )

if( NOT ${KICAD_INCLUDE_DIR} STREQUAL "KICAD_INCLUDE_DIR-NOTFOUND" )

    # attempt to extract the version information from sg_version.h
    find_file( KICAD_SGVERSION sg_version.h
        PATHS ${KICAD_INCLUDE_DIR}
        PATH_SUFFIXES kicad/plugins/3dapi
        NO_DEFAULT_PATH )

    if( NOT ${KICAD_SGVERSION} STREQUAL "KICAD_SGVERSION-NOTFOUND" )

        # extract the "#define KICADSG_VERSION*" lines
        file( STRINGS ${KICAD_SGVERSION} _version REGEX "^#define.*KICADSG_VERSION.*" )

        foreach( SVAR ${_version} )
            string( REGEX MATCH KICADSG_VERSION_[M,A,J,O,R,I,N,P,T,C,H,E,V,I,S]* _VARNAME $ ←
                {SVAR} )
            string( REGEX MATCH [0-9]+ _VALUE ${SVAR} )

            if( NOT ${_VARNAME} STREQUAL "" AND NOT ${_VALUE} STREQUAL "" )
                set( _${_VARNAME} ${_VALUE} )
            endif()

        endforeach()

        #ensure that NOT SG3D_VERSION* will evaluate to '0'
        if( NOT _KICADSG_VERSION_MAJOR )
            set( _KICADSG_VERSION_MAJOR 0 )
        endif()

        if( NOT _KICADSG_VERSION_MINOR )
            set( _KICADSG_VERSION_MINOR 0 )
        endif()

        if( NOT _KICADSG_VERSION_PATCH )
            set( _KICADSG_VERSION_PATCH 0 )
        endif()

        if( NOT _KICADSG_VERSION_REVISION )
```

```
            set( _KICADSG_VERSION_REVISION 0 )
        endif()

        set( KICAD_VERSION ${_KICADSG_VERSION_MAJOR}.${_KICADSG_VERSION_MINOR}.${ ←
            _KICADSG_VERSION_PATCH}.${_KICADSG_VERSION_REVISION} )
        unset( KICAD_SGVERSION CACHE )

    endif()
endif()


find_library( KICAD_LIBRARY
    NAMES kicad_3dsg
    PATHS
        ${KICAD_ROOT_DIR}/lib $ENV{KICAD_ROOT_DIR}/lib
        ${KICAD_ROOT_DIR}/bin $ENV{KICAD_ROOT_DIR}/bin
    DOC "Kicad scenegraph library path."
    )

include( FindPackageHandleStandardArgs )
FIND_PACKAGE_HANDLE_STANDARD_ARGS( KICAD
    REQUIRED_VARS
        KICAD_INCLUDE_DIR
        KICAD_LIBRARY
        KICAD_VERSION
    VERSION_VAR KICAD_VERSION )


mark_as_advanced( KICAD_INCLUDE_DIR )
set( KICAD_VERSION_MAJOR ${_KICADSG_VERSION_MAJOR} CACHE INTERNAL "" )
set( KICAD_VERSION_MINOR ${_KICADSG_VERSION_MINOR} CACHE INTERNAL "" )
set( KICAD_VERSION_PATCH ${_KICADSG_VERSION_PATCH} CACHE INTERNAL "" )
set( KICAD_VERSION_TWEAK ${_KICADSG_VERSION_REVISION} CACHE INTERNAL "" )
_EOF
```

Kicad and its plugin headers must be installed; if they are installed to a user directory or under `/opt` on Linux, or you are using Windows, you will need to set the `KICAD_ROOT_DIR` environment variable to point to the directory containing the KiCad `include` and `lib` directories. For OS X the FindPackage script presented here may require some adjustments.

To configure and build the tutorial code we will use CMake and create a `CMakeLists.txt` script file:

```
cd ${DEMO_ROOT}
cat > CMakeLists.txt << _EOF
# declare the name of the project
project( PLUGIN_DEMO )

# check that we have a version of CMake with all required features
cmake_minimum_required( VERSION 2.8.12 FATAL_ERROR )
```

```
# inform CMake of where to find the FindKICAD script
set( CMAKE_MODULE_PATH ${PROJECT_SOURCE_DIR}/CMakeModules )

# attempt to discover the installed kicad headers and library
# and set the variables:
#     KICAD_INCLUDE_DIR
#     KICAD_LIBRARY
find_package( KICAD 1.0 REQUIRED )

# add the kicad include directory to the compiler's search path
include_directories( ${KICAD_INCLUDE_DIR}/kicad )

# create a plugin named s3d_plugin_demo1
add_library( s3d_plugin_demo1 MODULE
    src/s3d_plugin_demo1.cpp
    )

_EOF
```

The first demo project is very basic; it consists of a single file with no external link dependencies other than the compiler defaults. We start by creating a source directory:

```
cd ${DEMO_ROOT}
mkdir src && cd src
export DEMO_SRC=${PWD}
```

Now we create the plugin source itself:

s3d_plugin_demo1.cpp

```
#include <iostream>

// the 3d_plugin.h header defines the functions required of 3D plugins
#include "plugins/3d/3d_plugin.h"

// define the version information of this plugin; do not confuse this
// with the Plugin Class version which is defined in 3d_plugin.h
#define PLUGIN_3D_DEMO1_MAJOR 1
#define PLUGIN_3D_DEMO1_MINOR 0
#define PLUGIN_3D_DEMO1_PATCH 0
#define PLUGIN_3D_DEMO1_REVNO 0

// implement the function which provides users with this plugin's name
const char* GetKicadPluginName( void )
{
    return "PLUGIN_3D_DEMO1";
}
```

```
// implement the function which provides users with this plugin's version
void GetPluginVersion( unsigned char* Major, unsigned char* Minor,
    unsigned char* Patch, unsigned char* Revision )
{
    if( Major )
        *Major = PLUGIN_3D_DEMO1_MAJOR;

    if( Minor )
        *Minor = PLUGIN_3D_DEMO1_MINOR;

    if( Patch )
        *Patch = PLUGIN_3D_DEMO1_PATCH;

    if( Revision )
        *Revision = PLUGIN_3D_DEMO1_REVNO;

    return;
}

// number of extensions supported; on *NIX systems the extensions are
// provided twice - once in lower case and once in upper case letters
#ifdef _WIN32
    #define NEXTS 7
#else
    #define NEXTS 14
#endif

// number of filter sets supported
#define NFILS 5

// define the extension strings and filter strings which this
// plugin will supply to the user
static char ext0[] = "wrl";
static char ext1[] = "x3d";
static char ext2[] = "emn";
static char ext3[] = "iges";
static char ext4[] = "igs";
static char ext5[] = "stp";
static char ext6[] = "step";

#ifdef _WIN32
static char fil0[] = "VRML 1.0/2.0 (*.wrl)|*.wrl";
static char fil1[] = "X3D (*.x3d)|*.x3d";
static char fil2[] = "IDF 2.0/3.0 (*.emn)|*.emn";
static char fil3[] = "IGESv5.3 (*.igs;*.iges)|*.igs;*.iges";
static char fil4[] = "STEP (*.stp;*.step)|*.stp;*.step";
#else
static char ext7[] = "WRL";
```

```
static char ext8[] = "X3D";
static char ext9[] = "EMN";
static char ext10[] = "IGES";
static char ext11[] = "IGS";
static char ext12[] = "STP";
static char ext13[] = "STEP";

static char fil0[] = "VRML 1.0/2.0 (*.wrl;*.WRL)|*.wrl;*.WRL";
static char fil1[] = "X3D (*.x3d;*.X3D)|*.x3d;*.X3D";
static char fil2[] = "IDF 2.0/3.0 (*.emn;*.EMN)|*.emn;*.EMN";
static char fil3[] = "IGESv5.3 (*.igs;*.iges;*.IGS;*.IGES)|*.igs;*.iges;*.IGS;*.IGES";
static char fil4[] = "STEP (*.stp;*.step;*.STP;*.STEP)|*.stp;*.step;*.STP;*.STEP";
#endif

// instantiate a convenient data structure for accessing the
// lists of extension and filter strings
static struct FILE_DATA
{
    char const* extensions[NEXTS];
    char const* filters[NFILS];

    FILE_DATA()
    {
        extensions[0] = ext0;
        extensions[1] = ext1;
        extensions[2] = ext2;
        extensions[3] = ext3;
        extensions[4] = ext4;
        extensions[5] = ext5;
        extensions[6] = ext6;
        filters[0] = fil0;
        filters[1] = fil1;
        filters[2] = fil2;
        filters[3] = fil3;
        filters[4] = fil4;

#ifndef _WIN32
        extensions[7] = ext7;
        extensions[8] = ext8;
        extensions[9] = ext9;
        extensions[10] = ext10;
        extensions[11] = ext11;
        extensions[12] = ext12;
        extensions[13] = ext13;
#endif
        return;
    }
```

```
} file_data;

// return the number of extensions supported by this plugin
int GetNExtensions( void )
{
    return NEXTS;
}

// return the indexed extension string
char const* GetModelExtension( int aIndex )
{
    if( aIndex < 0 || aIndex >= NEXTS )
        return NULL;

    return file_data.extensions[aIndex];
}

// return the number of filter strings provided by this plugin
int GetNFilters( void )
{
    return NFILS;
}

// return the indexed filter string
char const* GetFileFilter( int aIndex )
{
    if( aIndex < 0 || aIndex >= NFILS )
        return NULL;

    return file_data.filters[aIndex];
}

// return false since this plugin does not provide visualization data
bool CanRender( void )
{
    return false;
}

// return NULL since this plugin does not provide visualization data
SCENEGRAPH* Load( char const* aFileName )
{
    // this dummy plugin does not support rendering of any models
    return NULL;
}
```

This source file meets all the minimum requirements to implement a 3D plugin. The plugin does not produce any data for rendering models but it can provide KiCad with a list of supported model file extensions and file extension filters to enhance the 3D model file selection dialog. Within KiCad the extension strings are used to select the plugins which may be used to load a specified model; for example, if the plugin is `wrl` then KiCad will invoke each plugin which claims to support the extension `wrl` until a plugin returns visualization data. The file filters provided by each plugin are passed to the 3D file selector dialog to improve the browsing UI.

To build the plugin:

```
cd ${DEMO_ROOT}
# export KICAD_ROOT_DIR if necessary
mkdir build && cd build
cmake .. && make
```

The plugin will be built but not installed; you must copy the plugin file to KiCad' s plugin directory if you wish to load the plugin.

2.2 Advanced 3D Plugin

This tutorial walks the user through the development of a 3D plugin named "PLUGIN_3D_DEMO2". The purpose of this tutorial is to demonstrate the construction of a very basic scene graph which the KiCad previewer can render. The plugin claims to handle files of type `txt`. Although the file must exist in order for the cache manager to invoke the plugin, the file contents are not processed by this plugin; instead, the plugin simply creates a scene graph containing a pair of tetrahedra. This tutorial assumes that the first tutorial had been completed and that the CMakeLists.txt and FindKICAD.cmake script files have been created.

Place the new source file in the same directory as the previous tutorial' s source file and we will extend the previous tutorial' s CMakeLists.txt file to build this tutorial. Since this plugin will create a scene graph for KiCad we need to link to KiCad' s scene graph library `kicad_3dsg`. KiCad' s Scene Graph Library provides a set of classes which can be used to build the Scene Graph Object; the Scene Graph Object is an intermediate data visualization format used by the 3D Cache Manager. All plugins which support model visualization must translate the model data into a scene graph via this library.

The first step is to extend `CMakeLists.txt` to build this tutorial project:

```
cd ${DEMO_ROOT}
cat >> CMakeLists.txt << _EOF
add_library( s3d_plugin_demo2 MODULE
    src/s3d_plugin_demo2.cpp
    )

target_link_libraries( s3d_plugin_demo2 ${KICAD_LIBRARY} )
_EOF
```

Now we change to the source directory and create the source file:

```
cd ${DEMO_SRC}
```

s3d_plugin_demo2.cpp

```
#include <cmath>
// 3D Plugin Class declarations
#include "plugins/3d/3d_plugin.h"
// interface to KiCad Scene Graph Library
#include "plugins/3dapi/ifsg_all.h"

// version information for this plugin
#define PLUGIN_3D_DEMO2_MAJOR 1
#define PLUGIN_3D_DEMO2_MINOR 0
#define PLUGIN_3D_DEMO2_PATCH 0
#define PLUGIN_3D_DEMO2_REVNO 0

// provide the name of this plugin
const char* GetKicadPluginName( void )
{
    return "PLUGIN_3D_DEMO2";
}

// provide the version of this plugin
void GetPluginVersion( unsigned char* Major, unsigned char* Minor,
    unsigned char* Patch, unsigned char* Revision )
{
    if( Major )
        *Major = PLUGIN_3D_DEMO2_MAJOR;

    if( Minor )
        *Minor = PLUGIN_3D_DEMO2_MINOR;

    if( Patch )
        *Patch = PLUGIN_3D_DEMO2_PATCH;

    if( Revision )
        *Revision = PLUGIN_3D_DEMO2_REVNO;

    return;
}


// number of extensions supported
#ifdef _WIN32
#define NEXTS 1
#else
#define NEXTS 2
#endif

// number of filter sets supported
#define NFILS 1
```

```
static char ext0[] = "txt";

#ifdef _WIN32
static char fil0[] = "demo (*.txt)|*.txt";
#else
static char ext1[] = "TXT";

static char fil0[] = "demo (*.txt;*.TXT)|*.txt;*.TXT";
#endif


static struct FILE_DATA
{
    char const* extensions[NEXTS];
    char const* filters[NFILS];

    FILE_DATA()
    {
        extensions[0] = ext0;
        filters[0] = fil0;

#ifndef _WIN32
        extensions[1] = ext1;
#endif
        return;
    }

} file_data;


int GetNExtensions( void )
{
    return NEXTS;
}


char const* GetModelExtension( int aIndex )
{
    if( aIndex < 0 || aIndex >= NEXTS )
        return NULL;

    return file_data.extensions[aIndex];
}


int GetNFilters( void )
{
```

```
    return NFILS;
}


char const* GetFileFilter( int aIndex )
{
    if( aIndex < 0 || aIndex >= NFILS )
        return NULL;

    return file_data.filters[aIndex];
}


// return true since this plugin can provide visualization data
bool CanRender( void )
{
    return true;
}


// create the visualization data
SCENEGRAPH* Load( char const* aFileName )
{
    // For this demonstration we create a tetrahedron (tx1) consisting
    // of a SCENEGRAPH (VRML Transform) which in turn contains 4
    // SGSHAPE (VRML Shape) objects representing each of the sides of
    // the tetrahedron. Each Shape is associated with a color (SGAPPEARANCE)
    // and a SGFACESET (VRML Geometry->indexedFaceSet). Each SGFACESET is
    // associated with a vertex list (SGCOORDS), a per-vertex normals
    // list (SGNORMALS), and a coordinate index (SGCOORDINDEX). One shape
    // is used to represent each face so that we may use per-vertex-per-face
    // normals.
    //
    // The tetrahedron in turn is a child of a top level SCENEGRAPH (tx0)
    // which has a second SCENEGRAPH child (tx2) which is a transformation
    // of the tetrahedron tx1 (rotation + translation). This demonstrates
    // the reuse of components within the scene graph hierarchy.

    // define the vertices of the tetrahedron
    // face 1: 0, 3, 1
    // face 2: 0, 2, 3
    // face 3: 1, 3, 2
    // face 4: 0, 1, 2
    double SQ2 = sqrt( 0.5 );
    SGPOINT vert[4];
    vert[0] = SGPOINT( 1.0, 0.0, -SQ2 );
    vert[1] = SGPOINT( -1.0, 0.0, -SQ2 );
    vert[2] = SGPOINT( 0.0, 1.0, SQ2 );
```

```
vert[3] = SGPOINT( 0.0, -1.0, SQ2 );

// create the top level transform; this will hold all other
// scenegraph objects; a transform may hold other transforms and
// shapes
IFSG_TRANSFORM* tx0 = new IFSG_TRANSFORM( true );

// create the transform which will house the shapes
IFSG_TRANSFORM* tx1 = new IFSG_TRANSFORM( tx0->GetRawPtr() );

// add a shape which we will use to define one face of the tetrahedron;
// shapes hold facesets and appearances
IFSG_SHAPE* shape = new IFSG_SHAPE( *tx1 );

// add a faceset; these contain coordinate lists, coordinate indices,
// vertex lists, vertex indices, and may also contain color lists and
// their indices.

IFSG_FACESET* face = new IFSG_FACESET( *shape );

IFSG_COORDS* cp = new IFSG_COORDS( *face );
cp->AddCoord( vert[0] );
cp->AddCoord( vert[3] );
cp->AddCoord( vert[1] );

// coordinate indices - note: enforce triangles;
// in real plugins where it is not necessarily possible
// to determine which side a triangle is visible from,
// 2 point orders must be specified for each triangle
IFSG_COORDINDEX* coordIdx = new IFSG_COORDINDEX( *face );
coordIdx->AddIndex( 0 );
coordIdx->AddIndex( 1 );
coordIdx->AddIndex( 2 );

// create an appearance; appearances are owned by shapes

// magenta
IFSG_APPEARANCE* material = new IFSG_APPEARANCE( *shape);
material->SetSpecular( 0.1, 0.0, 0.1 );
material->SetDiffuse( 0.8, 0.0, 0.8 );
material->SetAmbient( 0.2, 0.2, 0.2 );
material->SetShininess( 0.2 );

// normals
IFSG_NORMALS* np = new IFSG_NORMALS( *face );
SGVECTOR nval = S3D::CalcTriNorm( vert[0], vert[3], vert[1] );
np->AddNormal( nval );
```

```
np->AddNormal( nval );
np->AddNormal( nval );

//
// Shape2
// Note: we reuse the IFSG* wrappers to create and manipulate new
// data structures.
//
shape->NewNode( *tx1 );
face->NewNode( *shape );
coordIdx->NewNode( *face );
cp->NewNode( *face );
np->NewNode( *face );

// vertices
cp->AddCoord( vert[0] );
cp->AddCoord( vert[2] );
cp->AddCoord( vert[3] );

// indices
coordIdx->AddIndex( 0 );
coordIdx->AddIndex( 1 );
coordIdx->AddIndex( 2 );

// normals
nval = S3D::CalcTriNorm( vert[0], vert[2], vert[3] );
np->AddNormal( nval );
np->AddNormal( nval );
np->AddNormal( nval );
// color (red)
material->NewNode( *shape );
material->SetSpecular( 0.2, 0.0, 0.0 );
material->SetDiffuse( 0.9, 0.0, 0.0 );
material->SetAmbient( 0.2, 0.2, 0.2 );
material->SetShininess( 0.1 );

//
// Shape3
//
shape->NewNode( *tx1 );
face->NewNode( *shape );
coordIdx->NewNode( *face );
cp->NewNode( *face );
np->NewNode( *face );

// vertices
cp->AddCoord( vert[1] );
cp->AddCoord( vert[3] );
```

```
cp->AddCoord( vert[2] );

// indices
coordIdx->AddIndex( 0 );
coordIdx->AddIndex( 1 );
coordIdx->AddIndex( 2 );

// normals
nval = S3D::CalcTriNorm( vert[1], vert[3], vert[2] );
np->AddNormal( nval );
np->AddNormal( nval );
np->AddNormal( nval );

// color (green)
material->NewNode( *shape );
material->SetSpecular( 0.0, 0.1, 0.0 );
material->SetDiffuse( 0.0, 0.9, 0.0 );
material->SetAmbient( 0.2, 0.2, 0.2 );
material->SetShininess( 0.1 );

//
// Shape4
//
shape->NewNode( *tx1 );
face->NewNode( *shape );
coordIdx->NewNode( *face );
cp->NewNode( *face );
np->NewNode( *face );

// vertices
cp->AddCoord( vert[0] );
cp->AddCoord( vert[1] );
cp->AddCoord( vert[2] );

// indices
coordIdx->AddIndex( 0 );
coordIdx->AddIndex( 1 );
coordIdx->AddIndex( 2 );

// normals
nval = S3D::CalcTriNorm( vert[0], vert[1], vert[2] );
np->AddNormal( nval );
np->AddNormal( nval );
np->AddNormal( nval );

// color (blue)
material->NewNode( *shape );
material->SetSpecular( 0.0, 0.0, 0.1 );
```

```
    material->SetDiffuse( 0.0, 0.0, 0.9 );
    material->SetAmbient( 0.2, 0.2, 0.2 );
    material->SetShininess( 0.1 );

    // create a copy of the entire tetrahedron shifted Z+2 and rotated 2/3PI
    IFSG_TRANSFORM* tx2 = new IFSG_TRANSFORM( tx0->GetRawPtr() );
    tx2->AddRefNode( *tx1 );
    tx2->SetTranslation( SGPOINT( 0, 0, 2 ) );
    tx2->SetRotation( SGVECTOR( 0, 0, 1 ), M_PI*2.0/3.0 );

    SGNODE* data = tx0->GetRawPtr();

    // delete the wrappers
    delete shape;
    delete face;
    delete coordIdx;
    delete material;
    delete cp;
    delete np;
    delete tx0;
    delete tx1;
    delete tx2;

    return (SCENEGRAPH*)data;
}
```

3 Application Programming Interface (API)

Plugins are implemented via Application Programming Interface (API) implementations. Each Plugin Class has its specific API and in the 3D Plugin tutorials we have seen examples of the implementation of the 3D Plugin API as declared by the header `3d_plugin.h`. Plugins may also rely on other APIs defined within the KiCad source tree; in the case of 3D plugins, all plugins which support visualization of models must interact with the Scene Graph API as declared in the header `ifsg_all.h` and its included headers.

This section describes the details of available Plugin Class APIs and other KiCad APIs which may be required for implementations of plugin classes.

3.1 Plugin Class APIs

There is currently only one plugin class declared for KiCad: the 3D Plugin Class. All KiCad plugin classes must implement a basic set of functions declared in the header file `kicad_plugin.h`; these declarations are referred to as the Base Kicad Plugin Class. No implementation of the Base Kicad Plugin Class exists; the header file exists purely to ensure that plugin developers implement these defined functions in each plugin implementation.

Within KiCad, each instance of a Plugin Loader implements the API presented by a plugin as though the Plugin Loader is a class providing the plugin' s services. This is achieved by the Plugin Loader class providing a public interface containing function names which are similar to those implemented by the plugin; the argument lists may vary to accommodate the need to inform the user of any problems which may be encountered if, for example, no plugin is loaded. Internally the Plugin Loader uses a stored pointer to each API function to invoke each function on behalf of the user.

3.1.1 API: Base Kicad Plugin Class

The Base Kicad Plugin Class is defined by the header file `kicad_plugin.h`. This header must be included in the declaration of all other plugin classes; for an example see the 3D Plugin Class declaration in the header file `3d_plugin.h`. The prototypes for these functions were briefly described in Plugin Classes. The API is implemented by the base plugin loader as defined in `pluginldr.cpp`.

To help make sense of the functions required by the base KiCad plugin header we must look at what happens in the base Plugin Loader class. The Plugin Loader class declares a virtual function `Open()` which takes the full path to the plugin to be loaded. The implementation of the `Open()` function within a specific plugin class loader will initially invoke the protected `open()` function of the base plugin loader; this base `open()` function attempts to find the address of each of the required basic plugin functions; once the addresses of each function have been retrieved, a number of checks are enforced:

1. Plugin `GetKicadPluginClass()` is invoked and the result is compared to the Plugin Class string provided by the Plugin Loader implementation; if these strings do not match then the opened plugin is not intended for the Plugin Loader instance.
2. Plugin `GetClassVersion()` is invoked to retrieve the Plugin Class API Version implemented by the plugin.
3. Plugin Loader virtual `GetLoaderVersion()` function is invoked to retrieve the Plugin Class API Version implemented by the loader.
4. The Plugin Class API Version reported by the plugin and the loader are required to have the same Major Version number, otherwise they are considered incompatible. This is the most basic version test and it is enforced by the base plugin loader.
5. Plugin `CheckClassVersion()` is invoked with the Plugin Class API Version information of the Plugin Loader; if the Plugin supports the given version then it returns `true` to indicate success. If successful the loader creates a PluginInfo string based on the results of `GetKicadPluginName()` and `GetPluginVersion()`, and the plugin loading procedure continues within the Plugin Loader’ s `Open()` implementation.

3.1.2 API: 3D Plugin Class

The 3D Plugin Class is declared by the header file `3d_plugin.h` and it extends the required plugin functions as described in Plugin Class: PLUGIN_3D. The corresponding Plugin Loader is defined in `pluginldr3D.cpp` and the loader implements the following public functions in addition to the required API functions:

```
/* Open the plugin specified by the full path "aFullFileName" */
bool Open( const wxString& aFullFileName );

/* Close the currently opened plugin */
void Close( void );
```

```
/* Retrieve the Plugin Class API Version implemented by this Plugin Loader */
void GetLoaderVersion( unsigned char* Major, unsigned char* Minor,
    unsigned char* Revision, unsigned char* Patch ) const;
```

The required 3D Plugin Class functions are exposed via the following functions:

```
/* returns the Plugin Class or NULL if no plugin loaded */
char const* GetKicadPluginClass( void );

/* returns false if no plugin loaded */
bool GetClassVersion( unsigned char* Major, unsigned char* Minor,
    unsigned char* Patch, unsigned char* Revision );

/* returns false if the class version check fails or no plugin is loaded */
bool CheckClassVersion( unsigned char Major, unsigned char Minor,
    unsigned char Patch, unsigned char Revision );

/* returns the Plugin Name or NULL if no plugin loaded */
const char* GetKicadPluginName( void );

/*
   returns false if no plugin is loaded, otherwise the arguments
   contain the result of GetPluginVersion()
 */
bool GetVersion( unsigned char* Major, unsigned char* Minor,
    unsigned char* Patch, unsigned char* Revision );

/*
   sets aPluginInfo to an empty string if no plugin is loaded,
   otherwise aPluginInfo is set to a string of the form:
   [NAME]:[MAJOR].[MINOR].[PATCH].[REVISION] where
   NAME = name provided by GetKicadPluginClass()
   MAJOR, MINOR, PATCH, REVISION = version information from
   GetPluginVersion()
 */
void GetPluginInfo( std::string& aPluginInfo );
```

In typical situations, the user would do the following:

1. Create an instance of `KICAD_PLUGIN_LDR_3D`.
2. Invoke `Open( "/path/to/myplugin.so" )` to open a specific plugin. The return value must be checked to ensure that the plugin loaded as desired.
3. Invoke any of the 3D Plugin Class calls as exposed by `KICAD_PLUGIN_LDR_3D`.
4. Invoke `Close()` to close (unlink) the plugin.
5. Destroy the `KICAD_PLUGIN_LDR_3D` instance.

3.2 Scenegraph Class APIs

The Scenegraph Class API is defined by the header `ifsg_all.h` and its included headers. The API consists of a number of helper routines with the namespace S3D as defined in `ifsg_api.h` and wrapper classes defined by the various `ifsg_*.h` headers; the wrappers support the underlying scene graph classes which, taken together, form a scene graph structure which is compatible with VRML2.0 static scene graphs. The headers, structures, classes and their public functions are as follows:

sg_version.h

```
/*
    Defines version information of the SceneGraph Classes.
    All plugins which use the scenegraph class should include this header
    and check the version information against the version reported by
    S3D::GetLibVersion() to ensure compatibility
 */

#define KICADSG_VERSION_MAJOR         2
#define KICADSG_VERSION_MINOR         0
#define KICADSG_VERSION_PATCH         0
#define KICADSG_VERSION_REVISION      0
```

sg_types.h

```
/*
    Defines the SceneGraph Class Types; these types
    are closely related to VRML2.0 node types.
 */

namespace S3D
{
    enum SGTYPES
    {
        SGTYPE_TRANSFORM = 0,
        SGTYPE_APPEARANCE,
        SGTYPE_COLORS,
        SGTYPE_COLORINDEX,
        SGTYPE_FACESET,
        SGTYPE_COORDS,
        SGTYPE_COORDINDEX,
        SGTYPE_NORMALS,
        SGTYPE_SHAPE,
        SGTYPE_END
    };
};
```

The `sg_base.h` header contains declarations of basic data types used by the scenegraph classes.

sg_base.h

```
/*
    This is an RGB color model equivalent to the VRML2.0
    RGB model where each color may have a value within the
    range [0..1].
 */

class SGCOLOR
{
public:
    SGCOLOR();
    SGCOLOR( float aRVal, float aGVal, float aBVal );

    void GetColor( float& aRedVal, float& aGreenVal, float& aBlueVal ) const;
    void GetColor( SGCOLOR& aColor ) const;
    void GetColor( SGCOLOR* aColor ) const;

    bool SetColor( float aRedVal, float aGreenVal, float aBlueVal );
    bool SetColor( const SGCOLOR& aColor );
    bool SetColor( const SGCOLOR* aColor );
};


class SGPOINT
{
public:
    double x;
    double y;
    double z;

public:
    SGPOINT();
    SGPOINT( double aXVal, double aYVal, double aZVal );

    void GetPoint( double& aXVal, double& aYVal, double& aZVal );
    void GetPoint( SGPOINT& aPoint );
    void GetPoint( SGPOINT* aPoint );

    void SetPoint( double aXVal, double aYVal, double aZVal );
    void SetPoint( const SGPOINT& aPoint );
};


/*
    A SGVECTOR has 3 components (x,y,z) similar to a point; however
    a vector ensures that the stored values are normalized and
    prevents direct manipulation of the component variables.
 */
```

```
class SGVECTOR
{
public:
    SGVECTOR();
    SGVECTOR( double aXVal, double aYVal, double aZVal );

    void GetVector( double& aXVal, double& aYVal, double& aZVal ) const;

    void SetVector( double aXVal, double aYVal, double aZVal );
    void SetVector( const SGVECTOR& aVector );

    SGVECTOR& operator=( const SGVECTOR& source );
};
```

The IFSG_NODE class is the base class for all scenegraph nodes. All scenegraph objects implement the public functions of this class but in some cases a particular function may have no meaning for a specific class.

ifsg_node.h

```
class IFSG_NODE
{
public:
    IFSG_NODE();
    virtual ~IFSG_NODE();

    /**
     * Function Destroy
     * deletes the scenegraph object held by this wrapper
     */
    void Destroy( void );

    /**
     * Function Attach
     * associates a given SGNODE* with this wrapper
     */
    virtual bool Attach( SGNODE* aNode ) = 0;

    /**
     * Function NewNode
     * creates a new node to associate with this wrapper
     */
    virtual bool NewNode( SGNODE* aParent ) = 0;
    virtual bool NewNode( IFSG_NODE& aParent ) = 0;

    /**
     * Function GetRawPtr()
     * returns the raw internal SGNODE pointer
     */
    SGNODE* GetRawPtr( void );
```

```
/**
 * Function GetNodeType
 * returns the type of this node instance
 */
S3D::SGTYPES GetNodeType( void ) const;

/**
 * Function GetParent
 * returns a pointer to the parent SGNODE of this object
 * or NULL if the object has no parent (ie. top level transform)
 * or if the wrapper is not currently associated with an SGNODE.
 */
SGNODE* GetParent( void ) const;

/**
 * Function SetParent
 * sets the parent SGNODE of this object.
 *
 * @param aParent [in] is the desired parent node
 * @return true if the operation succeeds; false if
 * the given node is not allowed to be a parent to
 * the derived object.
 */
bool SetParent( SGNODE* aParent );

/**
 * Function GetNodeTypeName
 * returns the text representation of the node type
 * or NULL if the node somehow has an invalid type
 */
const char * GetNodeTypeName( S3D::SGTYPES aNodeType ) const;

/**
 * Function AddRefNode
 * adds a reference to an existing node which is not owned by
 * (not a child of) this node.
 *
 * @return true on success
 */
bool AddRefNode( SGNODE* aNode );
bool AddRefNode( IFSG_NODE& aNode );

/**
 * Function AddChildNode
 * adds a node as a child owned by this node.
 *
 * @return true on success
```

```
    */
    bool AddChildNode( SGNODE* aNode );
    bool AddChildNode( IFSG_NODE& aNode );
};
```

IFSG_TRANSFORM is similar to a VRML2.0 Transform node; it may contain any number of child IFSG_SHAPE and IFSG_TRANSFORM nodes and any number of referenced IFSG_SHAPE and IFSG_TRANSFORM nodes. A valid scenegraph must have a single IFSG_TRANSFORM object as a root.

ifsg_transform.h

```
/**
 * Class IFSG_TRANSFORM
 * is the wrapper for the VRML compatible TRANSFORM block class SCENEGRAPH
 */

class IFSG_TRANSFORM : public IFSG_NODE
{
public:
    IFSG_TRANSFORM( bool create );
    IFSG_TRANSFORM( SGNODE* aParent );

    bool SetScaleOrientation( const SGVECTOR& aScaleAxis, double aAngle );
    bool SetRotation( const SGVECTOR& aRotationAxis, double aAngle );
    bool SetScale( const SGPOINT& aScale );
    bool SetScale( double aScale );
    bool SetCenter( const SGPOINT& aCenter );
    bool SetTranslation( const SGPOINT& aTranslation );

    /* various base class functions not shown here */
};
```

IFSG_SHAPE is similar to a VRML2.0 Shape node; it must contain a single child or reference FACESET node and may contain a single child or reference APPEARANCE node.

ifsg_shape.h

```
/**
 * Class IFSG_SHAPE
 * is the wrapper for the SGSHAPE class
 */

class IFSG_SHAPE : public IFSG_NODE
{
public:
    IFSG_SHAPE( bool create );
    IFSG_SHAPE( SGNODE* aParent );
    IFSG_SHAPE( IFSG_NODE& aParent );

    /* various base class functions not shown here */
```

```
};
```

IFSG_APPEARANCE is similar to a VRML2.0 Appearance node, however, at the moment it only represents the equivalent of an Appearance node containing a Material node.

ifsg_appearance.h

```
class IFSG_APPEARANCE : public IFSG_NODE
{
public:
    IFSG_APPEARANCE( bool create );
    IFSG_APPEARANCE( SGNODE* aParent );
    IFSG_APPEARANCE( IFSG_NODE& aParent );

    bool SetEmissive( float aRVal, float aGVal, float aBVal );
    bool SetEmissive( const SGCOLOR* aRGBColor );
    bool SetEmissive( const SGCOLOR& aRGBColor );

    bool SetDiffuse( float aRVal, float aGVal, float aBVal );
    bool SetDiffuse( const SGCOLOR* aRGBColor );
    bool SetDiffuse( const SGCOLOR& aRGBColor );

    bool SetSpecular( float aRVal, float aGVal, float aBVal );
    bool SetSpecular( const SGCOLOR* aRGBColor );
    bool SetSpecular( const SGCOLOR& aRGBColor );

    bool SetAmbient( float aRVal, float aGVal, float aBVal );
    bool SetAmbient( const SGCOLOR* aRGBColor );
    bool SetAmbient( const SGCOLOR& aRGBColor );

    bool SetShininess( float aShininess );
    bool SetTransparency( float aTransparency );

    /* various base class functions not shown here */

    /* the following functions make no sense within an
       appearance node and always return a failure code

        bool AddRefNode( SGNODE* aNode );
        bool AddRefNode( IFSG_NODE& aNode );
        bool AddChildNode( SGNODE* aNode );
        bool AddChildNode( IFSG_NODE& aNode );
     */
};
```

IFSG_FACESET is similar to a VRML2.0 Geometry node which contains an IndexedFaceSet node. It must contain a single child or reference COORDS node, a single child COORDINDEX node, and a single child or reference NORMALS node; in addition there may be a single child or reference COLORS node. A simplistic normals calculation function is provided to aid the user in assigning normal values to surfaces. The deviations from the VRML2.0 analogue are as follows:

1. Normals are always per-vertex.
2. Colors are always per vertex.
3. The coordinate index set must describe triangular faces only.

ifsg_faceset.h

```
/**
 * Class IFSG_FACESET
 * is the wrapper for the SGFACESET class
 */

class IFSG_FACESET : public IFSG_NODE
{
public:
    IFSG_FACESET( bool create );
    IFSG_FACESET( SGNODE* aParent );
    IFSG_FACESET( IFSG_NODE& aParent );

    bool CalcNormals( SGNODE** aPtr );

    /* various base class functions not shown here */
};
```

ifsg_coords.h

```
/**
 * Class IFSG_COORDS
 * is the wrapper for SGCOORDS
 */

class IFSG_COORDS : public IFSG_NODE
{
public:
    IFSG_COORDS( bool create );
    IFSG_COORDS( SGNODE* aParent );
    IFSG_COORDS( IFSG_NODE& aParent );

    bool GetCoordsList( size_t& aListSize, SGPOINT*& aCoordsList );
    bool SetCoordsList( size_t aListSize, const SGPOINT* aCoordsList );
    bool AddCoord( double aXValue, double aYValue, double aZValue );
    bool AddCoord( const SGPOINT& aPoint );

    /* various base class functions not shown here */

    /* the following functions make no sense within a
```

```
        coords node and always return a failure code

         bool AddRefNode( SGNODE* aNode );
         bool AddRefNode( IFSG_NODE& aNode );
         bool AddChildNode( SGNODE* aNode );
         bool AddChildNode( IFSG_NODE& aNode );
    */
};
```

IFSG_COORDINDEX is similar to a VRML2.0 coordIdx[] set except it must exclusively describe triangular faces, which implies that the total number of indices is divisible by 3.

ifsg_coordindex.h

```
/**
 * Class IFSG_COORDINDEX
 * is the wrapper for SGCOORDINDEX
 */

class IFSG_COORDINDEX : public IFSG_INDEX
{
public:
    IFSG_COORDINDEX( bool create );
    IFSG_COORDINDEX( SGNODE* aParent );
    IFSG_COORDINDEX( IFSG_NODE& aParent );

    bool GetIndices( size_t& nIndices, int*& aIndexList );
    bool SetIndices( size_t nIndices, int* aIndexList );
    bool AddIndex( int aIndex );

    /* various base class functions not shown here */

    /* the following functions make no sense within a
       coordindex node and always return a failure code

         bool AddRefNode( SGNODE* aNode );
         bool AddRefNode( IFSG_NODE& aNode );
         bool AddChildNode( SGNODE* aNode );
         bool AddChildNode( IFSG_NODE& aNode );
    */
};
```

IFSG_NORMALS is equivalent to a VRML2.0 Normals node.

ifsg_normals.h

```
/**
 * Class IFSG_NORMALS
 * is the wrapper for the SGNORMALS class
 */
```

```
class IFSG_NORMALS : public IFSG_NODE
{
public:
    IFSG_NORMALS( bool create );
    IFSG_NORMALS( SGNODE* aParent );
    IFSG_NORMALS( IFSG_NODE& aParent );

    bool GetNormalList( size_t& aListSize, SGVECTOR*& aNormalList );
    bool SetNormalList( size_t aListSize, const SGVECTOR* aNormalList );
    bool AddNormal( double aXValue, double aYValue, double aZValue );
    bool AddNormal( const SGVECTOR& aNormal );

    /* various base class functions not shown here */

    /* the following functions make no sense within a
       normals node and always return a failure code

        bool AddRefNode( SGNODE* aNode );
        bool AddRefNode( IFSG_NODE& aNode );
        bool AddChildNode( SGNODE* aNode );
        bool AddChildNode( IFSG_NODE& aNode );
     */
};
```

IFSG_COLORS is similar to a VRML2.0 colors[] set.

ifsg_colors.h

```
/**
 * Class IFSG_COLORS
 * is the wrapper for SGCOLORS
 */

class IFSG_COLORS : public IFSG_NODE
{
public:
    IFSG_COLORS( bool create );
    IFSG_COLORS( SGNODE* aParent );
    IFSG_COLORS( IFSG_NODE& aParent );

    bool GetColorList( size_t& aListSize, SGCOLOR*& aColorList );
    bool SetColorList( size_t aListSize, const SGCOLOR* aColorList );
    bool AddColor( double aRedValue, double aGreenValue, double aBlueValue );
    bool AddColor( const SGCOLOR& aColor );

    /* various base class functions not shown here */

    /* the following functions make no sense within a
```

```
        normals node and always return a failure code

        bool AddRefNode( SGNODE* aNode );
        bool AddRefNode( IFSG_NODE& aNode );
        bool AddChildNode( SGNODE* aNode );
        bool AddChildNode( IFSG_NODE& aNode );
    */
};
```

The remaining API functions are defined in `ifsg_api.h` as follows:

ifsg_api.h

```
namespace S3D
{
    /**
     * Function GetLibVersion retrieves version information of the
     * kicad_3dsg library
     */
    SGLIB_API void GetLibVersion( unsigned char* Major, unsigned char* Minor,
                                  unsigned char* Patch, unsigned char* Revision );

    // functions to extract information from SGNODE pointers
    SGLIB_API S3D::SGTYPES GetSGNodeType( SGNODE* aNode );
    SGLIB_API SGNODE* GetSGNodeParent( SGNODE* aNode );
    SGLIB_API bool AddSGNodeRef( SGNODE* aParent, SGNODE* aChild );
    SGLIB_API bool AddSGNodeChild( SGNODE* aParent, SGNODE* aChild );
    SGLIB_API void AssociateSGNodeWrapper( SGNODE* aObject, SGNODE** aRefPtr );

    /**
     * Function CalcTriNorm
     * returns the normal vector of a triangle described by vertices p1, p2, p3
     */
    SGLIB_API SGVECTOR CalcTriNorm( const SGPOINT& p1, const SGPOINT& p2, const SGPOINT& p3 ↩
        );

    /**
     * Function WriteCache
     * writes the SGNODE tree to a binary cache file
     *
     * @param aFileName is the name of the file to write
     * @param overwrite must be set to true to overwrite an existing file
     * @param aNode is any node within the node tree which is to be written
     * @return true on success
     */
    SGLIB_API bool WriteCache( const char* aFileName, bool overwrite, SGNODE* aNode,
        const char* aPluginInfo );

    /**
```

```
 * Function ReadCache
 * reads a binary cache file and creates an SGNODE tree
 *
 * @param aFileName is the name of the binary cache file to be read
 * @return NULL on failure, on success a pointer to the top level SCENEGRAPH node;
 * if desired this node can be associated with an IFSG_TRANSFORM wrapper via
 * the IFSG_TRANSFORM::Attach() function.
 */
SGLIB_API SGNODE* ReadCache( const char* aFileName, void* aPluginMgr,
    bool (*aTagCheck)( const char*, void* ) );

/**
 * Function WriteVRML
 * writes out the given node and its subnodes to a VRML2 file
 *
 * @param filename is the name of the output file
 * @param overwrite should be set to true to overwrite an existing VRML file
 * @param aTopNode is a pointer to a SCENEGRAPH object representing the VRML scene
 * @param reuse should be set to true to make use of VRML DEF/USE features
 * @return true on success
 */
SGLIB_API bool WriteVRML( const char* filename, bool overwrite, SGNODE* aTopNode,
            bool reuse, bool renameNodes );

// NOTE: The following functions are used in combination to create a VRML
// assembly which may use various instances of each SG* representation of a module.
// A typical use case would be:
// 1. invoke 'ResetNodeIndex()' to reset the global node name indices
// 2. for each model pointer provided by 'S3DCACHE->Load()', invoke 'RenameNodes()' ↩
    once;
//    this ensures that all nodes have a unique name to present to the final output ↩
    file.
//    Internally, RenameNodes() will only rename the given node and all Child subnodes;
//    nodes which are only referenced will not be renamed. Using the pointer supplied
//    by 'S3DCACHE->Load()' ensures that all nodes but the returned node (top node) are
//    children of at least one node, so all nodes are given unique names.
// 3. if SG* trees are created independently of S3DCACHE->Load() the user must invoke
//    RenameNodes() as appropriate to ensure that all nodes have a unique name
// 4. create an assembly structure by creating new IFSG_TRANSFORM nodes as appropriate
//    for each instance of a component; the component base model as returned by
//    S3DCACHE->Load() may be added to these IFSG_TRANSFORM nodes via 'AddRefNode()';
//    set the offset, rotation, etc of the IFSG_TRANSFORM node to ensure correct
// 5. Ensure that all new IFSG_TRANSFORM nodes are placed as child nodes within a
//    top level IFSG_TRANSFORM node in preparation for final node naming and output
// 6. Invoke RenameNodes() on the top level assembly node
// 7. Invoke WriteVRML() as normal, with renameNodes = false, to write the entire ↩
    assembly
//    structure to a single VRML file
```

```
// 8. Clean up by deleting any extra IFSG_TRANSFORM wrappers and their underlying SG*
//    classes which have been created solely for the assembly output

/**
 * Function ResetNodeIndex
 * resets the global SG* class indices
 *
 * @param aNode may be any valid SGNODE
 */
SGLIB_API void ResetNodeIndex( SGNODE* aNode );

/**
 * Function RenameNodes
 * renames a node and all children nodes based on the current
 * values of the global SG* class indices
 *
 * @param aNode is a top level node
 */
SGLIB_API void RenameNodes( SGNODE* aNode );

/**
 * Function DestroyNode
 * deletes the given SG* class node. This function makes it possible
 * to safely delete an SG* node without associating the node with
 * its corresponding IFSG* wrapper.
 */
SGLIB_API void DestroyNode( SGNODE* aNode );

// NOTE: The following functions facilitate the creation and destruction
// of data structures for rendering

/**
 * Function GetModel
 * creates an S3DMODEL representation of aNode (raw data, no transforms)
 *
 * @param aNode is the node to be transcribed into an S3DMODEL representation
 * @return an S3DMODEL representation of aNode on success, otherwise NULL
 */
SGLIB_API S3DMODEL* GetModel( SCENEGRAPH* aNode );

/**
 * Function Destroy3DModel
 * frees memory used by an S3DMODEL structure and sets the pointer to
 * the structure to NULL
 */
SGLIB_API void Destroy3DModel( S3DMODEL** aModel );

/**
```

```
     * Function Free3DModel
     * frees memory used internally by an S3DMODEL structure
     */
    SGLIB_API void Free3DModel( S3DMODEL& aModel );

    /**
     * Function Free3DMesh
     * frees memory used internally by an SMESH structure
     */
    SGLIB_API void Free3DMesh( SMESH& aMesh );

    /**
     * Function New3DModel
     * creates and initializes an S3DMODEL struct
     */
    SGLIB_API S3DMODEL* New3DModel( void );

    /**
     * Function Init3DMaterial
     * initializes an SMATERIAL struct
     */
    SGLIB_API void Init3DMaterial( SMATERIAL& aMat );

    /**
     * Function Init3DMesh
     * creates and initializes an SMESH struct
     */
    SGLIB_API void Init3DMesh( SMESH& aMesh );
};
```

For actual usage examples of the Scenegraph API see the Advanced 3D Plugin tutorial above and the KiCad VRML1, VRML2, and X3D parsers.

CPSIA information can be obtained
at www.ICGtesting.com
Printed in the USA
BVHW05s2015030518
515207BV00006B/48/P

9 781680 921274